ADVANCED DIEMAKING

Prepared under the direction of the Apprentice Subcommittee on Training

Advanced Diemaking

Resources and Materials of the National Tool, Die & Precision Machining Assn.

by D. Eugene Ostergaard

McGraw-Hill Book Company

New York

St. Louis

San Francisco

London

Toronto

Sydney

ADVANCED DIEMAKING

1234567890 (HD) 7432106987

NATIONAL TOOL, DIE & PRECISION MACHINING ASSN.
APPRENTICE SUBCOMMITTEE ON TRAINING RESOURCES AND MATERIALS

Herbert Harig (Chairman), Harig Products, Inc., Elgin, Illinois

Richard F. Moore (Vice Chairman), Moore Special Tool Co., Bridgeport, Connecticut

Jack Kleinoder (Vice Chairman), Volkert Stampings, Inc., Queens Village, New York

John D. Dewhurst, Arrow Tool Company, Inc., Wethersfield, Connecticut

Richard H. Ewing, Grand Valley Mfg. Co., Titusville, Pennsylvania

Carl A. Johnson, Jr., Port City Machine & Tool Co., Muskegon, Michigan

Howard H. H. Jones, Vulcan Tool Co., Dayton, Ohio

Louis M. Marussich, Genessee Instrument & Research Co., Division, Genessee Tool & Die Corp., Rochester, New York

Howard Otto, Hygrade Machine & Tool, Inc., Cleveland, Ohio

Jack H. Schron, Jergens Tool Specialty Co., Cleveland, Ohio

James R. Sommers, Conso Tool & Engineering, Inc., Dallas, Texas

Edward J. Stanek, Stanek Tool Corp., Milwaukee, Wisconsin

ACKNOWLEDGMENT

This is to acknowledge the time and effort given so unselfishly by the many National Tool, Die & Precision Machining Association members toward the creation of better text materials aimed at improving skills training in the metalworking industries. These men deserve the unreserved applause of their fellow association members and of all in the industry who benefit so greatly from such a worthy activity.

CHARLES L. BRINKMAN, *President*
National Tool, Die & Precision
Machining Assn.

PREFACE

"Advanced Diemaking" is a continuation of the necessary related training started in the book "Basic Diemaking," published by the McGraw-Hill Book Company in 1963. Since that time public and private schools, technical institutions, and in-plant training programs throughout the United States have widely accepted "Basic Diemaking" as their textbook for the beginning of tool and diemaking related training.

It is our hope that "Advanced Diemaking" will also be widely accepted, since it has been written to take up just where "Basic Diemaking" left off. We recommend that the logical point for an apprentice to start with this book is near the end of his second year of apprenticeship or at the beginning of his third year, depending on the amount of experience he has had in the shop.

As in "Basic Diemaking," explanations of the whys of diemaking have been given in each chapter and to every subject. Although the book progresses to the more advanced stages of complete dies, each subject is begun at its necessary foundation level and is developed to the point where the diemaker can understand completely the particular type of die discussed in each chapter.

We hope that the users of "Advanced Diemaking" will have had the opportunity of being taught by a qualified instructor the necessary basic knowledge of diemaking, using "Basic Diemaking" as the textbook. If not, it is our opinion that at the minimum a very conscientious study of "Basic Diemaking" should be completed before moving on to "Advanced Diemaking."

This textbook is an ideal reference and refresher manual for the journeyman tool- and diemaker as well as for the tool and die designer and engineer. There is much information applicable to their everyday work. It is our recommendation that diemakers purchase their own books or that employers have some copies available in a company library for employee use. Tool and die designers and engineers can also obtain much information applicable to their everyday work from this book.

Just as we recommended "Basic Diemaking" to be used as part of the curriculum of mechanical engineering at the college level, we also recommend "Advanced Diemaking." It is intended that the instructor, whether he be teaching apprentices or college students, should use the lecture approach in the classroom, with this textbook giving him his subject material. The student can study as homework a preassigned segment of the book and should be prepared for classroom discussions and/or tests following the lecture.

> HERBERT HARIG, *Chairman*
> *Apprentice Subcommittee on Training Resources and Materials*
> *National Tool, Die & Precision Machining Assn.*

CONTENTS

ESSENTIAL DIE-TO-PRESS RELATIONSHIPS

The subject of punch presses and kindred machines is a large one. The manufacture of these machines is in itself an entire industry. Because of the scope of the subject, any truly comprehensive study of these machines becomes, of necessity, a complete book in itself. Two such books are the "Power Press Handbook," published by the E. W. Bliss Press Company, and "Metalworking's Mechanical Press Handbook," published by *Metalworking* magazine.

Much specifically informative literature is readily available which is devoted to punch presses and kindred machines. This is in the form of catalogues and brochures published by the various manufacturers and pertaining to specific machines. They can be valuable study aids, in addition to their primary function of furnishing the exact and comprehensive specifications needed for production planning and die designing.

TYPICAL OBI PRESSES

The presses in Figs. 1·1 and 1·2 are typical open-back inclinable presses. They are referred to as "OBI presses." The press in Fig. 1·1 is equipped with tie rods. These give the press frame greater rigidity to resist possible deflection under heavy loads. The tie rods may be removed to provide greater accessibility if desired (in running lighter work).

The smaller press shown in Fig. 1·2 has some pertinent features which can be considered typical for other presses.

BASIC FEATURES OF A TYPICAL OBI PRESS

Figures 1·3 and 1·4 serve to illustrate essential construction features of a typical OBI punch press. As specified by one prominent maker of punch presses, some of these features are:

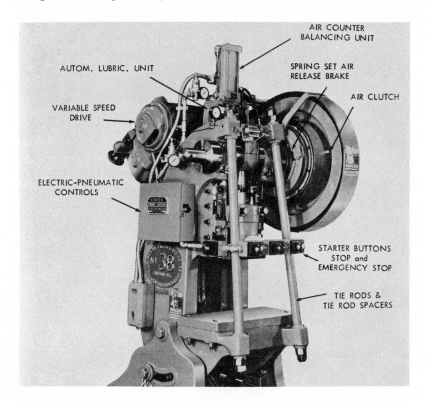

Figure **1·1** A typical OBI (open-back inclinable) punch press.

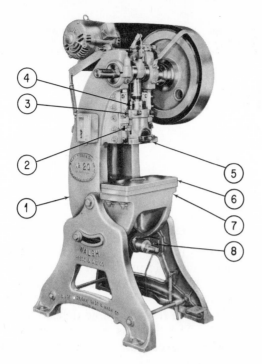

Figure **1·2** (1) Frame. (2) Knockout bar. (3) Ram-adjustment clamp. (4) Ram-adjusting nut. (5) Die-shank clamp. (6) Bolster plate. (7) Bed. (8) Inclining mechanism.

Figure **1·3** Frame of typical OBI press, showing bearings and gib alignment screws.

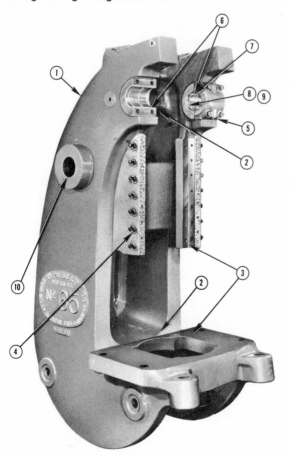

Frame (Fig. 1·3)

1. Reinforced, processed cast press frame; tensile strength over 45,000 psi
2. Large radii and T section designed for greater rigidity
3. Precision machining of press bed and gib mounting surface
4. Positive gib alignment assured by flat setscrews on both sides
5. Close tolerance of main bearing caps to press frame
6. Precision line-bored main-bearing housing
7. Replaceable, special bronze bearings, properly grooved
8. Precision line-honed main bearings (inside view)
9. Bearings hand-scraped to crankshaft for better line-up and longer bearing life
10. Back-gear drive bearings line-bored with main bearings

Ram and V ways (Fig. 1·4)

1. Large reinforced slide face
2. V bearings of slide precision ground, square to face within 0.002 in.
3. Precision-ground gib bearings, hand-scraped to slide
4. Front and back slide bearing surface lubricated independently
5. Slide V bearings grooved for proper lubricant retention
6. Precision-bored connection bearing
7. Honed, replaceable special bronze connection bearing, hand-scraped to crankshaft
8. Positive slide adjustment with oversized thread on ball socket
9. Positive slide adjusting clamp
10. Precision-bored die-shank clamping block
11. Die-forged and heat-treated pitman ball

DIE-TO-PRESS RELATIONSHIPS

It is self-evident that, if a die is to be run in a given press, the die must fit that press. To accomplish this, the die must be designed in accordance with the various press dimensions which pertain to the die-to-press relationship. These dimensions are normally taken from the press specification chart, or, if necessary, the required dimensions may be ascertained by actually measuring the specific press in which the die is to be run.

Shank diameter. Most of the pertinent die-to-press relationship dimensions will be evident. For example, it is obvious that the die-set shank diameter must agree with the diameter of the stem hole in the ram of the punch press. This may be accomplished by:

1. Making the die-set shank the same diameter as the stem hole. This is the most common (and usually the most desirable) practice.
2. Using a die set which has a shank smaller in diameter than the stem hole. The shank is then fitted with an adapter bushing to make it coincide with the stem-hole diameter. The use of this method is normally limited to special situations. As an example, it may be necessary to operate the die in different presses at different times. If the presses concerned have different stem-hole diameters, the die-set shank is made to the smallest stem-hole diameter and then fitted with adapters to suit the larger stem-hole diameters, when and as required. It is, of course, obvious that, if the die-set shank is larger than the stem hole, it will not be possible to mount the die in the press.

Die shut heights. By definition, the shut height of a die is the distance from the top surface of the upper shoe to the bottom surface of the lower shoe when the die is in its lowest operating position. When the die is being operated in the press, the press shut height and the die shut height coincide exactly. With cutting dies, the die shut height normally becomes slightly lower each time the die is sharpened (see Chap. 5, *Die Life*, in "Basic Diemaking"[1]). The resulting decrease in die shut height is most often compensated for by adjusting the press ram lower each time the die is set up in the press after sharpening.

Press shut heights. The range of shut heights for a typical punch press is illustrated in Fig. 1·5. Remember that the shut height is always measured with the press stroke at bottom dead center (BDC) position. In considering maximum shut heights, the ram adjustment is up at its highest stroke down position. In considering minimum shut heights, the ram adjustment is down—with the ram extended to its lowest position.

In view A the press is shown with the bolster plate removed. Distance H, from the top surface of the press bed to the bottom face of the ram, is the maximum vertical die space (shut height) possible for the press. On occasion, where die shut heights are high in relation to the press shut height, it may be necessary to operate with the bolster plate removed. However, this is not the most common practice, since it is generally

[1] D. Eugene Ostergaard, "Basic Diemaking," McGraw-Hill Book Company, New York, 1963.

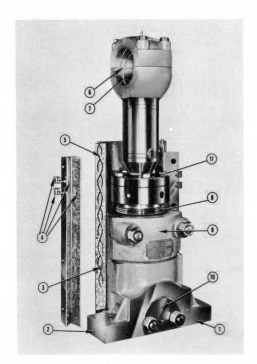

Figure 1·4   Ram and V ways of typical OBI punch press.

more desirable to use a bolster plate, as shown in view B.

In view B the bolster plate is shown in place on the press bed. This is the most common practice. The bolster thickness is indicated as B. The maximum shut height available for the die is H_1.

$$H_1 = H - B$$

In view C the bolster is in place and the ram has been extended downward a distance A equal to the length of its adjustment. Unless special provisions are made (such as a thicker bolster or the addition of spacers, etc.), this is the normal

Figure 1·5   Views showing shut heights H, H_1, H_2 of OBI punch press. View A: Stroke down, adjustment up. View B: Stroke down, adjustment up. View C: Stroke down, adjustment down.

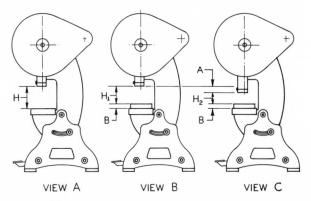

VIEW A   VIEW B   VIEW C

(STROKE IS DOWN IN ALL THREE VIEWS)

3

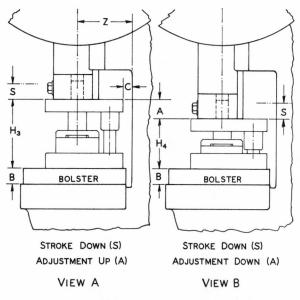

STROKE DOWN (S)
ADJUSTMENT UP (A)

VIEW A

STROKE DOWN (S)
ADJUSTMENT DOWN (A)

VIEW B

Figure 1·6 Schematic showing die-to-press shut-height relationships with ram adjustment up and with ram adjustment down.

minimum shut height H_2 available for the press-to-die relationship.

$$H_2 = H_1 - A$$

Typical shut-height relationship. A typical die-to-press relationship is pictured in Fig. 1·6. The die is a cutting die. Its shut height becomes lower and lower throughout its life because of sharpening attrition. When the die is new, the die-to-press relationship exists as shown in view A. View B depicts the relationship as it appears when the life of the die is expended. To refer to Figs. 1·5 and 1·6 in conjunction, the following limits have proved to be generally most practical for die-to-press shut-height relationships:

1. Where press shut height with stroke down, adjustment up, is H_1 and shut height of die when new is H_3, then, for small- and medium-size dies,

$$H_3 = H_1 - \tfrac{1}{8} \text{ to } \tfrac{1}{4} \text{ in.}$$

and for large dies

$$H_3 = H_1 - \tfrac{1}{4} \text{ to } \tfrac{1}{2} \text{ in.}$$

Figure 1·7 Lettered designations for punch-press dimensions which are charted in Fig. 1·8.

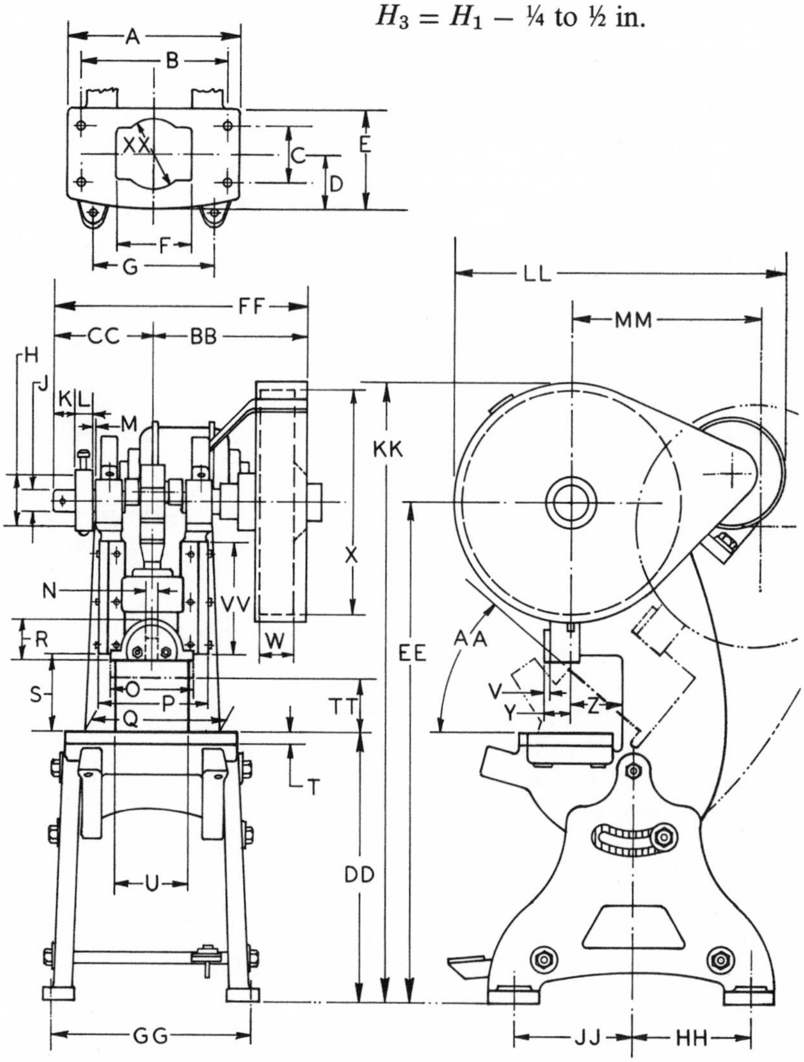

Making H_3 less than H_1 facilitates die setup in the press.

2. Where press shut height with stroke down, adjustment down, is H_2 and shut height of expended die is H_4, then

$$H_4 = H_2 + \tfrac{1}{8} \text{ in.}$$

For dies which have a constant shut height throughout their entire life, make

$$H_3 = H_1 - \frac{A}{2} \pm \tfrac{3}{8} A$$

Throat Depth. This dimension is shown as Z in Fig. 1·6. It is mentioned here for emphasis, because it is sometimes overlooked. When the die set or any other die component extends beyond

Figure **1·8** Chart for presses designated in Fig. 1·7.

	DIMENSIONS Per Drawing OF PRESS	No. 12 12 TON	No. 12X 12 TON	No. 18 18 TON	No. 20 20 TON	No. 20X 20 TON	No. 24 24 TON	No. 28 28 TON	No. 28X 28 TON	No. 38 38 TON	No. 38X 38 TON	No. 55 55 TON
A	Width of Bed L. to R.	15½	15½	18½	18½	19¼	21¾	21¾	21¾	27	27	32¼
B	Bolster Bolt Holes (Centers) L. to R.	13¼	13¼	16⅜	16⅜	16¾	19¼	19¼	19¼	23½	23½	28¼
C	Bolster Bolt Holes (Centers)	4½	4½	4½	4½	7½	7	7	7	7	11	11
D	Center of opening to front of Bed	4	4	5	5	5	6½	6½	6½	7¾	7¾	10
E	Depth of Bed—Front to Back	7½	9½	9½	9½	12¼	12	12	14½	14	19	18½
F	Oblong opening in Bed—WXD	5½x4	5½x4	7½x5	7½x5	7½x9	10x6½	10x6½	10x6½	11¾x7¾	11¾x7¾	14x10¾
G	Tie Rod Holes (Centers)	—	—	—	—	—	15½	15½	15½	18½	18½	21½
H	I. D. Brake Collar	3¾	3¾	4¾	4¾	4¾	5	5	5	7	7	8
J	Diameter of shaft — Main Bearing	1.750	1.750	2.250	2.250	2.250	2.500	2.500	2.500	3.000	3.000	3.750
	Diameter of shaft — Connection Bearing Dia.	2	2	3½	2½	2½	3	3	3	3½	3½	4½
K	Shaft projection beyond Brake	4½	4½	4⅞	4⅞	4⅞	4⅞	4⅞	4⅞	4⅞	4⅞	5⅛
L	Width of Brake Collar	1⅜	1⅜	1½	1½	1½	1¾	1¾	1¾	2½	2½	2½
M	Clearance of Brake	1/16	1/16	1/16	1/16	1/16	1/16	1/16	1/16	1/16	1/16	1/16
N	Stem hole diameter	1 9/16	1 9/16	1 9/16	1 9/16	1 9/16	1 9/16	1 9/16	1 9/16	2	2	2½
O	Face of slide—WXD	10x6¾	10x6¾	11x6¾	11x6¾	11x6¾	12¼x8⅜	12¼x8⅜	12¼x8⅜	14x10	14x10	17x11 3/16
P	Width of Frame	9¾	9¾	11½	11½	11½	13½	13½	13½	16	16	18
Q	Dimension across uprights	11¼	11¼	14½	14½	14½	17	17	17	21	21	25
R	Height—finished front of Slide	3¾	3¾	4	4	4	5	5	5	5½	5½	6½
S	Bolster to Gibs	8½	10⅞	9	10½	13	9	10¼	13½	12¾	15½	12½
T	Thickness of Bolster	1¼	1¼	1¼	1¼	1½	1½	1½	1¾	1¾	2¼	2¼
U	Distance between uprights	6½	6½	9	9	9	9½	9½	9½	12	12	16
V	Front of Slide to Cap	1/16	1/16	1/16	1/16	1/16	1/16	1/16	1/16	1/16	1/16	1/16
W	Width of Flywheel (Face)	3¼	3¼	4¼	4½	4½	5	5	5	5½	5½	6
X	Diameter of Flywheel or Gear	18	18	22	24	24	28	28	28	32	32	36¼
Y	Slide cap to center of bed	2½	2½	2⅝	2⅝	2⅝	3⅜	3⅜	3⅜	4	4	5⅛
Z	Throat C. Line of Press to back	4½	6	6	6	9½	6	6	10	7¼	12	9¼
A-A	Maximum Incline—DEGREES	45°	45°	45°	45°	45°	45°	45°	45°	45°	45°	30°
B-B	Press C. Line to extreme R. H.	15 13/16	15 13/16	18 5/16	18 5/16	18 5/16	21⅞	21⅞	21⅞	24 15/16	24 15/16	30 9/16
C-C	Press C. Line to extreme L. H.	11 7/16	11 7/16	13 3/16	13 3/16	13 3/16	14 13/16	14 13/16	14 13/16	17 5/16	17 5/16	20
D-D	Height—Floor to top of Bolster	32⅝	32¾	32¾	32¾	31¼	33	33	33	33¼	33½	34½
E-E	Height—Floor to C. Line of Shaft	57	59⅜	58¾	60¼	63¼	61⅜	63	67	68	73	77¾
F-F	Width—overall	27¼	27¼	31½	31½	31½	36¾	36¾	36¾	42¼	42¼	50 9/16
G-G	Leg hole centers L. to R. (Approx.)	21¾	21¾	22¼	26¾	23½	26¾	26¾	32	32	33	39¼
H-H	Leg hole centers—back to C. Line	10¾	13½	13½	16½	16½	16½	16½	24	24	26½	26½
J-J	Leg hole centers—front to C. Line	10¾	13½	13½	16½	16½	16½	16½	26	16	19½	19½
K-K	Height—overall	72	74⅜	73	75	76⅞	78	80	85	86	95	110
L-L	Overall F. to B.	30	30	35	35	35	44	44	46	48	60	64
M-M	Add to above when inclined 45°	22	24⅜	18	19	19	22	23	24	25	32	32
X-X	Diameter hole in Bed	5½	5½	7½	7½	9	9	9	9	10¾	10¾	15
T-T	Die space—Slide down Adj. up with std. stroke	6½	9	6½	7½	10	6½	7½	10	10	11	10
V-V	GIB LENGTH	12	12¾	13	13	13	15	15¾	15¾	16	17½	22
	ADJUSTMENT IN.	1½	1½	1½	1½	1½	2	2	2	2	2	2½
	STD. STROKE	1½	2	2	2½	3	2	2½	3	2½	4	2½

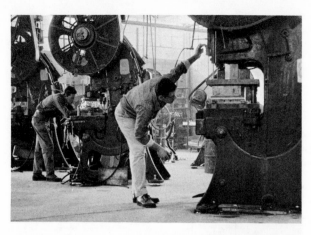

Figure 1·9 View showing a line of four OBI presses in a typical stamping plant. Die setters are setting up dies in the presses, in preparation for production runs.

the front of the press frame, clearance (shown as C) must be provided.

$$C = \text{⅛ to ¼ in. min.}$$

Bolster Openings. Remember that openings in the bolster plate are special. They are made to suit various applications or ranges of applications. Keep in mind that the die-shoe area must be large enough to extend an adequate distance beyond the bolster opening. Remember also that,

unless special provision is made, slugs or blanks which pass through the die must also pass freely through the bolster-plate and press-bed openings.

Feed height. For dies which are fed manually, the feed height is not critical. However, when dies are used in conjunction with automatic feeding devices, the height of the stock line of the die must be within the range permitted by the feeding device.

Other dimensional relationships. The relationships which have been described and discussed up to this point have been presented here for the following reasons:

1. The relationships are not immediately obvious and require study for the thorough understanding which is essential to diemaking proficiency.
2. Experience has shown that certain relationships, although obvious, are all too often overlooked.

The other press dimensions and die-to-press relationships may be readily determined by referring to the press specification chart or by examining and measuring the actual press, if necessary.

A typical press specification diagram and chart as supplied by one press manufacturer appears in Figs. 1·7 and 1·8.

CHAPTER 2

AUTOMATIC FEEDS

GENERAL BACKGROUND

A very important consideration for any given job is the choice of the most economical and efficient feed to be used with it. Many factors govern the selection of a press feed for coil and strip stock. Some of these are the degrees of accuracy needed, the width and thickness of the stock, the speed and flexibility required of the feed, the length of the production run, the kind of work performed, the construction of the die, and the use or nonuse of straighteners.

Basic feed types. There are two basic types of feed used with coil and strip stock, namely, slide feeds and roll feeds. Many manufacturers, however, offer variations on the basic types that differ widely in cost and performance characteristics. This makes the problem of feed selection more complex. A general knowledge of the types of feeds available is essential to sound selection.

Most roll and slide feeds, particularly in the more common sizes, are manufactured by specialists. With a few major exceptions, press manufacturers purchase this type of equipment from feed manufacturers rather than building it themselves. The reasoning for this is quite obvious. Feed making is a relatively light manufacturing operation in comparison with press building. The plant that is geared to press manufacture would have to maintain separate facilities and equipment for feed manufacture. Most press manufacturers prefer to keep their operation divorced from feed manufacture.

The common practice in the industry is for the press manufacturer to provide roll or slide feeds at the option of the buyer.

Feeds for existing equipment. The market for feeds is not confined to new equipment. It also includes furnishing feeds for existing equipment. This results from the increasing trend toward press automation in the stamping industry. This trend, in turn, results from stronger competition,

foreign and domestic, and a continuing effort to get costs down. The most fertile area for reducing costs in the stamping industry is that of man-hours. Automatic feeding is an efficient and readily available means of exploiting this area. Feed selection thus becomes a critical function of the equipment specifier.

This trend toward automation of presses has resulted, in recent years, in the marketing of many new types of roll and slide feeds by established feed builders and by newcomers to the field. Some of these offer innovations that are of genuine worth. One of the largest buyers of roll and slide feeds is the engineer in the small stamping plants who may have little experience with automatic feeds or whose experience may be confined to one type. To assist this buyer and his more experienced counterpart in their job of selection, field-proved examples of existing types and the method by which they operate will be described in this chapter. It is equally important that the diemaker be acquainted with the basic feeds.

It would not be practical to attempt to describe and/or discuss the products of all feed manufacturers. Therefore, the feeds which are described in the following paragraphs have been selected as typical examples.

MECHANICAL SLIDE FEEDS

Mechanical slide feeds are offered by a number of manufacturers in a variety of sizes and capacities. The basic principle of the mechanical slide feed is the use of a feed block actuated between positive stops that advances the material the exact distance required at each stroke. Mechanical slide feeds have inherently high accuracy. They are particularly suitable for use with coil stock. When strip stock is used, it is necessary to feed the strip ends into the press manually.

Adjustment of mechanical slide feeds may be somewhat critical when dies with pilots are used. After the feed block has pushed the stock for-

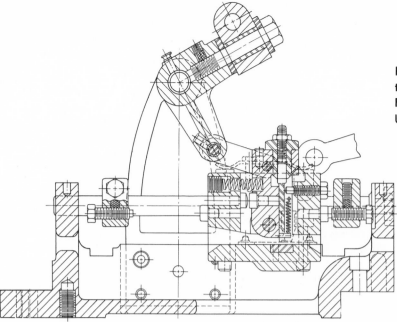

Figure **2·1** This line drawing illustrates the mechanical slide feed pictured in Fig. 2·2, views *A*, *B*, and *C*. Feed is a U.S. Tool Company, Inc. model.

ward, a drag or roller check holds the stock from sliding backward on the return stroke of the feed block. Since the stock is not completely free at this point, the check restricts backward motion; it must be located accurately by the feed so that the pilots can engage without distorting the pilot holes. This is usually accomplished by feeding short, which permits the pilots to pull the strip into position. This action is described and illustrated in Chapter 8 of "Basic Diemaking."

Figure 2·1 shows a cross section through a typical mechanical slide feed.

Feeding thin stock. When thin stock is to be fed with the slide feed, stock guides should be used to overcome any tendency of the stock to buckle. Buckling is usually caused by interference in the die. Such interference will, of course, affect all types of feeds. Buckling can be overcome to some degree by the use of stock guides. These are flat plates that support the stock from below. Stock guides are generally necessary when the stock strip is less than $\frac{1}{32}$ in. thick. For feeding very thin material, roll feeds have certain advantages. These will be discussed in a later section.

Typical mechanical slide feeds. Typical of many mechanical slide feeds is a popular stock model offered by a major supplier. It is powered by the crankshaft of the press, as are most feeds of this type. The rotation of the press is transmitted to the feed through an eccentric mounted on the crankshaft. The eccentric may be a simple one-piece unit keyed to the crankshaft, or it may be adjustable. Adjustable eccentrics are more expen-

sive, but they make it possible to vary the feed with relationship to the rotation of the crank shaft. Where frequent changes in feed length are expected, the adjustable type should receive strong consideration, since it simplifies timing.

The feed block is mounted on hardened slide rods running through the body of the feed block parallel to the feed direction. The block is free to reciprocate on the slide rods. The linkage of the feed block to the eccentric is provided by an adjustable connecting rod. The feed end of such a connecting rod can be seen connected to the feed block linkage at the top of the feed in Fig. 2·2.

Mounted in the feed block is a feed-blade holder with an adjustable feed blade, usually carbide-tipped. The feed blade or gripper plate alternately grips the material during the feed stroke and releases on the return stroke. The action is very similar to that of a carpenter's plane.

Drag plugs in the feed block are provided to supply tension between the block and the slide rods on which it rides. These have a braking action and are adjustable. The basic motion of the feed block is provided by the eccentric. Feed length is controlled by using adjustable stops.

The direction of feed, left to right, right to left, or front to back, is governed by the location of the crankshaft extension on the press and, of course, the arrangement of the die. If a mechanical slide feed which feeds left to right, or vice versa, is desired on a press with a front-to-back crankshaft, it can be provided by using appropriate linkage.

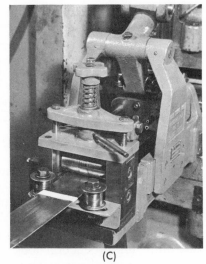

| (A) | (B) | (C) |

Figure **2·2**   View A: Tape on stock strip shows progress. The feed block is fully retracted in this view. View B: Gripper plate has engaged, and stock strip is being pushed into the die. View C: Feed stroke has been completed. Press ram is down. Note position of tape.

To ensure against the possibility of slippage, most mechanical-slide-feed users install a drag unit. This is simply a pair of plates covered with brake lining through which the stock passes. It is mounted in front of the feed. Roller checks are used when marking of the stock is objectionable. These are hardened steel rolls with a one-way clutch that permits the stock to move only in a forward direction.

Most mechanical slide feeds provide sufficient power to pull stock through plain straighteners. This is a definite advantage of this type of equipment, since the cost of a powered straightener is eliminated.

Mechanical slide feeds in the intermediate sizes are usually mounted to the bolster of the press. Many users, particularly of the smaller sizes, mount mechanical slide feeds to the die and consider the feed as part of the die. This can be practical because of the low initial cost of the feed. Die-mounted feeds reduce setup time.

For many operations, particularly blanking and light drawing operations on metal ⅛ in. and less in thickness, mechanical slide feeds offer outstanding economies. Figure 2·3 shows another typical mechanical slide feed.

AIR SLIDE FEEDS

Like mechanical slide feeds, air slide feeds use a feed block and blade, usually carbide-tipped, to push the stock into the die. Unlike mechanical feeds, they are not powered by the crankshaft of the press but are actuated by air pressure applied to a cylinder. Timing an air slide feed is commonly accomplished by means of a cam, which may be

attached to the press ram or to the crankshaft. Many other methods of controlling these feeds are also practical. For example, there is at least one commercial model of air slide feed in wide use which can be used with a timing device that causes the feed to control the press. This is a useful procedure when the press is faster than the feed.

Since they are not operated by the crankshaft, air slide feeds can be used to feed in any direction and feeding time can be reduced to less than 180° of crankshaft rotation. This is essential to

Figure **2·3**   A simple but efficient version of a mechanical slide feed is manufactured by the Producto Machine Company. This type of feeder is easily set up by using slide blocks made from round stock cut to size and faced.

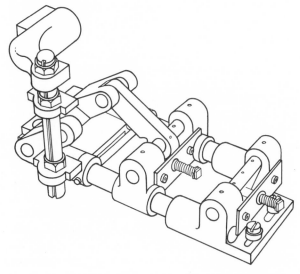

9

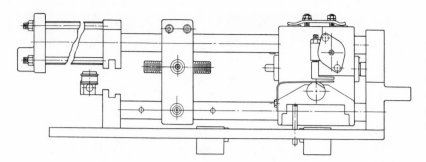

Figure **2·4** Air slide feeds are versatile. They are not dependent upon press action for operation and can be used wherever an adequate supply of shop air at 60 to 100 psi is available.

some types of progressive forming or drawing operations. (It should be remembered that this is also a feature of some types of mechanical slide feeds.)

Air slide feeds should receive serious consideration for production jobs where long feed lengths and small press tonnages are required. Very often, when other feed types are employed on such jobs, it is necessary to use a heavier press than would be otherwise needed in order to get the required feed length. The size of the press has no bearing on the size of air slide feed that can be used. By using electric counters to operate the press on every second cycle, a 40-in. feed can be obtained from a 20-in. air slide feed. Counters are furnished by one manufacturer that can operate up to 6 cycles and a maximum feed length of 144 in.

Other advantages of air slide feeds are their adaptability to hydraulic presses or other presses without accessible crankshafts and the ease and speed with which the required feed length can be set. In many cases, air slide feeds can provide sufficient pull to make the use of plain stock straighteners feasible.

The major disadvantages of air slide feeds include the cost of providing a reliable source of shop air at 80 to 100 psi and the inherent speed limitations of any mechanism that must wait for

air to exhaust and for a piston to return to position on each stroke. Speed limitations for one manufacturer's medium-duty models are 150 strokes per minute at 6 in. feed and 60 strokes per minute at 24 in. feed. This is considerably less than the speed possible with mechanical slide feeds but it is entirely adequate for most press operations in the average stamping plant. Figure 2·4 shows a typical air slide feed.

HITCH FEEDS

Hitch feeds have been in general use for more than a quarter of a century. They resemble mechanical slide feeds in that the stock is pushed forward by a gripper plate. Again, the action is similar to that of a carpenter's plane. Unlike mechanical slide feeds, the hitch feed is operated by a cam mounted on the punch holder, the operation being independent of any connection to the crankshaft. Hitch feeds can be used to feed stock in any direction and can be used on presses that do not have accessible crankshafts.

The actual propelling force is generated by one or more springs that are compressed by the action of the cam as the punch holder descends. The springs feed the stock into the die on the upstroke of the press. Figure 2·5 shows a hitch feed.

Hitch feeds are among the most inexpensive of all press feeding devices, and it is common prac-

Figure **2·5** The Dickerman hitch feed is a very popular and reliable feeder. Its action is readily apparent from an examination of this line drawing. Some hitch feeds use cylinders instead of gripper plates.

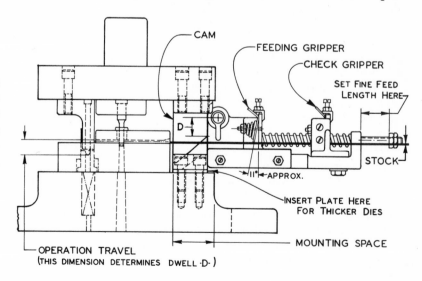

tice in the stamping industry to mount hitch feeds permanently on the dies with which they are used. They are very well suited to fast blanking operations as well as for use with progressive and piloted dies. They are not suited to the feeding of wide, heavy materials. Hitch feeds available at present can handle stock up to 8 in. wide and 0.031 in. thick. A model exists that can feed stock up to 0.050 in. thick, but only in narrower widths.

A disadvantage of hitch feeds is the necessity of machining a cam for each feed-length and press-stroke combination desired. This disadvantage has been overcome to a large extent by the development of a simple formula that can be used with a template, furnished by the feed supplier, to generate the appropriate cam shape. Ordinary toolroom equipment is all that is needed for machining the cams.

A variation of the hitch feed, similar in that the propelling force is derived from springs which are compressed by cam action, uses stock-gripping cylinders in place of a gripper plate. In this respect, this type of feed resembles a roll feed. The cylinders operate on the principle of an overriding clutch. They rotate freely in one direction and lock instantly against rotation in the other direction. This makes movement of stock between the cylinders possible in one direction only. Models of this die feed are available that can handle stock to 6 in. wide. Generally, hitch feeds are not well suited to jobs requiring very long feed lengths. Because of the cam action, the feed length is restricted to a distance which does not require an impractical degree of angle for the cam.

A third type of spring-powered feed is available that makes greater feed-length settings possible. This is accomplished by incorporating a rack slide into the body of the feed, a feature which doubles the potential feed length. This type of press feed, like that discussed in the previous paragraph, has a stock release which opens the gripping cylinders, making it suitable for feeding dies which are equipped with pilots. It is an open-throat design. Since it grips only the edge of the material being fed, very wide stock widths can be handled. This type of feed has proved to be particularly suitable for use with draw-form dies.

ROLL FEEDS (Figs. 2·6–2·8)

Roll feeds are widely used throughout the stamping industry. They are available in sizes suitable for use with almost any size and thickness of stock and are used in every type of presswork ranging from simple blanking jobs to complex blanking and drawing operations involving

Figure **2·6** Cleanly designed roll feed made by the E. W. Bliss Company.

the use of progressive dies. Roll feeds, as a rule, are somewhat more expensive than the simpler types of slide feeds designed for feeding coil or strip stock. For a given job under a given set of circumstances, however, a roll feed may be the most economical type. The nature of the stamping industry is such that the cost of accessory equipment may be written off in terms of literally millions of pieces produced. Therefore, first cost becomes relatively insignificant.

Basically, a roll feed consists of a pair of rolls that can turn in only one direction. They exert pressure on the stock by means of springs or other devices. They are rotated by the motion of the press crankshaft. As they rotate, they push the stock forward a distance that is a function of the angle of rotation.

Other than size, the basic differences among roll feeds are the manner by which the motion of the press slide or the rotation of the crankshaft is transmitted to the feed rolls and the method by which roll lifters, if they are employed, are actuated. Other differences are largely refinements developed to meet specific circumstances.

Roll feeds of all types are very suitable for use with extremely thin materials or for feeding materials with finely polished surfaces. By substituting hard chromium-plated rolls for the standard ground-steel feed rolls, polished surfaces will not be scored or otherwise marked during feeding. Rubber- or plastic-coated rolls can also be used with soft finished or prepainted stock.

There are two advantages to be gained by using roll feeds for feeding very thin stock. By using

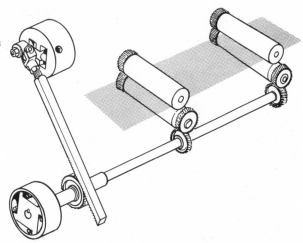

Figure **2·7** Drawing illustrates feed manufactured by the F. J. Littell Machine Company.

patterned rolls, a flange can be formed to stiffen the stock. This flange is, of course, formed on a waste edge of the stock. The roll feed can also be located to pull the stock through the die rather than pushing it. This eliminates buckling. The most desirable method of feeding extra-thin stock, however, is to use double roll feeds. This arrangement is a very common one in the stamping industry for all classes of material. Roll feeds are mounted on opposite sides of the die and synchronized so that the stock between them is

Figure **2·8** Double rack-and-pinion feed is mounted on a Warco 125-ton press.

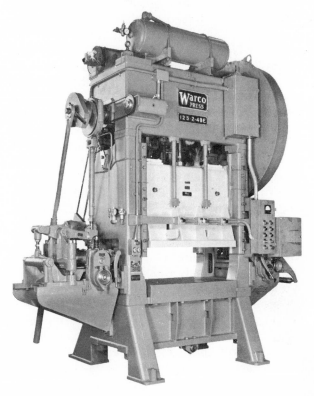

always under slight tension. No buckling is possible.

Roll feeds eliminate manual feeding of end sections when strip stock is processed. Double roll feeds are particularly suitable when a sizable scrap skeleton remains after the press operation.

One of the oldest and most reliable of all roll feeds is the rack-and-pinion type illustrated in Fig. 2·7. The driving disk at the top makes a full 360° turn with each stroke of the press. It actuates the feed rolls through on overrunning clutch during the upstroke. The feed illustrated is a double roll type, widely used in the stamping industry.

Rack-and-pinion roll feeds are available in almost all sizes, but they are usually thought of in connection with relatively heavy stamping and drawing operations on both OBI and straight side presses. On larger presses it is common to use double roll feeds of the rack-and-pinion type that are actually incorporated in the press bolster. This makes for extreme rigidity.

A typical rack-and-pinion roll feed is mounted on the press by adjustable brackets, to provide for a variety of die heights. It is powered by a driving disk that is connected to a hub attached to the press crankshaft. Rotation of the disk on the hub sets the feed length and also makes it possible to adjust feed timing. This is essential in progressive die work. The driving disk makes a full 360° turn with each stroke of the press.

During the first half revolution, the driving disk pulls a rack upward. The rack revolves a drive shaft through an overrunning clutch. The drive shaft revolves the lower feed roll by means of spiral gears. The lower feed roll, through a gear connection, rotates the upper feed roll. The stock strip is between the upper and lower rolls and is subject to the pressure exerted by them. Thus, when the rolls revolve, they cause the stock strip to move through the die.

As the rack reaches the top point of its up stroke, the feeding half of the cycle is complete. When the revolving driving disk starts the rack down, the overrunning clutch is automatically disengaged so that the feed rolls are motionless during the downward travel of the rack. During this period, the stock is located in the die, the stamping is accomplished, and the ram starts on its upward stroke. At the halfway point of the upward stroke, a new feeding cycle begins.

In specifying roll lifters for rack-and-pinion feeds the nature of the work to be done must be considered. For blanking and simple progressive die work, standard roll lifters are adequate. For progressive forming or drawing, another type of lifter should be considered. Either an eccentric or a cam roll type will provide the more precise timing which is generally required for such work.

Bypass automatic roll lifters or their equivalent should be considered where early piloting is necessary or when deep forming or drawing is being performed in progressive dies.

A chain-driven roll feed (Fig. 2·9). An interesting feature of another successful type of roll feed is the use of a chain drive rather than an eccentric. The feed rolls turn constantly, rather than intermittently. Power for driving the feed rolls is transmitted by a chain drive from the sprocket mounted on the drive shaft of the feed itself. This type of feed is furnished with an adjustable chain tightener so that interchangeable sprockets can be used to develop any desired ratio between press and feed.

The lower rolls on the feed are driven by the feed drive shaft by means of bevel gears. The lower rolls in turn drive the upper rolls through special spur gears that remain in constant mesh. The upper rolls are mounted in floating bearings that rest on the cams of a release shaft. During feeding, the upper rolls are held against the stock by adjustable springs. To provide intermittent feeding, the upper rolls are lifted from the stock by a release mechanism operated by a trip arm attached to the ram of the press. The trip arm can be set so that it will break contact between the rolls and the stock at any desired point in the stroke of the ram by operating a camshaft that lifts both ends of the rolls in their bearings.

Feeding of the stock starts as soon as the rolls start to lift. This makes it possible to use any part of the press stroke for feeding purposes. By using appropriate sprockets, this type of feed can be used to obtain a long feed during any part of the crankshaft revolution. This is an advantage in feeding combination dies or progressive dies, where a large part of the stroke is used for drawing or forming. Since the length of the feed is not dependent on the speed of the press or the length of the stroke, this type of feed can generate long feeds on short stroke operations.

A cam-driven feed. A unique type of roll feed used in underdrive presses has some interesting features. This feed is used primarily in high-production high-speed operations. Instead of the springs used in conventional roll feeds to provide pressure on the upper feed roll, air pressure is used. The pressure is adjustable, by means of a valve, to suit the material and feed conditions. The brakes are water-cooled.

The most unusual feature of this feed is the

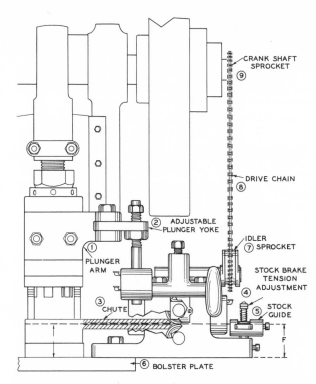

Figure **2·9** Unusual roll feed by the Wittek Manufacturing Company is chain-driven from press crankshaft.

method by which it is driven. A cam is mounted on the crankshaft to push against an air-backed plunger. The contour of the cam can be changed to permit feeding in longer or shorter periods of the press stroke. This is a distinct advantage because, with the feed period shorter than the standard 180° feeding period of the conventional feed, it is possible to draw deeper shells with the same stroke of the press. Conversely, feeding with a longer period makes it possible to operate the press faster, thus producing more parts while keeping the actual feeding speed of the material within normally accepted limits.

The cam-actuated plunger rocks a lever, the opposite end of which is attached to a rack that drives the feed roll. Moving the fulcrum on which the lever pivots changes the feed length. It is possible to move this fulcrum while the press is running. This can facilitate adjusting and correcting the feed length.

Wedge-type roll feed. Another kind of roll feed is the wedge type. The basic mechanism is quite simple, consisting of a bronze arm mounted between two hardened steel disks. The disks have flanged rims. The bronze arm and the steel disks are mounted on a common shaft. The disks are keyed and setscrewed to the shaft, and the arm is free to turn. A wedge-shaped dog, cut out at the sides to fit the flanges of this disk, is mounted so

13

that its lower end rests in a cutout in the bronze arm hub, while the other is linked to the arm by a coil spring.

When the arm is turned clockwise on the shaft by rotation of the press crankshaft, pressure is exerted by the cutout wall of the hub on the lower end of the wedge. This clamps the edges of the wedge cutouts against the flanges of the disks and revolves the feed rolls.

The disks themselves are hardened to Rockwell C62-65. To prevent disk wear, the wedges are hardened to a slightly lesser degree. This type of feed has given good service in combination with multiple-stage progressive dies in comparatively light operations. It is somewhat limited with respect to length of feed, but geared versions can feed up to 20 in. of 12-in.-wide stock.

Versatility of roll feeds. One of the important factors in considering roll feeds is their extreme range and flexibility. Roll feeds are widely used for feeding very narrow stock and fine wire. They are also available for feeding extremely heavy and broad widths of stock. The same basic principle is applicable.

Roll feeds are often incorporated into feeding machines that are independently powered. They may or may not include straighteners and coil cradles.

Other feed types of interest to stampers are dial feeds, hopper feeds, vibratory feeds, some types of transfer feeds, and a number of specialized feeds that have been developed to meet specific requirements. Of these, dial and special feeds are discussed in the following text.

Figure **2·10** Operator performs two jobs with this dial feed. Press is a 21-B inclinable. Feed is manufactured by Bliss.

DIAL FEEDS

The use of dial feeds with mechanical presses, though a relatively new technique, is growing rapidly.

Prior to World War II, only a few truly accurate dial feeds were available to the press user, although many stamping shops successfully used simplified Geneva drives to power index tables of various kinds. Dial-fed presses were available from press builders, but their use was limited, and relatively low labor costs made it difficult to justify them from the standpoint of economy.

Many dial-feed types are now available to the stamping plant. Some of these can be supplied with new presses as an integral part of the press. Many of the dial feeds supplied by press builders are manufactured by outside sources, for the very good reason that their manufacture is a field in itself. Variations of these dial feeds can usually be purchased as separate items for installation on existing equipment.

The increase in use of dial feeds stems from the growing need for high productivity in stamping operations. The dial feed, either manually supplied or hopper supplied, can offer substantial labor savings.

A simple illustration might be that of a 50-ton OBI press used for a second operation—coining a drawn part such as an outlet box, for example. To equip such a press with a dial feed would cost in the neighborhood of $4,000 if one widely used type of equipment were specified. Installation of the dial feed to produce such a workpiece would slightly more than double production under normal conditions. If the job volume were great enough, direct labor savings alone would recover the cost of the equipment in a relatively short time.

Corollary savings include the possibility of eliminating one or more presses or of using auxiliary equipment such as hoppers to permit one operator to take care of more than one machine. This is often done.

General description. Basically a dial feed is a rotating table. It may be built into the press bed, or it may be fixed to the press bolster, or it may be a separate piece of equipment. Its function is to position one or more dies under a punch or punches mounted on the press slide. It may also be used to carry blanks or partially completed workpieces between a fixed punch and die.

The dial feed may be powered by the press crankshaft or independently. Units of the latter type are usually more expensive, but they have unique advantages.

The heart of any dial feed is the mechanical principle by which it operates. This may be a simple ratchet-and-pawl arrangement. It may be a system of dogs and pins. It may be a barrel-type indexing cam of great complexity. All three methods give good service in specific applications. The cam-operated dial feed has the widest acceptance in the press industry.

Application range. The proper specification of dial-feeding equipment is a function of the part to be fed. This determines the type of drive that should be selected, the diameter of the dial table, the degree of accuracy required, and the number of stations on the dial. The possible volume of work of a given description is an influencing factor.

Dial feeds can be applied to blanking, coining, staking, piercing, bending, forming, and drawing operations. The only limiting factor is the physical capacity of any given dial feed in relation to the size of the tooling as dictated by the size and/or nature of the work. Dial feeds have been applied to presses exceeding 125 tons capacity. Unfortunately, many stampers who could otherwise use dial feeds to good advantage think of them only in terms of relatively light assembly operations or as second-operation equipment for the screw-machine industry, etc.

Some of the available dial-feed types. Some dial feeds that have given good service are described in the following text. Although it does not encompass all available makes of equipment, the description will give the reader some indication of what is available and some of the factors that should be considered in selecting equipment.

One of the most widely used versions of the cam-operated dial feed is that manufactured by the Federal Press Company. This organization builds presses with and without dial feeds. It also makes dial feeds that can be installed on almost all other makes of presses.

This dial feed is powered by the rotation of the crankshaft through a meter-gear drive and shaft or through chains and gears. The crankshaft rotation is transmitted to a hardened indexing cam that moves the table through a system of cam followers. The use of a cam provides extreme accuracy. To prevent possible misalignments, a series of holes are jig-bored around the circumference of the dial plate. As the dial indexes to each position, a spring-loaded pin, mounted beneath the dial, enters the hole. The pin serves as a protective device. If the pin does not enter the hole, the clutch will not engage and the ram cannot descend.

The dial feeds offered by this maker can be provided in virtually any diameter and number of indexing stations. They can also be provided with independent drives. They are high-precision equipment and are usually installed at the Federal plant.

A different kind of cam-operated dial feed is that made by the Ferguson Machine Corporation. The cam is of a special design that has been extensively used on assembly equipment for many years and that takes into consideration three types of acceleration.

Two preloaded antifriction bearing followers are in contact with the cam rib at all times. In the dwell position there is no clearance between the cam rib and the followers. The accuracy of this indexing drive, it may be noted, is closer than 0.001 in.

Ferguson equipment is also furnished in the form of a high-speed press feed with an integral bolster. The dial and the dies may be removed as a unit, or the index table and bolster may be detached from the press. It is designed to be driven by the press crankshaft. Ferguson drives can be installed on almost any make of press. They are offered as original equipment by several major press builders.

The E. W. Bliss Company uses the principle of the indexing cam in its dial feed, manufactured primarily for use on Bliss presses.

Other manufacturers of cam-type indexing equipment are the Swanson-Erie Corporation and the Standard Tool and Manufacturing Company. Both these makers provide integral indexing units that are widely used in machining and assembly operations. The basic equipment can be applied to presswork.

Typical of the specialized equipment that these manufacturers can provide is a Swanson-Erie machine, based on a turret-type indexing-machine chassis that performs automatic feeding as well as two piercing, two lancing, and two stenciling operations. The press units are actually attachments to the indexing chassis. Sequential press operations are performed about the periphery of the turret. This method is particularly profitable in operations involving small parts on which several light press jobs must be done.

A relatively simple and inexpensive dial feed is manufactured by the Benchmaster Manufacturing Company. This feed can be applied to any small press. Rotation is by means of an indexing plate.

The outer circumference of the indexing plate is equally divided into the desired number of stations with V-shaped notches. The notches are engaged by a round-nose spring-loaded pawl

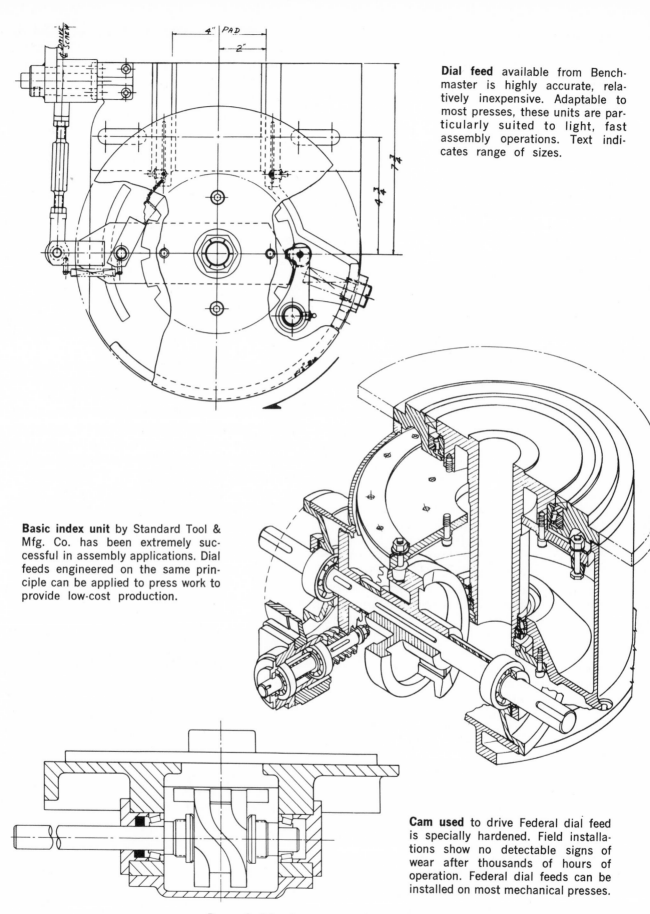

Dial feed available from Benchmaster is highly accurate, relatively inexpensive. Adaptable to most presses, these units are particularly suited to light, fast assembly operations. Text indicates range of sizes.

Basic index unit by Standard Tool & Mfg. Co. has been extremely successful in assembly applications. Dial feeds engineered on the same principle can be applied to press work to provide low-cost production.

Cam used to drive Federal dial feed is specially hardened. Field installations show no detectable signs of wear after thousands of hours of operation. Federal dial feeds can be installed on most mechanical presses.

Figure **2·11**   Some types of dial-feed drives.

operating on a rocker. The rounded section seats in the V.

This equipment has an unusually long table dwell for punch engagement and withdrawal from the die. With 12 stations, the table is completely stationary during 220° of crankshaft rotation.

Benchmaster equipment is available in table diameters of 12 and 15 in. Stock equipment can be furnished with 8, 10, or 12 stations. More stations are available on special order. This equipment is relatively inexpensive yet highly accurate. It should receive consideration in specifying dial feeds for light operations.

Both rotary index tables and dial feeds are manufactured by the Bellows Company and have been widely used in conjunction with machine tools as well as presses. Typical is the company's model BRET-260.

This index table has a 1-in. mild-steel table top which rotates on a cast-iron subplate. Tapered bushings are press-fitted into the bottom of the perimeter of the table, 1 in. inside the circumference. The bushings are engaged by an air-powered tapered shot pin that locks the table in exact position at the end of each indexing stroke of an air motor. The motor's piston rod indexes the table, operating through a rack-and-gear mechanism interlocked with an air-operated ratchet pawl. The piston stroke is cushioned on the advance stroke. The cushioning action can be regulated.

Maximum turning effort (in in. per lb) of the table is 30 times the air pressure applied, usually 60 to 125 psi. Shop air is used. This equipment is available in 4, 6, 9, 12, or 18 stations in standard models. Tables with up to 36 stations are available on special order.

Selecting a dial-feed type. The press user who wishes to employ dial feeds has a wide range of equipment from which to select the feed best suited to his needs. The cost of dial feeds ranges from a few hundred to several thousands of dollars. The cost reflects, to a great extent, the size, speed, and accuracy of the equipment.

The question of which equipment is best for a given job can best be answered by personnel specializing in the field. The dial-feed makers mentioned in this section maintain extensive field representation, as do builders whose equipment is not discussed here.

While the question "Which feed shall I use?" is best answered by specialists, it can be positively stated that dial feeds of one description or the other offer much the same economies in second operations as roll feeds and other auto-

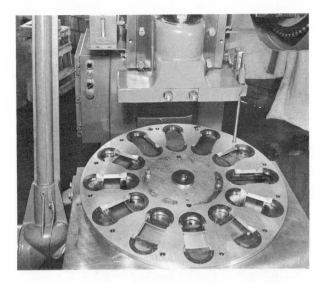

Figure **2·12** Pockets on this Federal dial feed are special. Maker can provide almost any conceivable shape.

mation devices offer to coil-stock users. In today's highly competitive markets, dial feeds should receive the most serious consideration by the specifier of stamping equipment and accessories.

Their use should not be confined merely to light operations, although it is in this area that they have had the widest acceptance. There are many repetitive operations involving the use of blanks or partly worked metal shapes where a dial feed could be applied in a manner that would increase production.

The stamping industry has made great advances in the domain of other metalworking processes, primarily because of chip elimination. Further

Figure **2·13** This Bellows rotary-feed table with arbor press boosted bearing production 100 percent.

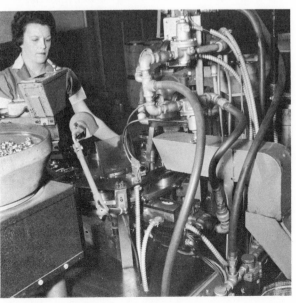

Figure **2·14** Specialized version of a roll feed made by the Automatic Feed Company was designed for unusually high-speed service.

gains will have to be based on increased efficiency. Dial feeds offer one of the proved methods for increasing efficiency.

SPECIAL FEEDS

Another feed category, called "special" feeds for want of a more definitive term, deserves the study of the equipment specifier. For reasons of space, it is not feasible to attempt to list all the available special feeding equipment. The selection that follows will serve to illustrate the range of work that these feeds can do. It bears out an

Figure **2·15** Out-feed side of press with coil-stock cradle and straightener in background. Stock strip 48 in. wide by 0.06 in. thick is automatically fed by Ses-Matic feeder.

earlier premise that there are extremely few press-feeding operations, primary or secondary, that cannot be made automatic.

Some special-feed examples. The potential economies that can result from automatic press feeding are often startling. A Detroit firm was hand feeding 14 × 0.06-in. coil stock to a punch press. Production was 14,000 pieces per day. An air feed was installed, not to increase production, but to eliminate die damage resulting from operator fatigue. Die damage was eliminated, as planned. Production also increased to 33,000 pieces per day.

The air feed referred to was made by the Special Engineering Service, Inc. (a Dearborn, Mich., firm). Its equipment is marketed under the name Ses-Matic. Ses-Matic air and gripper feeds are available in stock models. The company also furnishes specialized equipment. Typical is a feed made for molded extrusions in which the clamping surfaces are made to fit the extrusion precisely.

Another special Ses-Matic feed handles a job that requires six 10-in. feed strokes followed by one 2-in. feed stroke. An electrical counter and a solenoid establish the cycle.

Many Ses-Matic special feeds are adaptations of standard feeds. Most makers of roll, slide, air, and hitch feeds will engineer their equipment to fill special needs. The Automatic Feed Company (Napoleon, Ohio) has done some particularly valuable work in this area. When standard equipment can be used for special work, the basic cost is usually reduced. The point to be noted is that most shapes can be automatically fed and that the cost may be far less than a casual estimate would indicate.

A unique storage feeder was designed by the Campbell Machines Company (Detroit, Mich.) to feed a part that would not seem to lend itself to automation. Two sizes of connecting rod are oriented and fed to a mechanical press for a straightening operation. The storage feed is vibratory. The feed reorients the rod so that it hangs from the wrist-pin boss with the long axis of the yoke parallel to the direction of travel. A second-stage orienter turns the rods 90°, putting the cross axis of the yoke parallel to the travel. The rods are fed to the press at the rate of 1,500 pieces per hour.

While not an extreme case, this feed does indicate that even complex shapes can be fed automatically.

Not all special feeds are made by feed specialists. Several press builders have done outstanding work in developing special feeds that are basic to

their presses. Typical of this class is a shuttle feed
made by the Federal Machine and Welder Company and installed on a 250-ton Warco press.

The feed carries the parts from a receiving station on the conveyor to the work station in the
press by means of mechanically operated fingers.
This is done during the downward stroke of the
press. As the press stroke continues, the fingers
return and mechanically operated discharge fingers bump the part against locating blocks in the
die. The discharge fingers then move out of the
way, and the stroke is completed. After the dies
reopen, the discharge fingers reverse direction
and displace the part from the die. At the same
time they trip a limit switch and reset the cycle.

This is only one of many special feeds designed
into presses by the Federal Machine and Welder
Company. Such integral feeds, of course, are
usually suitable only for high-volume operation.

Another feed, and a most unusual one, was
designed by the Ferracute Machine Company for

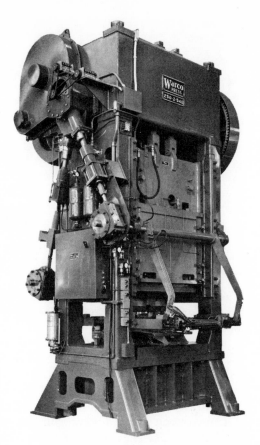

Figure 2·16 Shuttle-type feed
shown here was made by the Federal
Machine and Welder Company. It
is installed on a 250-ton Warco
press. The cycle is fully automatic.

Figure 2·17 Chain feed on a
Ferracute embossing press makes
rocker arms, two at a time, at 30
strokes per minute.

Figure **2·18** Noteworthy feature of this Flexofeed is the ease and speed of converting from feeding blanks to feeding coil stock.

use on its E-401 embossing press. The feed consists of a chain with cavities in which workpieces are placed. These are fed to the front of the press and drop out the back on completion.

The workpiece is a rocker arm for intake and exhaust valves. They are made two at a time at 30 strokes per minute. Total production is 3,600 pieces per hour. Changing the chain to provide different cavities gives this special feed more

Figure **2·19** Sahlin Iron Hands, usually associated with unloading the work, can also be designed to feed the work into the die.

flexibility than would be apparent from a casual consideration.

A different kind of flexibility was the object of the Precision Welder and Flexopress Corporation in designing its Flexofeed, a special feed available on its line of high-productivity straight-side automatic presses.

The Flexofeed was designed to fill the gap that exists when a high-speed press is idle. It makes it possible to change over from blanks to coil stock or from one size of blank to another in about the same time that it takes to change a die. These feeds are designed to suit the application (or applications) and become an integral part of the press.

An excellent example is a Flexofeed designed for a clutch-plate job. Clutch plates are used in automatic transmissions for automobiles. They are blanked in a variety of diameters ranging from 4 to 6 in. Since the job was to be run at 200 strokes per minute, it was obvious that there would be idle press time.

A gripper mechanism was incorporated in the feed so that the idle time could be used with a standard progressive die using coil stock. Actual production of all parts at present exceeds 250 per minute.

Another application calls for 0.014-in. coil stock, 40 in. wide, to be fed in 15-in. increments. Regular production of 80 strokes per minute is being maintained. Other jobs using this same equipment range up to 42 in. wide and run at speeds that vary from 40 to 120 strokes per minute.

It should be pointed out that almost all press builders can and will design special feeds into their presses. As stated previously, however, a very high production volume is usually needed to justify the extra expense.

A category of special feed that simulates the action of the human hand and arm to unload the work has given useful service in many stamping plants. A typical example is the Iron Hands feed of the Sahlin Engineering Company, Inc.

Sahlin feeds are available from stock to fit any type of mechanical press. They may be independently driven, or they may be powered from the press crankshaft. Models are available that can feed workpieces up to 12 oz in weight and 36 sq in. in area. Installations of this feed have increased production up to 400 percent.

Also simulating the action of the human operator is the Pas-It feeder made by Press Automation Systems, Inc. (Warren, Mich.). This feed can be used with any OBI press. It consists of a preloading station in which blanks are placed.

An air-powered arm picks work from the station and inserts it in the die. The arm can be equipped with mechanical fingers. The mechanical-finger sets can be specially designed to accommodate unusual shapes. For some work, it may be desirable to equip the arm with a vacuum pickup or with a magnetic pickup. The various finger sets, pickups, etc., can be interchanged. Feeding capacity ranges from 2,000 to 3,600 piece parts per hour.

Most of the press feeds so far discussed were installed to eliminate die damage, to speed up production, and/or to increase safety factors. However, another important reason for the installation of press-feeding equipment is to provide a practical means for the handling of bulky and/or heavy material. The McKay Machine Company (Youngstown, Ohio) and Automation Associates, Inc. (Madison Heights, Mich.) are among the numerous manufacturers who have done outstanding work in developing this kind of equipment.

Any study or consideration of the potential of automatic feeds makes it quite clear that the majority of primary stamping operations can be accomplished most economically by feeding coil or strip stock, with roll, slide, air, or hitch feeds (or variations of these feeds) used. It also becomes clear that many secondary operations can be made more efficient by the use of automatic feeding devices. Dial feeds and/or special feeds can be adapted to almost any conceivable part or shape.

Why, then, are so many presses still fed by hand when automatic feeds have so much to offer? Probably because of two basic misconceptions.

The first misconception has to do with initial cost. Actual prices have not been mentioned here, since the cost of special feeds is a function of the part to be fed. However, in a very general way, it can be said that most special feeds will pay for themselves within one year. Very often they will pay for themselves in weeks. This is in

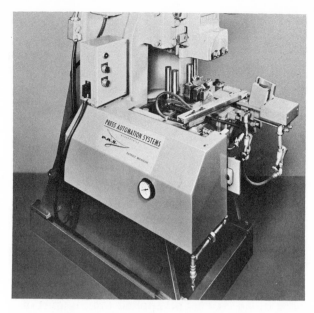

Figure **2·20** Typical of feeds that simulate the action of the human hand and arm is this Pass-It feeder, made by Press Automation Systems, Inc. Press is a Niagara.

terms of production and man-hours alone. The intangible benefits such as operator and equipment protection are bonuses.

The second misconception is that automatic feeds are not justified unless the production volume per given piece part is extremely high. The answer to this is that many press feeds, conventional and special, are far more flexible than they were only a relatively short time ago. Installation and adjustment time has been given a great deal of attention by feed makers. It is no longer necessary to have runs high up in the thousands to justify automatic feeding.

The man who specifies equipment for the stamping plant should examine every job, especially those which are repetitive. He will find it easier to justify automatic feeds than it has ever been in the past. The potentials of increased production, greater safety, more accurate loading, and other factors can no longer be disregarded.

CHAPTER 3

INVERTED DIES

Production applications are encountered from time to time which either require the use of inverted construction or are facilitated by it. The principle of inversion may be applied to the complete die, or it may be applied to only part of a die, as with a progressive die having one or more inverted stations.

It will be best to become familiar with and understand single-station inverted dies before attempting to consider the relative inversion of stations in progressive dies. One of the most representative types of inverted dies appears in Fig. 3·1. The entire die is mounted in a manner vertically reversed to that of a conventional blank-through die. The female (die-block) member is mounted to the punch shoe of the die set and moves with the press ram. The punch is mounted on the die shoe, which is secured to the bolster plate and/or the press bed, whichever is appropriate for the particular application.

The piece parts produced do not pass through the die opening but are ejected from it at each stroke of the press. (There are exceptions to this, but they are unusual and not pertinent to this discussion.)

Figure **3·1** Vertical section through a typical inverted blanking die.

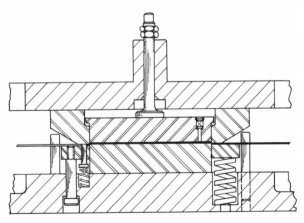

UTILITY CONSIDERATIONS

As with any other die design configuration, there must be reason for using inverted die constructions. Certain factors pertaining to die utility are inherently associated with inverted dies:

1. Press cushions or other equipment mounted in the press bed do not interfere with piece-part disposal.
2. Piece parts may be produced which are too large to pass conveniently through the press bed or bolster plate.
3. A solid bolster plate may be used under this type of die, thereby providing additional support to resist deflection in performing very heavy work. (Factors 2 and 3 do not apply to compound dies or any others which may have scrap passing through the lower die shoe.)
4. If the die is equipped with a preloaded shedder (spring-actuated or the equivalent), the piece parts produced will have a much better degree of flatness than if they were produced by a blank-through die. In fact, even when the shedder is actuated by a positive knockout, inverted dies tend to produce somewhat flatter blanks than blank-through dies. This is largely due to the fact that the blanks are immediately return-ejected from the die opening instead of being forced clear through it.
5. When gaging of the piece parts can be accomplished in a practical manner, secondary operations such as trimming and shaving are often well suited to being performed with inverted dies.

SHEDDING AND STRIPPING

The piece parts are expelled from the die opening by the shedder. The shedder may be either the compression type or the positive type.

Compression type. Compression shedders may be actuated by springs, rubber cushions, hydraulic devices, or pneumatic devices. These shedders are customarily referred to in a specific manner as "spring" shedders, "hydraulic" shedders, etc. They are also referred to in the generic sense as "pushback" shedders.

Positive type. Positive shedders are actuated by positive knockout arrangements which strike against the knockout bar of the punch press or, in some instances, against a specially constructed knockout device. Positive shedders can be appropriately referred to as "percussion" shedders.

As with almost all die components, there are numerous variations and modifications of the above basic shedder types necessitated by specific individual die and production requirements. The particular shedder most suitable for a given application depends upon the nature of the piece part and the production facilities.

With reference to single-station inverted dies, the shedders are most typically either spring-actuated or driven by a positive knockout arrangement which is actuated by the punch-press knock-out bar. For these dies, and speaking from the die-operating standpoint, it can also be generalized that positive shedders are usually more desirable than compression shedders.

Positive shedder proportions. The action of a typical percussive shedder is presented in sequential stages in Figs. 3·2 to 3·5.

In Fig. 3·2 the die is pictured as it would appear during the downstroke before contacting the stock material. This is also the way the various components would be related when the punch holder assembly is removed from the die shoe assembly for bench-checking by the diemaker. In either case the proportional relationships should exist as shown here. The shedder flanges rest on the die opening ledge at P. The jam nuts are seated against the top of the shank at C. The nuts serve as a stop to provide and maintain the clearance gap B. At this stage, the knockout must not be in contact with the shedder. A clearance gap (B) is mandatory. It is also essential for the face of the shedder to protrude beyond the die face a distance A. Minimum dimensions for these relationships should be

$$A = \tfrac{3}{64} \text{ in.}$$
$$B = 0.005 \text{ in.}$$

It should be emphasized that the above dimensions are minimums and are not to be considered as desirable relationships. Avoid working to the minimums. Average optimum dimensions are

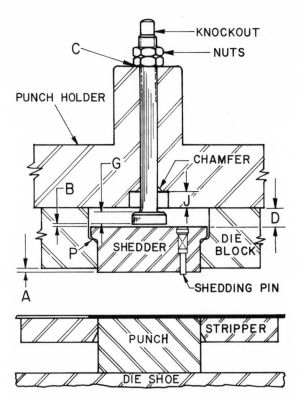

Figure **3·2** Press ram descending (downstroke).

$$A = \tfrac{1}{16} \text{ in.}$$
$$B = \tfrac{1}{64} \text{ in.}$$

These allowances may (and often should) be increased for large work. Cruder work, especially, may require larger allowances at A and B. However, if dimensions A and B are increased significantly, then gap D may require a compensatory increase.

Depth J of the clearance pocket provided for the knockout flange should afford ample clearance for the flange. This also applies to the horizontal dimensions of the pocket. However, in cases where such pockets are exceptionally deep and/or wide, check and verify that the structural integrity of the punch holder in the area of the shank is not endangered.

In Fig. 3·3 the die is shown as it would appear in its closed position at the bottom of the press stroke. The inset view depicts proportions W and H for flanged shedders. These should be

$$W = \tfrac{1}{16} \text{ in. min.}$$
$$H = 1\tfrac{1}{2} \ W \text{ min.}$$
$$H > 1\tfrac{1}{2}W \text{ whenever practical}$$

In order to alleviate cracking tendencies during (or after) heat treatment, always provide a junction fillet where shown (F). Do not make these corners dead sharp. Of necessity, these fillets

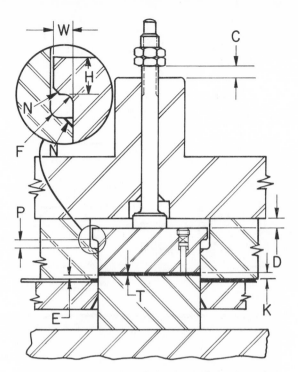

Figure **3·3**   Die closed (bottom of press stroke).

may have to be quite small. However, any fillet is better than no fillet: a fillet radius of 0.010 in. is far superior to a sharp corner. Clearance chamfers N for the fillets should be carefully done and held to a safe minimum size. Generally, the flange area should not be heat-treated harder than

Figure **3·4**   Press ram ascending (upstroke).

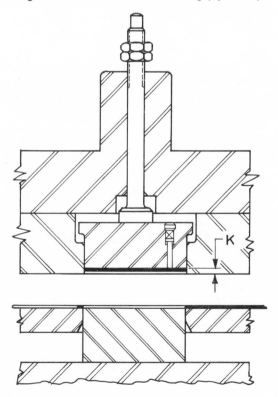

Rockwell C47 even in those applications where the balance of the shedder is made harder.

The stock material thickness is designated as T. E indicates the distance the punch enters the die opening at the closed position. The shedder is now elevated into the die opening a distance $K = E + T$. The total shedder travel is $P = A + K$. (A is, of course, the protrusion distance shown in Fig. 3·2.) Clearance distance C will now be $C = P - B$. At this stage, gap D should normally be a minimum of $2\frac{1}{2}T$ or $\frac{1}{8}$ in., whichever is greater. These figures are minimums and may often be considerably greater. It is readily apparent that the existence of gap D will facilitate die setup in the press. In addition to this, an adequate space at D is an important safety factor. It can (and does) happen that for some reason such as shedding-pin or knockout malfunction, etc., the blank is not totally ejected clear of the die. In the event of such a mishap, gap D should permit at least two extra blanks to be driven accumulatively into the die opening before the back of the shedder is driven against the punch holder. This gives the operator an opportunity to notice the malfunction and stop the press. Or a fail-safe switch can be installed which will be actuated if the shedder is driven farther upward by a "double." The switch will then shut off the press before any damage occurs. Dies of this type have been made where gap D was eliminated in an attempt to flatten the blank. However, spanking the blank by bottoming the shedder has proved to be more wishful than practical and introduces an unnecessary hazard besides. Note the action of the shedding pin at this stage. It has been forced upward against its spring. The compressive force of the spring is now stored until it is needed to complete the action at the top of the press stroke.

In Fig. 3·4 the die has opened, and the upper assembly is ascending with the press ram. The stripper has acted to strip the stock strip from the punch. The lateral compressive forces which are inherent in the cutting action cause the blank to be retained within the die cavity at depth K. Therefore, the various component relationships of the upper assembly are maintained the same as they were at Fig. 3·3 when the die was closed.

Figure 3·5 depicts the proper relationship as it would appear at the instant the press ram reaches the highest point of the press stroke. At this stage the proper relationship is

$$A_1 = P_1$$
$$C = \frac{1}{2}P$$

On the assumption that the shedder is made to

the optimum dimensions given with Fig. 3·2, the actual dimensions at Fig. 3·5 would be

$$A = \tfrac{1}{32} \text{ in.}$$
$$P = \tfrac{1}{32} \text{ in.}$$
$$C = \tfrac{1}{64} \text{ in.}$$

The condition shown is an instantaneous condition. The shedder and the knockout shaft immediately drop free, restoring the relationships shown in Fig 3·2.

Necessity for proper relationships. The major reasons underlying the foregoing shedder relationships are:

1. Diemaking is facilitated, since absolute dimensional exactitude is not required. It is easy to understand, for example, that working to the minimums specified at Fig. 3·2 demands much more of the diemaker than working to either the average optimum allowances or the larger allowances, as suggested.
2. Die setup in the press is much easier when the die is made with adequate shedder-to-knockout allowances.
3. Trouble-free running: inadequate shedder proportions and/or allowances are a source of trouble in the course of die operations.
4. Safety: an inadequate shedder-to-knockout arrangement can be hazardous in relation to both equipment and personnel.

Shedder-to-press relationship. The diagram (Fig. 3·6) serves to illustrate another possible condition which influences shedder proportions. It represents the rotary path of the crankshaft eccentric in a punch press. This path is the crank circle. The rotary motion is converted by the pitman into the reciprocating motion of the ram, resulting in the press stroke S, which is equal to the diameter of the crank circle. The top of the press stroke coincides with the top-dead-center (TDC) position of the crankshaft.

If the press should happen to stop at some point X before TDC, the effective knockout travel at this point would be shorter by the amount Y.

$$Y = R - R \cos L$$

EXAMPLE

$$R = 2 \text{ in.} \qquad L = 5°$$

Then

$$Y = 2 - 2 \ (0.996) \qquad \text{or} \qquad Y = 0.008 \text{ in.}$$

A poorly proportioned shedder with inadequate knockout allowances might fail to eject the blank

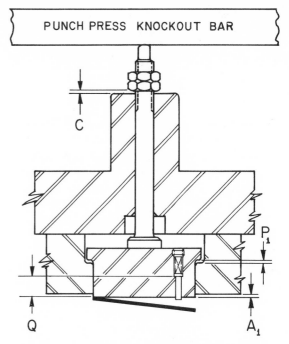

PUNCH PRESS KNOCKOUT BAR

Figure **3·5**   Top of press stroke (TDC position).

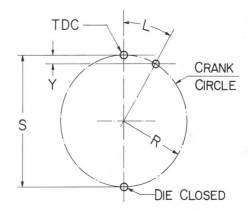

R = RADIUS OF CRANK CIRCLE

S = PRESS STROKE = 2R

Figure **3·6**   Diagram: Press-crankshaft action.

from the die opening under these circumstances. It is true that, if the press motion is now started again, the shedder will push the blank out of the opening when the crank passes through the TDC position. However, most of the knockout impact effect will be lost. The ram will then be accelerating on its downstroke, and the blank may be caught before it clears the die area, resulting in possible damage and/or safety hazard.

The above may or may not be very likely to happen, but a properly proportioned shedder-knockout combination can completely eliminate the possibility of such a mishap. This, combined

25

with the safety and operating advantages should serve to emphasize the desirability of adequate proportions and allowances—especially since, in the great majority of cases, a properly proportioned shedder-knockout combination is actually easier to build.

Shedding-pin function. The manner in which a shedding pin functions is apparent from examination of Figs. 3·2 to 3·5. What may not be so readily apparent is the importance of this function. The importance of an adequately functional shedding pin (or its equivalent) cannot be overemphasized.

The stock material may be coated with a rustproofing or other protective solution. Even if the stock is cleaned before it is to be run in the die, a slight residual deposit may remain. Also, various lubricants are often applied to the stock material in order to facilitate die working. It is obvious that any liquid or gummy deposit on the stock material will cause the blanks to stick to the face of the shedder. It is the function of the shedding pin (or its equivalent) to eliminate this possibility. Because of this, shedding pins are often called "oil" pins. The designation oil pin can, however, be misleading and is therefore inappropriate.

It can (and will) occur that absolutely clean, dry stock material will adhere to the shedder face because of atmospheric pressure. Therefore, regardless of stock material condition, the installation of shedding pins (or the equivalent) must be considered to be absolutely necessary.

Be sure to check and verify that dimension Q (Fig. 3·5) will be adequate for the die life requirement of the specific application.

Riddance action for a very delicate shedder. A rather unusual shedder and shedding-pin combination is pictured in Fig. 3·7. The illustrated die is an inverted blanking die. The drawing has been made out of proportion for purposes of illustration. The width of the die opening, W, was considered too small for a more conventional spring-pin installation (W was 0.014 in.). Dimensions W and P indicate the rectangular shape of the shedding pin, which has a round head, as shown. Shedder dimension S was shortened to provide the necessary space at P. A study of the illustration will reveal that the shedding-pin effect is functionally the same as that of a more conventional shedding pin. The actual die proved to be somewhat touchy in operation at first, because it was found that the spring-pressure requirement was rather exacting. When the spring was too

strong, it distorted the blank by bending the end of the blank downward. When the spring was too weak, the end of the blank was distorted in the opposite direction and the distorted end tended to stick in the die opening. However, once the optimum spring pressure was determined, the die proved to be satisfactory.

Shedding vents. These are generally nothing more than a hole provided through the shedder which enables a jet of air to blow the part from the shedder face in the manner pictured in Fig. 3·8. Pressure air A is blown into the space behind the shedder and vented through the hole provided in the shedder, forcing the blank away from the shedder face. A secondary air blast is often necessary to blow the blank clear of the die area. The air jets must be properly timed, and it will be better if the secondary air jet B is timed very slightly later than jet A. Shedding vents are especially well suited for applications where the shedder is delicate and would be seriously weakened by the installation of a shedding pin (the shedding pin would also be delicate in such an application).

Except for special instances such as those described above, the shedding pin should normally be the preferred method of ensuring that the die is rid of the blank. More die setup time is usually required for shedding vents, and there is no definite saving as far as diemaking is concerned. In fact, if commercially available spring pins are used as shedding pins, they can produce some economies in making the die.

Location. The shedding pin (or its equivalent) should be located out toward the periphery of the shedder, rather than in the center. The purpose of this is to provide better leverage for the shedding-pin action. This principle applies also to large shedders in which a number of shedding pins may be incorporated. The pins should be located so as to provide an unbalanced action which will yield a leverage effect. Another method of producing imbalance for leverage is to increase the spring force for one or more of the pins, if and as required.

Most inverted dies (very large dies may be excepted) using positive shedders are run in inclined open-back presses. After the shedder has driven the blank out of the die cavity, the blank simply drops through the opening in the back of the press. An air blast may be required to assist and ensure such disposal of the blank. If the press is not inclined, then some ejection provision (an air jet is the most common method) will

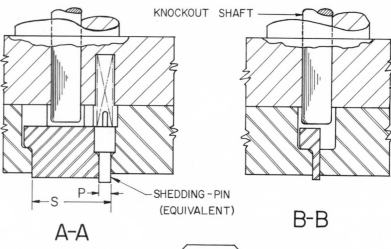

KNOCKOUT SHAFT

A-A

SHEDDING – PIN
(EQUIVALENT)

B-B

Figure **3·7**   Die with shedder divided
in order to secure shedding-pin action.

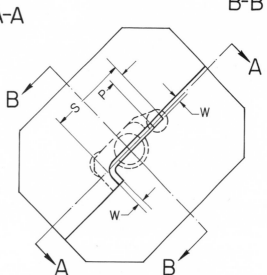

PLAN VIEW OF DIE FACE

Figure **3·8**   Shedding vent (air hole) in shedder.

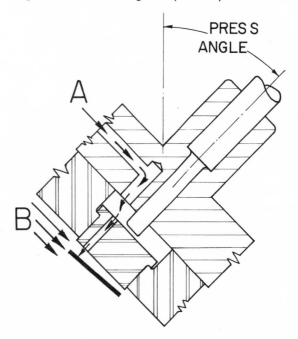

PRESS
ANGLE

quite probably be indispensable to practical operation of the die. Because of these operating circumstances, it has been found that the best
location for the shedding pin is toward the front
of the die. This has proved to be the most favorable location when blank disposal is to the rear,
which is most frequently the direction of disposal.
The foregoing discussion can be summed up and
stated very briefly:

Whenever practical, locate the shedding pin
out toward the shedder periphery and in the area
opposite to the direction of disposal. One exception to the above general rule is round shedders.
In plain, round inverted dies the shedder is often
free to rotate about its center. The spring-pin
assembly must, of course, be fully incorporated
within this kind of shedder. The site of the spring
pin will change if and as the shedder rotates.
Barring a few possible exceptional cases, the fact
that the location of the shedding pin may change
from time to time is generally disregarded. It is
not normally considered necessary to go to the
trouble of keying the shedder just to be certain

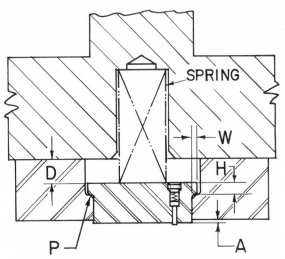

Figure **3·9** Basic compression shedder.

that the shedding pin (or equivalent) remains in the most desirable location. This would not apply, of course, to a spring-pin assembly which is partly in the shedder and partly in some fixed member of the die.

It can be stated very briefly that the purpose of shedding pins and shedding vents is to rid the shedder of the blank (or piece part or slug). Therefore, it might be more appropriate to refer to shedding pins and shedding vents as "riddance" pins and "riddance" vents, respectively. In fact, it might even be advantageous to coin, by derivation, the word "ridder" to be used in speaking collectively of riddance pins and riddance vents.

Compression shedders. In appearance, the shedder of Fig. 3·9 is identical to those of Figs. 3·1 to 3·5. This shedder, however, is fundamentally different because its action is compressive instead of percussive. This inherent difference affects the proportional relationships of the shedder. Dimen-

Figure **3·10** Spring pressure transmitted to shedder via transfer pins.

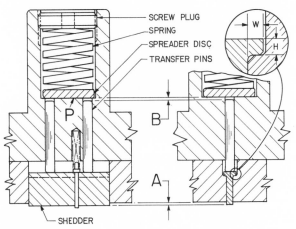

sionally speaking, the differences are slight, but they do exist.

Figure 3·9 depicts the shedder relationships as they would appear when the upper (punch-shoe) assembly is removed from the lower (die-shoe) assembly. The relationships exist in this manner throughout the press cycle except for the short period of contact with the stock material at and near the bottom of the press stroke. The shedder flanges are seated against the die opening ledge at P. The force existing at P is equal to the pre-load pressure exerted by the springs. Flange proportions H and W should be

$$H = 2W \text{ min.}$$

Flange strength should be in proportion for the spring pressure. Space D should be treated the same as it would be if the die were equipped with a positive shedder.

Theoretically speaking, protrusion distance A could be zero (flush with the die face). Practically speaking, however, it will range from zero to $\frac{1}{16}$ in., depending upon the individual application. If the shedder is intended to push the blank back into the stock strip, dimension A should be close to zero for light-gage stock material. For heavier material, protrusion A may range from zero to 0.005 in.; more than this is not likely to be advantageous. For light-gage stock material when the blank area is relatively large it will be best to install two or more shedding pins. These should be located symmetrically with respect to the blank contour. For heavier stock material, shedding pins may not be necessary in a pushback shedder. However, a number of other factors may influence the success of a pushback operation. Therefore, with hardened shedders, it is generally wise to provide (before heat treating) holes which will permit the incorporation of spring pins in the shedder if they should prove to be necessary.

For applications in which the shedder does not push the blank back into the stock material, protrusion distance A may be increased, if desired, to facilitate diemaking. For these shedders, shedding-pin considerations are generally the same as for positive shedders.

Compression shedders with transfer pins. The construction of Fig. 3·10 incorporates transfer pins to transmit the spring pressure to the shedder. The length of the transfer pins is made to provide a clearance B, as shown. Therefore, the preload pressure is applied at P and is not applied to the shedder flanges. With transfer-pin constructions it is not normally necessary for the keepers (in this case, shedder flanges) to carry the spring load. As a result, the strength proportions for the keepers would not be as critical as otherwise (refer to Fig. 3·9).

For constructions equivalent in principle to that shown in Fig. 3·10, keeper strength may be less than for those which are required to resist the spring pressure. It is possible that, in some instances, it might be desirable to take advantage of this fact. For example, flange proportions H and W (inset view) could be made

$$H = W \qquad \text{provided that } B > \text{zero}$$

In principle, this applies for all compression shedders, no matter what method is used to retain them. If B is made equal to zero, then the keepers should be made strong enough to ensure carrying the spring load under service conditions for the entire life of the die.

The possible hazards associated with inadequate keepers are obvious. If clearance gap B is made larger than protrusion distance A, the shedder will not be effective. Therefore the relationship should be either

$$A = B \qquad \text{or} \qquad A > B$$

If the shedder is intended to act as a pushback shedder in blanking light-gage stock material, then A should generally be equal to B plus $\frac{1}{1,000}$ to $\frac{5}{1,000}$ in. The exact proportions may have to be determined experimentally when the die has reached the tryout stage of construction.

The construction which is shown in Fig. 3·11 has the clearance gap at C, which keeps the shedder in a preloaded condition at all times. This is seldom desirable and should generally be avoided if possible. In many cases where shedders were made to function in this way it may have been due to a lack of analysis in relation to the shedder function. If, for any reason, this construction is employed, remember that a transfer pin (or pins) makes it possible to apply very strong pressures to very small shedders. Therefore, strongly proportioned keepers are necessary any time the construction is such that they must carry the spring load.

PUSHBACK DIES

Normally, when a compression shedder is used in conjunction with a compression stripper, the blank is pushed back into the stock material from which it was cut. This action is shown sequentially in Fig. 3·12. The shedding pin is not shown in the drawings, in order to simplify the presentation. The die is equipped with a plunger which transfers the spring pressure to the shedder.

In view 1 the upper die assembly is descending

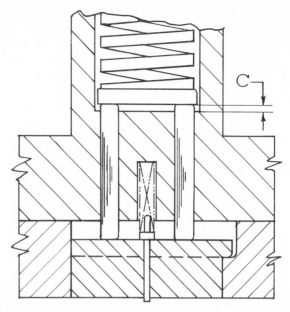

Figure **3·11** Preload pressure transferred to keeper flanges.

with the downstroke of the ram and is about to contact the stock strip. The relationships are shown as they would exist at this stage or at any time the die is in an open condition. The stripper is flush with the top face of the punch. The plunger flange is seated at C. The shedder flanges rest on the die opening ledge at P. Shedder protrusion distance is indicated as A. B is the clearance gap between the transfer plunger and the shedder. The stock material thickness is called T.

In view 2 the relationships are shown as they would exist when the die is closed at the bottom of the press stroke. The punch has cut the blank from the stock strip, displacing the blank a distance E into the die opening. The punch does not necessarily enter the die opening. In fact, many pushback applications will be more successful if the punch does not completely penetrate the stock strip. Practically speaking, penetration distance E may be $\frac{1}{2}T$ to slightly more than T, depending upon the penetration depth necessary to perform the cutting action. For very thin stock material it is not generally practical to attempt a partial penetration. The stripper travel is equal to E, since the stripper is forced downward (in compression) this amount. Shedder travel $P_1 = A + E$. Plunger travel $C = A - B + E$, which is the amount the shedder spring will be compressed in addition to the preload. It is obvious that stripper travel E and plunger travel C_1 are generally quite small, causing only a relatively slight increase in their respective spring pressures. This accounts for the comparatively high preload compression which is normally required.

29

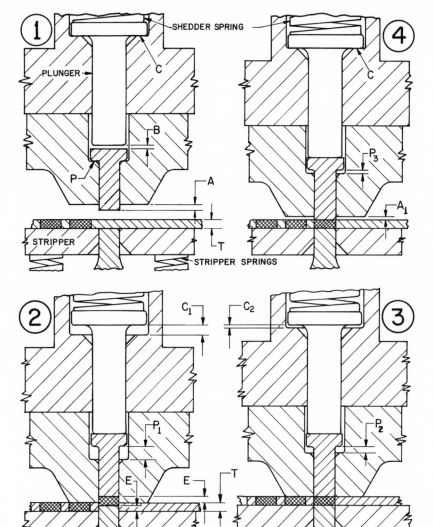

Figure **3·12**   Pushback sequence.

In view 3 the die has now opened a distance equal to E as the ram moves upward on the return stroke. At this stage, $P_2 = A$, and $C_2 = A - B$. In applications where B is made equal to A, C_2 would be equal to zero at this stage. If $B < A$, then the sequence develops as pictured in view 4.

View 4 applies to shedders where $A > B$. Here the die has opened farther a distance equal to A_1. This dimension would be $A_1 = A - B$. The remaining (free-fall) travel of the shedder would be $P_3 = A_1$ or $P_3 = A - B$, also. Immediately following this stage, the shedder drops to its original position (view 1), which remains unchanged throughout the balance of the cycle.

In analyzing the function sequence in Fig. 3·12, it is a good idea to assign dimensional values to the primary factors A, B, T, and E (just as you could be required to do if you were actually making such a die). Then, using these dimensions, determine what the actual relationships would be at each stage of the sequence. For example, suppose that $T = 0.050$ in., $A = 0.020$ in., $B = 0.016$ in., and $E = 0.8T$. Then determine what the actual dimensions would be for C_1, P_1, C_2, P_2, A_2, and P_3 on the basis of the assigned values. This type of practice is well worthwhile. By assigning various primary dimensions and proceeding through the sequence, a thorough and lasting understanding can be achieved in a short time.

Importance of proper shedding action. This chapter has emphasized the importance of proper shedding action. There are two reasons for this:

1. As far as simple inverted dies are concerned the shedder, in association with its means of actuation, can be considered to be a predominant feature of the die.
2. A thorough comprehension of the inverted shedder function is essential to many other applications. However, it is wiser and better to analyze and study the shedder function in these simple surroundings, rather than in more

30

complex constructions which might deemphasize it. It will be found that the proportions and relationships are generally valid for practically all inverted constructions.

It should be noted that, in spite of the length and detail of the discussion, only one basic shedder configuration (the flanged shedder) has been used as an example. However, the reasoning which has been employed is valid for all shedders. The diemaker who studies and understands this exposition can directly apply the reasoning to any other shedder configuration. For reference to other typical shedder constructions see "Basic Diemaking."

Incomplete pushback. In the preceding illustration (Fig. 3·12) and discussion, it is assumed that the shedder will push the blanks back to a flush condition in the strip. It is not always practical to attempt to achieve an exactly flush condition by using only shedder pressure. In some cases the pushback is totalized in the next station. That is, the face surface of the die block contacts the partly returned blank and forces it to a flush position. Obviously, to accomplish this, the stripper springs must be strong enough to immobilize the stock strip until the blank is forced into the flush condition.

Occasionally, conditions will be encountered where it is better to avoid attempting to achieve a totally flush pushback relationship. For these occasions the die face can be relieved in a manner similar to that pictured in Fig. 3·13. Here, a shallow offset X is provided in the die face to afford clearance for the returned blank, as shown.

SOME GENERALITIES FOR INVERTED DIES

If the die set is equipped with a shank, the shank area is likely to be critical. It will often be inherently necessary to have cavities and/or holes machined in the shank area. The diemaker should check and verify the structural integrity of the shank attachment before machining. If it seems necessary, because of the size or location of a cavity, check for the method of shank attachment also. Steel punch holders may have the shank welded in place; semisteel punch holders may have integrally cast shanks; punch holders made of either material may be provided with inserted shanks. If the die set has an inserted shank, be especially certain that the soundness of the attachment will not be threatened because of clearance pockets, etc. For critical applications, the method of shank attachment should be clearly ascertained when the die set is being ordered.

The inverted dies shown here operate on the return-ejection principle. That is, the blank (or slug) does not pass through the die opening. Angular clearance is not required (and should not be used) for die openings that operate on this principle.

Whenever practical, the strippers for these dies

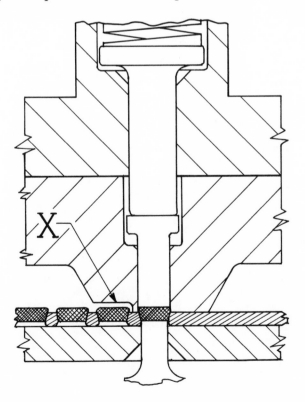

Figure **3·13** Die block relieved to clear incomplete pushback condition.

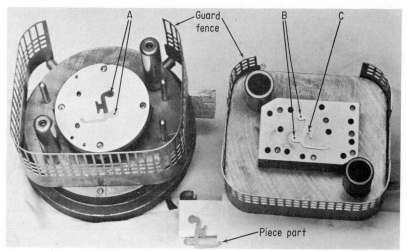

Figure **3·14** A high-precision inverted type of blanking die which produces the piece part shown in the foreground.

are made of mild steel and left soft. Pushback dies, however, will normally require that both the shedder and the stripper be hardened.

When stripper bolts are used to retain shedders, play it safe. Be certain that they are adequate in size and sufficient in number. Also give due consideration to stripper bolt locations. Be sure that they are strategically located to provide a well-balanced containment of the pressures and forces imposed upon the component. Stripper bolt locations should be distributed in such a manner as

to preclude any bowing, warping, or cocking of the component they retain.

The die shown in Fig. 3·14 has a diagonal-post die set composed of a round die shoe combined with a rectangular punch holder. The die operates within the attached guard fence provided for operator safety. The guard fence is open at the rear to permit ejection of the piece part. Holes (*A*) in the punch and (*B*) in the shedder are construction holes. The shedding pin is located at *C*.

CHAPTER 4

COMPOUND DIES

The term "compound die" is applied to dies in which two or more cutting operations, typically piercing and blanking, are performed in the same single station and completed during the same single press cycle. The action of the piercing punch-die functions must be directionally opposed to the action of the blanking (or equivalent) punch-die functions. If the piercing punches do not act in the opposite direction with respect to the blanking punch, the die should not be classified as a compound die.

A station in a progressive die may supply the attributes of a compound die. If and when a compound station is incorporated in a progressive die, the die as a whole is customarily referred to as a "progressive" compound die.

The term compound die is restricted to cutting functions (most typically, piercing and blanking). When forming or deforming operations (forming, drawing, coining, etc.) are combined with cutting operations (most typically, blanking and/or piercing) in a single station die, the die is called a "combination die." These will be described and discussed later on when appropriate.

It may not be absolutely necessary for compound dies to be inverted in the customary sense. However, in view of the fact that, by definition, the respective cutting actions for the piercing and blanking functions must be directionally opposed, it is necessary to invert one or the other of these functions. The most logical result of this opposed cutting relationship is that the great majority of compound dies are inverted in the customary sense described in Chap. 3. In fact, the addition of an opposed piercing function within a conventional inverted blanking die would convert that die into a compound die.

A TYPICAL, FUNDAMENTAL COMPOUND DIE

A representative compound-die configuration appears in Fig. 4·1. It is a "positive" compound die, so called because the shedder is actuated by a positive knockout arrangement.

The blanking die block is a component part of the upper assembly mounted to the punch holder. This assembly is thereby attached to (and moves with) the press ram. The side walls adjacent to the cutting edges of the blanking-die opening should be straight (90° to the face plane and base surface of the die block). The die employs the return-ejection principle described earlier for plain inverted dies and does not require angular clearance in the blanking-die opening. Angular clearance is not only unnecessary in these openings—it can also be undesirable in relation to piece-part burr factors and die-life considerations. In addition to this, the presence of angular clear-

Figure 4·1 A typical, fundamental compound die. Die is equipped with a positive shedder which is directly actuated by a knockout rod.

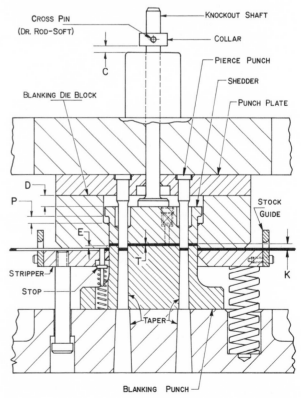

ance in these blanking die openings can have a decidedly detrimental effect on those dies where the shedder is intended to guide and/or support the pierce punches.

The blanking punch is mounted on the die shoe, which is secured to the bolster plate or, on suitable occasion, directly to the press bed.

The punches or perforators which pierce the required openings in the blank are located within the die opening area, as is necessary. The pierce punches are most often retained in a punch plate in some manner similar to that shown. The pierce punches are often supported and/or guided by the shedder. If this is the case, the shedder would be considered a "guiding" shedder and it, in turn, would have to be guided, usually by making the shedder to the desired guide fit in the die opening. This is generally true for smaller dies and is especially true for applications which require small and delicate pierce punches. The pierce die openings corresponding to the pierce punches are, of necessity, contained within the blanking punch. These piercing functions do not use the return-ejection principle: these (and all such) pierce die openings must be provided with angular clearance in the same manner as for any other conventional pierce die openings.

The corresponding openings which permit the scrap slugs to pass through the die shoe should also be tapered. This is especially important for compound dies because they are so often run in presses which are inclined at an angle. Experience has proved that dies which ran satisfactorily in an upright position would jam and be damaged when they were run in an inclined position. This was found to be due to the fact that the slug clearance holes through the die shoe were not tapered. When taper was added to these openings, the dies gave no further trouble when they were run in presses which were inclined.

In the illustration, the die is pictured as it appears when closed at the bottom of the press stroke. The upper assembly has completed its descent. The proportional relationships C, D, E, K, and P are indicated as they exist at this stage of the cycle. The stock material has been forced downward on the blanking punch. At this stage, the piece part (or blank) has been cut out of the stock strip and is contained within the blanking die opening. Since downward movement of the blanked portion was prevented by the face surface of the blanking punch, the pierce punches have penetrated through the blank.

The proportional relationships at other stages of the cycle will be the same as those described earlier, in Chap. 3. The operational sequence for this die is identical to that given for inverted plain blanking dies of the positive shedder type. Also, the proportional relationships given for inverted dies are directly applicable to this die. Values for the designations C, D, E, K, and P may be used interchangeably between Fig. 3·3 and Fig. 4·1. Therefore, it follows that the relationships for the significant cycle stages (Figs. 3·2 to 3·5) given for plain inverted dies are also valid for the compound die in Fig. 4·1. These relationships may be applied by direct association to this die specifically and, in principle, to compound dies in general.

COMPOUND DIES WITH THRUST PLATES AND INDIRECT KNOCKOUTS

Another quite typical positive compound die is pictured in Fig. 4·2. This die is very similar to the previous die except for the knockout construction and the addition of a thrust plate. These differences in construction are necessary because the piece-part requirements are different: the required piercing function is now located in the central area of the piece-part blank. The presence of the pierce punch in the center of the die opening will not permit a centrally located knockout shaft to be extended directly into contact with the shedder. Instead, a spreader plate is used to provide a bridge effect, transmitting the knockout force to the shedder via the transfer pins. Knockout arrangements of this kind are commonly called "indirect" knockouts.

A thrust plate is introduced between the punch plate and the punch holder. An adequate thrust plate of some sort is essential to this type of die construction. The thrust plate provides a backup for the pierce punch, preventing the punch from being displaced upward into the knockout cavity. Thickness requirements for these thrust plates are proportional to the span of the knockout cavity and the punching force required for the piercing operation. Therefore, thrust-plate thickness will vary according to the specific application and must, of course, be adequate for that application. If thickness is adequate, thrust plates may often be left soft to facilitate diemaking. However, this is also contingent upon the individual application. As an aid to deciding whether or not the thrust plate should be hardened, refer back to Fig. 4·1. If the punch or punches in question would not require a hardened backup in these circumstances, then a hardened backup will not generally be required for the circumstances existing in Fig. 4·2, *provided that the thickness of the thrust plate is adequate.*

For heat-treated thrust plates of this kind

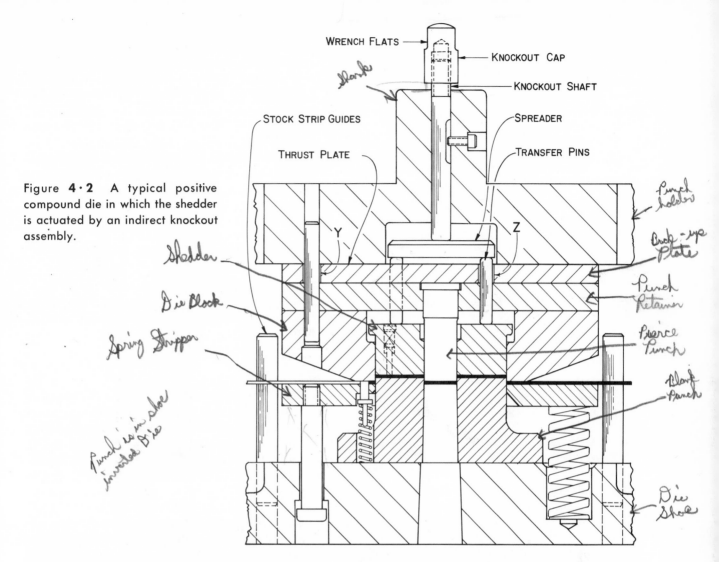

Figure **4·2** A typical positive compound die in which the shedder is actuated by an indirect knockout assembly.

The following labels appear on the figure:

WRENCH FLATS
KNOCKOUT CAP
KNOCKOUT SHAFT
STOCK STRIP GUIDES
SPREADER
THRUST PLATE
TRANSFER PINS
Shank
Y
Z
Punch holder
Back-up Plate
Punch Retainer
Pierce Punch
Blank Punch
Die Shoe
Shedder
Die Block
Spring Stripper
Punch is in shoe inverted Die

(which span a cavity), a hardness approximating a spring temper or somewhat harder is usually appropriate. This would be in the range Rockwell C45-54. If the plate thickness appears to be approaching the minimum, use the lower half of the above hardness range.

A common practice with hardened thrust plates of this sort is to provide clearance holes (Y) for the dowels. When this is done, the transfer-pin holes are also often cleared as indicated at Z. If it is felt that the thrust plate should support the transfer pins (or if there is any other reason for immobilizing the thrust plate), then separate smaller dowels may be used to dowel the thrust plate to the punch plate, thereby unitizing these components.

The presence of the thrust plate may influence selection of the die set. On those occasions where a steel punch holder might be deemed desirable for backing up the pierce punches, the thrust plate supplies a steel backup surface, permitting the use of a semisteel or cast-iron punch holder.

This is mentioned because the use of a cast punch holder may yield a slight economic advantage. Obviously, our earlier discussion (Chap. 3) concerning punch-holder cavities applies here also. The diemaker should verify the structural integrity of the punch holder, especially in relation to the security of the shank.

Generally, the punch plate is left soft, although special applications and/or very high production requirements may, on occasion, make it desirable to heat-treat it. However, in relation to dies in general, hardened punch plates are considered to be the exception rather than the rule.

Construction and relationships for floating spreaders. In Fig. 4·2 the die is shown in the conventional closed position. In Fig. 4·3 the upper die assembly is shown as it would appear if removed from the lower assembly in order to depict the shedding-system relationships as they should exist when the die is open. In principle, the relationships are the same as those described here-

35

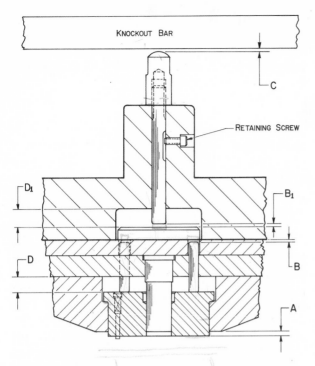

KNOCKOUT BAR

C

RETAINING SCREW

D₁

B₁

D

B

A

Figure 4·3 Knockout-to-shedder-to-die relationships for compound die with floating-type spreader plate.

tofore in regard to similar shedding functions. There is, however, a slight variation. The reasoning which applies to the relative proportions of the shedding system is merely extended to allow for the presence of the floating-type spreader plate. Doing this reveals, simply, the need for an additional small clearance gap at B_1. Optimum proportions for this shedding system can be determined by association with the previous discussion (refer to Fig. 3·2) plus allowing for the introduction of clearance gap B_1.

PROCEDURE

1. Analyze the drawing to estimate clearance-gap requirements at C, B_1, and B from the viewpoint of die setup and operation. Analysis reveals the need for a clearance allowance at C to facilitate setting the punch press knockout bar (refer to Fig. 3·5). It also becomes apparent by examination that a minimal clearance will be satisfactory for both B_1 and B. Further study reveals not only that it will be satisfactory to minimize B_1 and B but that it will probably be advantageous to do so, since all three gaps C, B_1, and B must be absorbed by protrusion distance A.

2. Analyze these clearance gaps with regard to facilitating diemaking. In this light, it is readily apparent that it will be easy to provide a very small gap at B, while a slightly larger gap at

B_1 will be desirable. Therefore, it is logical to make $B_1 > B$. Actually, both gaps are kept minimum, but the practical minimum for B_1 is larger than the minimum practical at B.

3. Check protrusion distance A to be certain that the dimension at A is large enough to absorb the total slack travel $B + B_1 + C$. With the slack eliminated from the system the remaining protrusion distance A_1 must still be sufficient to ensure a safely adequate shedding action.

EXAMPLE

To determine A_1,

$$A_1 = A - (B + B_1 + C)$$

assume the following dimensions (in inches):

$$A = 0.063 \quad B = 0.004 \quad B_1 = 0.012 \quad C = 0.016$$

then

$$A_1 = 0.063 - (0.004 + 0.012 + 0.016)$$
$$= 0.031$$

This can be considered a normally adequate shedding system. It will permit a setting error of $\pm\frac{1}{64}$ in. at the knockout bar and still ensure a shedder-protrusion distance of 0.015 in. to absorb a shorter effective knockout travel if the press should stop before TDC position (refer to Fig. 3·6).

Association with other applications. While it is true that the above dimensions may actually be suitable in many instances, they are not given here for that purpose. They were assigned merely to illustrate the example and only as a guide. It must be understood that actual dimensions for any individual die must be determined according to that specific application. To attain proficiency, it will be of definite value to assign different values to the relationships and then work them out to see whether or not they will be practical: associate them with different conditions such as small work, large work, fine work, crude work, etc., and reason them out. Then, by association, use the procedure and example as a guide for different shedding-system constructions, eliminating or adding values, as required.

In addition to the determination and checking of suitable shedding-system proportions, the procedure and example can be employed to eliminate hesitation and risk in the following manner. Suppose that the diemaker discovers that the transfer pins have been inadvertently made slightly shorter than was originally intended. Will it be too risky to use them as is? Should they be discarded and new ones made? Should compensation be made by perhaps reducing the thrust-plate thickness? This reasoning applies to any of the components. A thorough understanding of the principles which influence die proportions plus reliable and efficient procedures for determining their adequacy can be the difference between a mediocre diemaker and a truly proficient one. (This, of course, applies to die designers as well as to diemakers.)

THE KNOCKOUT CONSTRUCTION

Figure 4·3 also serves to accentuate the fact that the dimension at D_1 should be greater than the space provided at D (the strength of the punch holder in the shank area being always kept in mind, however).

With this knockout arrangement the spreader plate is subject to percussive effects against the knockout shaft and against the transfer pins. The knockout cap is subject to impact against the knockout bar of the punch press. For these components, a hardness in the range Rockwell C45-57 is generally appropriate. Use the lower half of the range when the component proportions are such that toughness is more desirable than hardness, and vice versa. For light- to medium-duty applications employing loose transfer pins as shown, standard dowels are often used as transfer pins. If this is done, the dowel ends should be finished by grinding smooth and flat with only a minimum of material removed. The plane of the ends should be nicely perpendicular to the longitudinal axis of the dowel. The ends of the dowels should be slightly chamfered to absorb any tendency to swell, which may induce spalling of the pin and/or binding in the hole.

The retaining screw represents one method of keeping the knockout shaft in assembly. Its primary purpose is to prevent the shaft from falling out when the die is being handled or transported. It also ensures that the shaft will remain in assembly with the die during storage periods. In addition, this screw can be an asset to diemaking when the knockout shaft is assembled with threaded components such as jam nuts or the threaded cap shown in the illustration. The retaining screw will prevent rotation of the shaft, which can facilitate seating and securing any components which may be threadedly engaged to the shaft. A groove or a flat is provided in the shaft to clear the retainer. The retainer must not cause binding or interfere in any way with the required shaft motion. Be sure that the clearance slot is long enough to provide ample clearance beyond the possible shaft travel in either direction.

Sometimes, dies are designed using a headless setscrew instead of a cap screw as shown here. Setscrews used in this manner are very likely to be troublesome, either binding the shaft or failing to keep it in assembly. Using a cap screw in the manner shown will permit positive control of its relationship to the shaft, eliminating binding and ensuring satisfactory retention of the shaft.

Relationships for unitized knockout. Figure 4·4 illustrates the die as it would appear if it were equipped with a unitized knockout assembly. Proportional relationships for the shedding system would then exist as indicated. Compare this drawing with the previous drawing to decide whether or not the difference in construction might influence the proportions of the shedding system. Comparative analysis of the working of the shedding systems reveals that in Fig. 4·4 it will be better to make gap B_1 slightly smaller than gap B. Then, in the event of a maladjustment at C, the spreader will bottom against the thrust plate before the shedder flanges contact the retaining ledges at P. Note that the shedding system is proportioned to bottom first at C and then at B_1 before bottoming at P (or B). This is a fundamental principle for positive shedding systems: the construction should avoid permitting the knockout components to stack up to a solid drive against the shedder keepers. Sometimes, knockouts are used which do not employ a shaft-mounted stop. This, of course, eliminates C from the system, and such knockouts cannot be stopped at C. However, the

Figure **4·4** Shedding-system relationships for compound die with unitized knockout assembly.

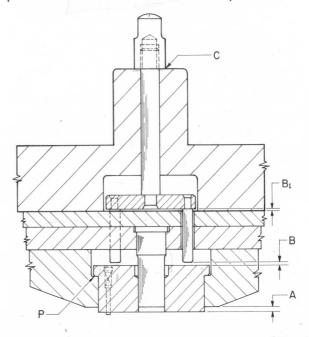

above principle still applies: these knockouts should make contact at B_1 first, to provide the clearance gap at B.

In order to avoid any possible confusion, we have shown and discussed flanged shedders. However, the principles underlying the proportional relationships are valid for positive shedding systems in general even though the constructions differ. For a study of different shedding-system constructions refer to "Basic Diemaking." It should be emphasized that a comprehensive study of the above basic volume is a prerequisite to the study of the applications presented here.

EJECTION SPACE

There exists, understandably, some confusion in regard to the terms "shedding," "stripping," and "ejecting." We use these terms here as follows:

Shedding. The act of expelling the work material from the die opening

Shedder. The die component which physically contacts the work material to perform the act of shedding

Stripping. The act of removing the work material from the punch

Stripper. The component which physically contacts the work material to perform the act of stripping

Ejection. The act of expelling the work material from the die as a whole

Ejector. A mechanism or means for performing the act of ejection

Most compound dies (and inverted blanking dies) are not equipped with mechanical ejectors. The work is usually gravity-dropped or else air-ejected as described earlier (Chap. 3). Large work may sometimes be manually unloaded, or special mechanical unloaders may be employed. Delicate work may also require the use of special unloading devices or procedures in order to prevent damage to the work produced.

In speaking of ejection, positive compound dies are called "top-delivery" dies because the piece part is ejected from the die at the top of the press stroke (this term is applied to all inverted-type dies equipped with positive shedders). With all top-delivery dies, due consideration must be given to the amount of space required to ensure total ejection. Total ejection normally means that the piece parts must be ejected entirely clear of the press. To accomplish this, it is, of course, essential for the piece parts to be ejected clear of the area occupied by the die. It is expected that the die designer will incorporate adequate ejection space in the design of the die. It is further expected that the diemaker will verify that adequate ejec-

tion space has been provided. He will do this in the course of his familiarization study of the design drawings—before making the die. The most common oversight in regard to ejection space is insufficient distance between the guideposts when the dies are mounted on back-post die sets. Therefore, check especially that the guideposts will not interfere with ejection of the piece part.

BURR-SIDE AND COMPOUND DIES

One of the noteworthy features of compound pierce-and-blank dies is the burr-side effect. Piece parts produced by these dies have only one burr side. That is, the burr side of openings pierced within the piece part will agree with the burr side of the blanked outer contour of the piece part. This characteristic burr-side effect can be a major consideration which influences the decision to build a compound die in order to produce a given piece part.

The rules which apply to burr-side location are:

1. The burr side of a blank or of a slug is *always* toward its respective punch.
2. The burr side of a pierced opening is *always* toward its respective die opening.

Therefore, the burr side on the outer periphery of the blank will be toward the blanking punch. Since the pierce-die opening is contained in the blanking punch, the burr side of the pierced opening in the blank will also be toward the blanking punch.

The burr-side effect as related to compound dies is evident from examination of the amplified schematic illustration (Fig. 4·5).

CUTTING CLEARANCE AND COMPOUND DIES

With compound dies, the blanks (piece parts) do not pass through the die opening: they are return-ejected. Therefore, angular clearance is not incorporated in the blanking-die openings of compound dies. The absence of angular clearance can influence the amount of cutting clearance to be provided between the blanking punch and blanking-die opening. This cutting clearance is called C in the schematic drawing (Fig. 4·6). Since the sidewalls of the die opening are parallel to the sidewalls of the punch, cutting clearance C will remain constant throughout the life of the die. Because the amount of clearance remains constant, it is practical to make the die with a larger cutting clearance at C than would be the case otherwise. There are several reasons why it might be desirable to be able to use a larger clearance. Some of these are:

1. Diemaking facility. Various diemaking pro-

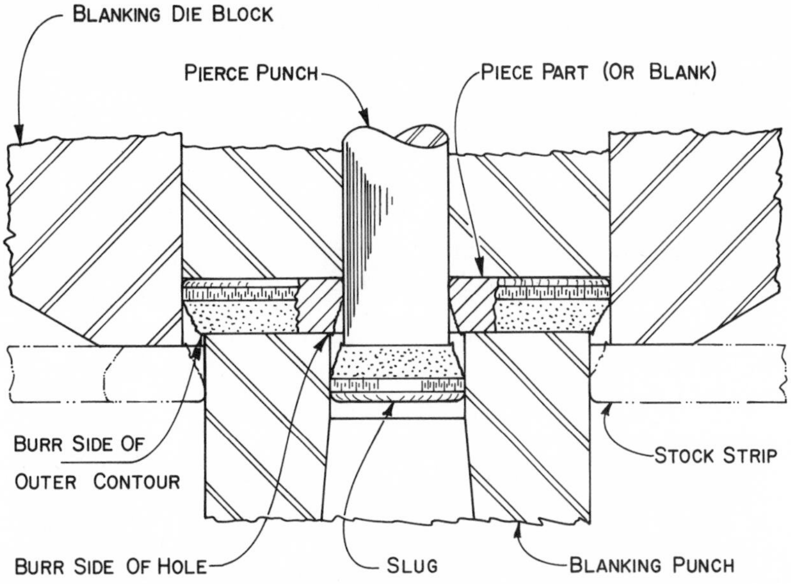

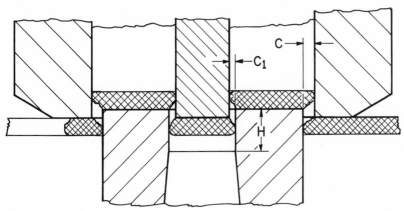

Figure **4·5** The burr-side relationship which is characteristic for compound dies.

BLANKING DIE BLOCK

PIERCE PUNCH

PIECE PART (OR BLANK)

BURR SIDE OF OUTER CONTOUR

STOCK STRIP

BURR SIDE OF HOLE

SLUG

BLANKING PUNCH

cedures may be facilitated. The work can be somewhat less exacting because the dimensions related to the clearance space will not ordinarily have to be so precisely controlled. This advantage is generally in direct proportion to the size and complexity of the blanking contour.

2. Cutting force. Larger cutting clearances tend to reduce the cutting force requirements to some degree. This may be desirable for large blanks and will be more desirable in cases where relatively delicate die constructions are necessary.

3. Attrition. The rate of wear on the cutting edges of the punch and die at the blanking contour may be favorably influenced because of the larger initial clearance.

The first two reasons stated above are more important than the third. All three reasons are generally considered as advantageous side effects which are inherent in dies which use the return-ejection principle. Thus, they would usually be secondary rather than primary reasons for deciding which kind of die would be most suitable for

a given application. However, there can be exceptional conditions which could benefit by association with the above reasons. Therefore, awareness and understanding of these conditions are essential to proficiency in diemaking.

Differential cutting clearance. Because it is worthy of emphasis, it should be stated that the foregoing cutting-clearance discussion applies solely to the blanking function, *not* to the piercing functions. As described earlier in this chapter, the die openings for the piercing functions are contained within the blanking punch. The resulting slugs (if the die is a conventional compound die) pass through the blanking punch and the die shoe. Therefore, the die openings for the piercing functions must be treated as described in the discussion of Fig. 4·1. Since these pierce-die openings must be tapered, they will eventually increase in size as a result of sharpening. This can influence the amount of cutting clearance which is provided for the piercing function (C_1, Fig. 4·6). Be-

Figure **4·6** Cutting-clearance relationship for compound die.

cause of this, compound dies are often made with a smaller initial cutting clearance for the piercing function C_1. Exceptions to this would be:

1. Low-production dies where the number of sharpenings would not increase cutting clearance C_1 by any significant amount.
2. Dies for average to high production requirements where the height H of a cutting land may help to provide adequate life before the clearance increase at C_1 becomes objectionable. Sometimes, height H is made slightly higher than normal as a compensatory measure. This, however, can be dangerous, especially with delicate punches or if the pierced opening is located relatively close to the blanking periphery.
3. Another practice is to use a minimal degree of angular clearance in the pierce-die openings. The degree of angular clearance considered minimal varies, of course, with the quality of the opening in question; it can be as little as $\frac{1}{8}°$ per side for a high-quality ground or lapped opening or $\frac{1}{4}°$ per side for a filed opening. Here again, be careful of pierced openings which are located close to the blanking periphery.
4. Still another method which may, at times, be considered is a double angle clearance, minimal angle toward the top of the opening and a larger angle toward the bottom of the opening (this may be especially desirable for filed openings).
5. High-production dies where replaceable pierce-die inserts may be incorporated within the blanking punch. The relative sizes of the components and the location of the pierced openings with respect to the blanking periphery will emphatically influence the practicality of such inserts.
6. Another practice is to make the size of the piercing punch close to the minimum permissible size and then replace the punch (when it becomes necessary) with a slightly larger punch to compensate for the increase in cutting clearance. For obvious economic reasons, this method is normally restricted to round punches, rather than to punches which are other than round.

The above considerations may be applicable in quite a number of specific applications. The diemaker must be aware of this and must comprehend the reasoning behind these considerations. However, it remains a fact that for the majority of applications the most practical method is to use a minimum initial cutting clearance at C_1 and a larger cutting clearance at C.

Blanking size related to die life. When a blank-through die is sharpened below its cutting land, the die opening becomes larger. This is due to the presence of the angular clearance, which is a vital feature of blank-through die openings. Since the blank derives its size from the die opening, blanks produced by blank-through dies become correspondingly larger each time the die is sharpened.

A compound die does not have angular clearance in its blanking-die opening. Therefore, sharpening the die has no effect on the size of this opening. As a result, the size of the blanks produced remains constant throughout the entire life of a compound die. This constancy of blank size contributes to the established reputation of compound dies for producing uniformly accurate blanks to very close tolerances.

PIERCING IN PROXIMITY TO BLANKING

When holes must be pierced in proximity to the blank edge, the blanking punch should be made as strong as possible. One method of accomplishing this is to give the blanking punch a pyramid configuration similar to those pictured in Fig. 4·7. For round blanks, the blanking punch is usually made with the pyramid shape extending entirely around the blanking circumference, as it appears in view 1. This will usually facilitate both diemaking and maintenance. For irregular blank contours (rectangular, etc.), it is often advantageous to localize the pyramid effect to the required area adjacent to the proximal piercing. In this case, the pyramid configuration would not be made entirely around the blanking periphery, and a cross section of the punch would appear as shown in view 2.

Height A of the cutting sidewall of the blanking punch is related to the proximity distance F: if F is narrower, A must be made shorter. In order to minimize height A, the stripper opening is deeply relieved (H), leaving a minimal straight sidewall B in the stripper opening. In extreme cases, the B dimension may be reduced to zero. To be practical, a life-clearance dimension of $\frac{1}{16}$ in. at D would be the minimum. Clearance dimension D will diminish each time the blanking punch is sharpened. The pyramid contour is then ground away, as required, to ensure clearance at D. This grinding is represented by the dotted lines at G and G_1.

The cutting force at the blanking edge will

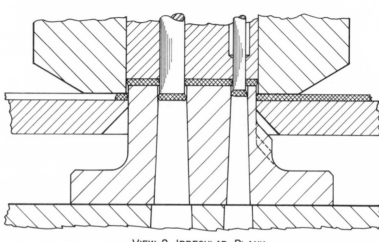

Figure **4·7** Integrally reinforced blanking punch for piercing close to edge (compound die).

PIERCE PUNCHES

VIEW 1 ROUND BLANK

VIEW 2 IRREGULAR BLANK

tend to crowd the proximal piercing punch. For smaller piercings, especially, it may be necessary to alleviate crowding by shortening the pierce punch an amount $C = 0.75T$. This is generally the practical minimum amount. For most applications, make $C = T$.

It is readily apparent that entry distance E must be limited to the smallest feasible amount. Do not dismiss this as the setup man's problem. To guard against overentry, setup blocks (sometimes called "bumpers") should be installed on dies of this kind. When installing these blocks, be certain that their location will not interfere with ejection of the piece part.

A COMPOUND DIE WITH PIERCE PUNCH MOUNTED IN THE DIE BLOCK

Construction comment. The compound die in Fig. 4·8 does not require a punch plate or a thrust plate. The piercing punch is a pedestal-type punch. Its base diameter A is large enough to span adequately the knockout spreader cavity

in the punch shoe. Its flange thickness E must be thick enough to resist the sudden and repeated impact forces imposed by the cutting action, plus an adequate safety margin for mishaps.

A diemaking procedure for this type of construction. In the course of making this die, the blanking-die block can be set up in an internal grinder (or equivalent machine). Diameter B and diameter A in the die block can then be ground in this one setup. Grinding the two diameters in the same setup will assure concentricity for these diameters. If desirable, surfaces D and D_1 may also be cleanup ground in this same setup, ensuring that these surfaces are truly perpendicular to diameters A and B. Stock removal at D and D_1 should be absolutely minimal to facilitate this kind of grinding in this kind of setup.

Diameters A and C on the piercing punch can be externally ground in one setup. This will ensure concentricity for these two diameters. Punch flange diameter A should be fitted nicely to its

41

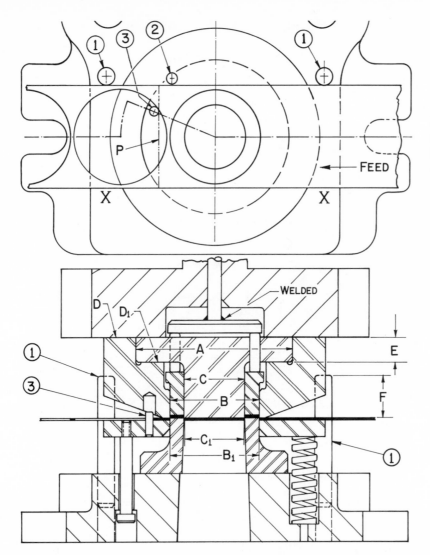

mating counterbore in the die block. If this is done, punching diameter C and blanking diameter B will be concentric when in assembly.

The idea of using single setups for concentric grinding can also be applied to the blanking punch. Cutting diameter B_1 and pierce die diameter C_1 can be externally-internally ground in one setup. This procedure, of course, ensures concentricity for these two diameters. It may or may not be desirable to face-grind the face surface of this punch in this same setup, to ensure perpendicularity of the face to the sidewalls. The desirability of face-grinding in this setup depends upon other factors in the finishing approach. For example the punch base surface could be finish-ground first, in close approximation to perpendicularity with the vertical axis of the punch. The punch could then be set up against this surface for internal-external grinding, etc. (A similar procedure could also be applied to grinding surface D of the blanking-die block.)

Procedures other than those described above

may be used to accomplish the same results. In fact, other procedures may be more desirable at times. This would depend upon the sum of all conditions pertaining to the individual situation. However, the described procedure will ensure a nicely concentric die (and piece part) and can facilitate the overall aspects of making the die.

Stock guides and stop: construction and function. In this die, there is no provision for guiding the front edge of the stock strip. This is a common enough practice for dies of this general type, which are run in inclined presses. The absence of front guides can facilitate diemaking to a slight degree. However, they usually are not eliminated because of this. When they are not used, it is because it is felt that their absence will facilitate feeding. Since the die is inclined to the rear, the back edge of the stock strip tends to rest against the rear guide.

The die of Fig. 4·8 has two guide pins (1) pressed into the die shoe and located tangent to

42

the desired rear edge line of the stock strip. Whenever possible such pins should be located in the manner shown, outside the area covered by the die block and stripper. If this is done, it will not be necessary to provide clearance for these pins in either of the above components. Standard dowel pins of suitable diameter and length are generally appropriate for this purpose. The guide pins extend vertically above the feed line a distance F, which must be high enough to ensure ease of feeding. A smaller guide pin (2) is pressed in the stripper. It, too, is located tangent to the back gage line. The auxiliary guide pin comes into play when the stock strip is being started. Its purpose is to facilitate strip alignment when the lead end of the strip is at the starting position P. A standard dowel pin is generally a logical choice for solid auxiliary-guide-pin applications where conditions are the same as those illustrated.

The auxiliary pin need not extend as far above the stripper as the main guide pins (refer to F). It should, however, extend higher than the stop pin (3). Both the auxiliary pin and the stop pin require matching clearance holes in the die block as shown in the sectional view for (3). These clearance holes should be deep enough to provide the necessary die-life factor.

For the stop pin, too, a standard dowel pin will often be satisfactory from the production viewpoint and desirable as far as diemaking is concerned. Refer to the plan view of Fig. 4·8, and note the location of the stop pin. When the stock strip is fed against it, a wedging action develops, tending to force the strip against the back guides. This is a desirable principle which should be followed whenever the blank contours and other conditions such as grain direction, burr side, etc., will permit. Actually, the location of this stop pin accomplishes four desirable objectives:

1. The pin is far enough from the cutting edges to ensure that its matching clearance hole in the die block will not weaken the die in this area.
2. The stop-pin location influences the location of the auxiliary guide pin. In this application the stop-pin location permits the auxiliary guide pin also to be located farther from the cutting edges. Therefore, provision of a clearance hole for the auxiliary guide pin is facilitated.
3. The stop pin can act as a primary stop without causing undue stock-material consumption in spite of the fact that it accomplishes objectives 1 and 2.
4. The stop pin provides the wedging action described earlier, which is an asset to feeding the stock strip.

Objectives 1 and 2 cited above pertain to the use of solid-type pins. Objectives 3 and 4 could apply to any type of stop.

If it is felt that it will also be desirable to guide the front edge of the strip, simply install two more guide pins located at X in the illustration. The front guide pins would be the same kind and size as the rear guide pins (1).

DIE AND PUNCH INSET IN SHOES

The die shown in Fig. 4·9 can be considered to produce the same piece part as the die in Fig. 4·8. Construction of the two dies is identical except that the die shown in Fig. 4·9 has its blanking-die block fitted into a counterbore in the punch shoe and its blanking punch fitted into a counterbore in the die shoe.

Study the drawing (Fig. 4·9). Then, by association with the previous die, decide what your diemaking procedures would be for this die. Analyze particularly the possibilities introduced by the fact that the die block and punch are set into their shoes. Determine how this can be advantageous. Be thorough. Record each step of your procedure. Then, analyze your procedure, and revise it until you are satisfied that you have attained an efficient diemaking procedure for this die. Be sure of the practicality of your work sequence. It can be educational to make several comparison studies of the die. We suggest the following:

1. Assume that you are to make the die in a shop

Figure **4·9** Compound die with die block and blanking punch inset-mounted (in shoes).

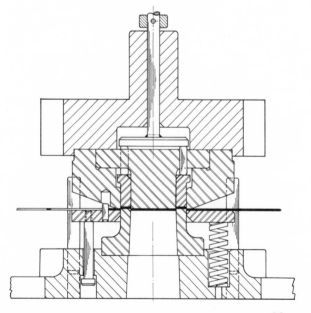

which has only the necessary minimum of equipment.

2. Assume that you are to make the die in a shop that has everything in the way of diemaking equipment.

3. If you are employed in a die shop, assume that you are to make the die in that shop. The equipment of most shops, naturally enough, will be somewhere between the above equipment for (1) and (2).

4. Assume differing piece-part requirements, such as materials from which the piece part is to be made, accuracy requirements, and production-quantity requirements.

The foregoing procedure of analysis and comparative study is a practice which can be invaluable in modern apprenticeship. It can also be of inestimable value to the designer, the engineer, the journeyman diemaker, and the supervisor. This is an unequivocal statement of fact. Today's diemaker does not merely serve an apprenticeship and then repeatedly make the same dies over and over again. He is far more than that. He works in a world of constantly advancing technological change. He should constantly adapt to new conditions and improvise creatively when required. His entire career can be one of learning and advancement. This is why diemaking can be such an exceptionally interesting and rewarding career.

COMPOUND DIE: COMPOSITE CONSTRUCTION

The piece part. A piece part is pictured in Fig. 4·10. Examination of the drawing indicates that a compound die is a most logical choice for producing this piece part as specified. The resulting die is pictured in Fig. 4·11. This die employs

Figure **4·10**   Piece part produced by die as shown in Fig. 4·11.

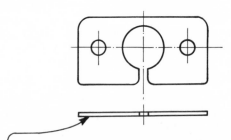

BURR SIDE OF HOLES AND PERIPHERY

FLATNESS — 0.004" T.I.R.

DIEMAKER NOTE:—

MATCH-CUTS ON PERIPHERY ARE NOT

ACCEPTABLE

composite construction for the die block and for the stripper, too.

Analyzing the die construction. The stripping unit is composed of a stripper plate (1) and a spring plunger (2). This construction was necessitated by the narrowness of the isthmus, which is part of the blank periphery. (1) and (2) are two separate components. Each is individually actuated for the performance of the stripping act. Nevertheless, the two components function as though they were one for the act of stripping. The plunger spring must be strong enough to ensure that the bulblike scrap tab does not bend downward and stick in the blanking punch. Other than this, the balance between spring forces is not so critical as it might seem at first glance. This is due to the laminal effect which exists during the stripping act. That is, the scrap stock material is sandwiched between the stripper face and the die face, which prevents the scrap from bending upward.

The blanking-die opening is created by the two die-block sections (3) and (3_1) plus another component (4). This other component (4) looks like a punch. It is made like a punch. It is also mounted in the punch plate like a punch. However, in spite of all its punchlike features, in this die (4) is not a punch. It creates part of the periphery of the blanking-die opening and is a functional part of this opening.

The stop pin (6) and the auxiliary rear guide pin (7) are spring pins, commonly called "disappearing pins." They do not require clearance holes in the die face. Therefore, they may be situated close to the cutting edges.

The stock-strip guides (8) are narrow bars screwed to the ends of the stripper plate. They are shaped to create an aperture through which the stock strip is fed. The front and rear walls of the apertures guide the strip across the die area. The height of the aperture at H must permit the strip to be lifted over the stop pin for feeding purposes. Or the stock strip may be flexed in an arc to clear the stop pin. Both methods are used, depending upon the practicality of flexing the stock strip and also upon operator preference.

Note the feed direction. Observe that the die has been made to conform with the most favorable feeding condition. The blank-to-strip orientation is such that the projecting scrap tab trails the feed direction. It is evident by examination that if the strip were fed in the opposite direction the scrap tab could quite possibly cause interference with feeding.

Examination of the illustration reveals another interesting fact. If the two small piercings (5) were not present, the die would no longer be a

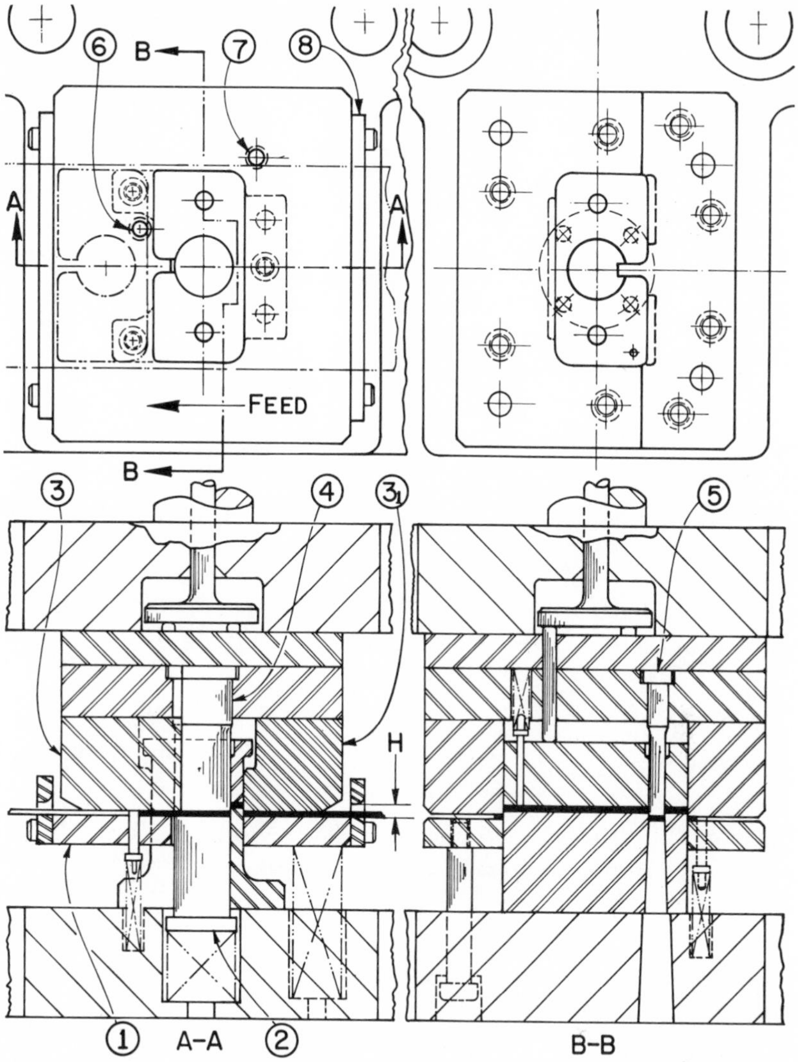

Figure **4·11** Compound die with composite die block and stripper.

compound die. It would then be a plain inverted blanking die in spite of the fact that it incorporates every other component normally considered to be a feature of a compound die.

This die is not cited here as a construction curiosity. It is a valid die design which satisfied some rather stringent piece-part specifications. It would make an interesting study and discussion to assume the following:

1. Assume that the piece-part specifications did not include the burr-side requirements. How and why might this affect the decision to make a compound die for this part?
2. Assume that, in addition to assumption 1, the flatness requirement had not been a necessary piece-part specification.
3. Assume that, instead of assumptions 1 and 2, only the match-cut restriction had been removed from the piece-part requirements. What might this imply as far as the choice of die type is concerned?

At this stage, it is not necessary to make a de-

tailed analysis of the possible die types resulting from the above assumptions—only practical possibilities need be considered. However, it could be quite informative to engage in such a study after becoming familiar with various progressive die principles and constructions. Therefore, it is suggested that the serious reader refer back to the above assumptions after he has studied the various progressive dies which are discussed later in this book.

COMPOUND DIE: ANGLED ORIENTATION

Figure 4·12 pictures a typical L-shaped piece part. A grain direction of 45° is specified, which dictates the orientation of the blank in relation to the stock strip. However, it is readily apparent that, even if the piece part did not have the specified grain direction, it would still be most logical to orient the blank at 45° in the stock strip. Rotating these blanks to 45° permits them to be interposed in the strip for maximum economy of stock material as shown at strip *A* and strip *B* in the diagram.

45

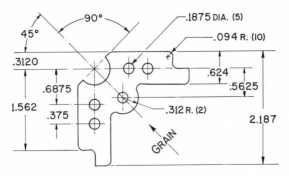

NOTE:— PART IS SYMMETRICAL

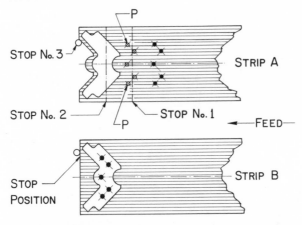

Figure 4·12   Piece-part and comparison-strip layouts. Strip A: Produced by progressive die. Strip B: Produced by compound die.

Analysis of comparative strip layouts. For purposes of comparison, two stock strips are shown. Each layout depicts the strip as it would appear after the first complete blank had been produced from it.

If the blank were produced by a progressive die, the strip would appear as shown in strip *A*. The operating sequence to produce the first blank would be:

1. Lead end of strip is fed to primary stop (No. 1). Press is tripped to produce the five pierced holes.

2. Lead end of strip is fed to secondary-stop position (No. 2). On the downstroke the pilots enter the two holes indicated as *P*. The pilot action qualifies the feed to register the strip. As the ram continues its descent, a partial blank is produced because the lead end of the strip lies across the blanking-die opening. The partial blanking will cause the cutting force to tend to displace the punch laterally to the left. This must be taken into account in the die construction.

3. Strip is fed to final stop (No. 3). Note that the location of this stop is not tangent to the lead

end of the strip. The stop acts against the blanked-out opening in the strip. The press cycle is then repeated and produces a complete blank, as shown.

The above sequence is described as though the die were manually fed. If the strip were mechanically fed, the presence of actual die stops at No. 2 and No. 3 would not be necessary. However, the sequence would be unaltered, and the resulting stock-strip skeleton would be identical for either kind of feeding.

This strip assumes that it is permissible to apply pilots in the piece-part holes at *P*. If this were not so (and it may not always be permissible), it would be necessary to increase the stock-material consumption in order to provide space for pilot holes in the scrap portion of the stock strip.

In strip *B* the equivalent strip is shown as it would appear if produced by a compound die. Only one stopping position is required. There are no pilots. There is no need for partial blanking. With the compound die it is obviously simpler to start the strip through the die. This is one of the favorable features inherent in compound dies which applies to interposed blank orientation in the stock strip. The above described conditions are characteristics of compound dies. These conditions are due to the fact that compound dies are single-station dies.

The die construction. The die in which this piece part was produced appears in Fig. 4·13. The stock-strip guides for this die are four standard dowel pins (1). The pins are press-fitted into the stripper plate. They are located outside the area covered by the blanking-die block assembly. The auxiliary back guide pin (3) and the stop (2) are spring pins. The blanking punch (4) is an offset pedestal-type punch in order to provide maximum access for machining and grinding in making the punch. The blanking-die block is a composite sectional assembly consisting of two die-block sections (6) and (7) and the pseudo punch (5).

Examination of the die-block construction will reveal another favorable aspect of single-station compound dies. It is not necessary to convert the piece-part dimensions to suit the angled blank orientation. The die-block assembly and the punch plate can be made by direct reference to the piece-part dimensions, because the exterior sides of these components are dimensionally parallel to the dimensional pattern of the piece part. After the die-block and punch-plate assembly is completed, it is simply mounted at the required blank orientation angle (in this case 45°, as shown on the inverted plan view of the upper die assembly).

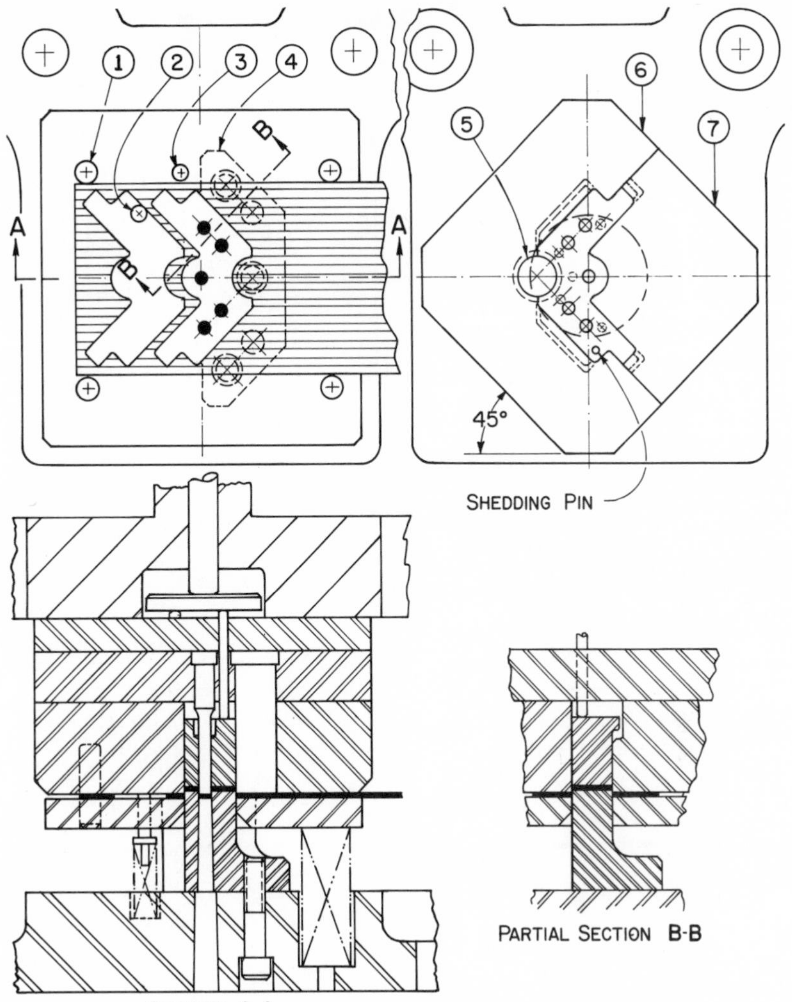

Figure **4·13** Compound die, blanks angled and interposed.

SHEDDING PIN

45°

SECTION A-A

PARTIAL SECTION B-B

A SEMICOMPOUND DIE

The piece part. Figure 4·14 depicts a piece part which has a width W. Its grain direction is also specified. Dimensionally this piece part was required to be very accurate and consistent, except for width W, which was permitted a tolerance of $\pm \frac{1}{64}$ in. Because of the rather generous tolerance for W, it was decided to use strip stock whose width was equal to W. It is quite apparent that this procedure would effect a worthwhile saving in regard to stock-material consumption, owing to elimination of the need for both front and back scrap webs.

The die construction. Consideration of the above circumstances resulted in the die shown in Fig. 4·15. This die is not actually a compound die. It is, however, similar to a compound die, and because of this it is called a "semicompound" die. This die can ensure a common burr side for only the cutting actions performed by it. It cannot ensure a common burr side for the entire blank. Therefore, it cannot ensure all the results consid-

ered characteristic for true compound dies. Because of this it is considered to be a semicompound type of die.

Figure **4·14** Piece part produced by semicompound die in Fig. 4·15.

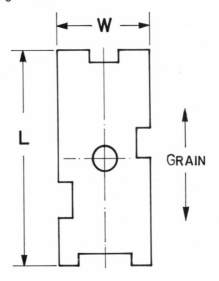

47

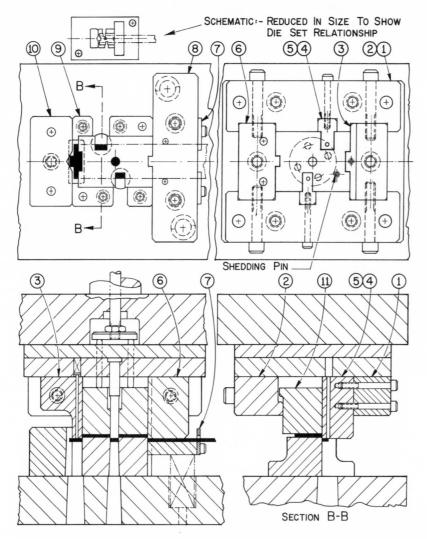

SCHEMATIC:- REDUCED IN SIZE TO SHOW DIE SET RELATIONSHIP

SHEDDING PIN

SECTION B-B

Figure **4·15** Semicompound die. Main components are: (1) Notched yoke block. (2) Notched yoke block. (3) End cutting block. (4) Notching insert. (5) Notching insert. (6) End cutting block. (7) Stock guides. (8) Spring-actuated stripper. (9) Pedestal-type punch. (10) Stop block. (11) Shedder.

The die is mounted on a diagonal-post die set as depicted by the reduced-size schematic. The majority of the die components are numbered (1) to (11). The call-out for (1) to (7) is repeated at the sectional views in order to help visualize the association of these details in the assembly.

The upper die-block assembly consists of two end cutting blocks (3) and (6) and two notching inserts (4) and (5). These are fitted into the two notched yoke blocks (1) and (2). This group of components is cross-bolted together to achieve a unitized assembly as shown. The unitized assembly can then be mounted just as though it were a solid die block. The shedder (11) is retained vertically by the ledges provided in the yoke blocks. Shedder ledges are not (and should not be) provided in the end cutting blocks (3) and (6). Locating the ledges where shown simplifies die construction and future maintenance as well. In addition the die will be stronger, and die life is enhanced.

The lower assembly consists of the spring-actuated stripper (8), a pedestal-type punch (9) which has its flanges cleared out where required

to facilitate diemaking, and a stop block (10). The stop block also provides lateral confinement for the end slug, permitting this slug to be disposed of through the die shoe. A V-shaped notch is shown in this stop block. The notch acts to centralize the strip each time the latter is fed to the stopping position.

Standardized commercially available stock guides (7) are attached to the stripper. As purchased, these guides were hardened and ready to mount. Two standard dowel pins are incorporated in the stripper to act as auxiliary stock-strip guides. It is apparent by examination that the narrowness of the stripper limits the effectiveness of the auxiliary stock-strip guides. However, the centering notch in (10) tends to alleviate this condition.

The notch detail. Holes are provided in (3), (4), and (5) (Fig. 4·15) to permit the installation of spring pins if this should prove necessary because of slug pulling. In the case of the die we are discussing here the notches were made as pictured exaggeratedly in Fig. 4·16. The sides of the notches were very slightly tapered to produce a dovetailed effect, as shown. Shallow notching operations can be quite troublesome in relation to slug problems. However, a dovetail taper of as little as 0.002 in. per side can be very effective in the elimination of slug problems inherent in notching operations. The notch contour must, of course, be larger at the bottom of the notch, as shown, in order to lock the slug laterally within the die opening.

Fitting the shedder. The shedder (11) (Fig. 4·15) in this die is a guiding shedder: it provides support for the round perforator. Therefore, the shedder must be guided, in this case by properly fitting it to the die cavity. The entire shedder contour could, of course, be made a slip fit to the die cavity. However, doing this would entail needless exacting work on the part of the diemaker. In the case of the die we are now discussing, the shedder was fitted as shown exaggeratedly in Fig. 4·17. A clearance of approximately 0.005 in. was provided where indicated by the double lines. The single lines indicate the slip-fitted areas.

A COMPOUND DIE WITH AN
EXTENDED STOCK GUIDE

The most typical provisions for guiding stock strips in compound dies are those shown intermittently in Figs. 4·1 to 4·15. Occasionally, however, some not so typical stock-guiding provision may be desired. For example the construction of Fig. 4·18, for a compound die, is rather less orthodox as far as stock guiding is concerned.

Here, the stripper is made longer than usual. It extends shelflike to the infeed side, projecting beyond the area covered by the die block. A back gage bar (1), a shelf plate (2), and a top plate (3)

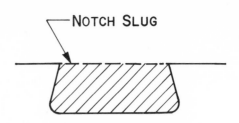

Figure **4·16**   Notch detail (exaggerated).

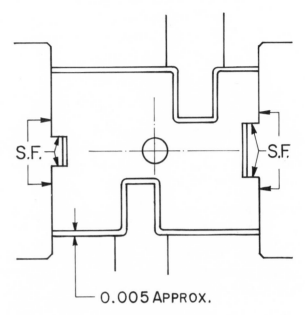

Figure **4·17**   Exaggerated schematic showing how shedder is fitted to die opening.

are mounted in assembly on the projecting part of the stripper plate, as shown.

A guide pin (4) is provided for the front edge of the strip. This front guide pin, too, is located in the area projecting beyond the die block. There-

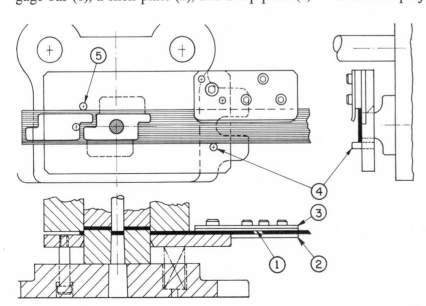

Figure **4·18**   A compound die with extended stock guide mounted on stripper plate. (1) Back-gage bar. (2) Shelf plate. (3) Top plate. (4) Front guide pin. (5) Rear guide pin.

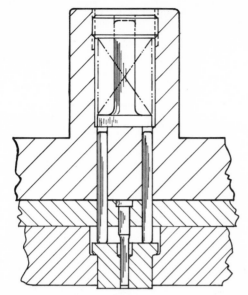

Figure **4·19** Small compound die equipped with compression shedder which is actuated by spring pressure transmitted through transfer pins.

fore, in this and similar cases, the front guide pin is logically a solid pin, press-fitted in the stripper. An auxiliary rear guide pin (5) is often necessary. This may be a solid pin if circumstances permit and if desired. In many applications, the auxiliary rear guide pin may be eliminated, if the extended back guide is long enough to provide adequate alignment for the stock strip.

COMPOUND DIES WITH COMPRESSION SHEDDERS

As described in Chap. 3, *Inverted Dies*, compound dies, too, may incorporate compression shedders in their construction. Figure 4·19 depicts one such construction which is generally well suited to smaller dies. In principle, this action is the same as that described for Fig. 3·10.

The schematic of Fig. 4·20 represents another compound die which is equipped with a compression shedder. This shedder is actuated by springs and is suspended by stripper bolts.

The basic principle of compression shedders

for compound dies is the same as for inverted dies. The discussions in Chap. 3 which described shedding action, proportions, and relationships may all be applied to compound dies.

The major reasons for employing compression shedders in compound dies are:

1. The piece part has very stringent flatness requirements.
2. The piece part may be such that it is quite susceptible to distortion or damage from the fall which results when a positive shedder is employed. This will be noted especially in relation to large, relatively fragile piece parts and to secondary-operation dies where the piece parts have previously formed projections, etc.
3. The available press equipment may influence the choice of shedder actuation.

COMPOUND DIE GENERALITIES

Flatness. Compound dies are noted for their ability consistently to produce piece parts which will satisfy very exacting flatness specifications. This ability is due to the favorable combination of work strains induced in the workpiece by the manner in which a compound die performs. This quality is inherent in compound dies in general and is especially notable in compound dies equipped with compression shedders. It is not generally good practice to bottom the shedder in an attempt to flatten the workpiece by spanking. In fact, doing this will seldom (if ever) improve piece-part flatness, and it will certainly introduce a condition which is much better avoided. In regard to flatness, compound pierce and blank dies are superior to progressive pierce and blank dies for producing flat and distortion-free blanks.

Consistent accuracy. Compound dies are noted for producing accurate piece parts. This accuracy is consistent throughout the life of the die.

Burr side. For piece parts produced in compound dies the burr side of the pierced holes will be on

Figure **4·20** A compound die, larger than that of Fig. 4·19, with spring-actuated shedder. Springs act directly against shedder.

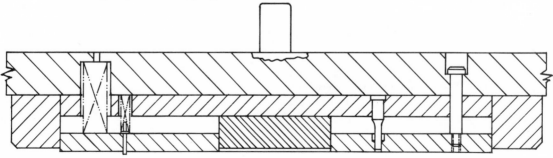

the same side of the piece part as the burr side of the blanked periphery.

Applications. In addition to running strip stock (in coil, if desired), compound dies are well suited for working with unit stock. On occasion this feature may be taken advantage of to produce piece parts from scrap pieces left over from other jobs. Certain secondary operations, too, may be efficiently performed by compound dies.

Large dies. Because compound dies are single-station dies, they may be employed to produce piece parts which are too large to be practical for production in a progressive die.

Two-pass dies. Compound dies can be successfully applied where multiple-pass (usually two-pass) feeding is desired. This, too, is because compound dies are single-station dies.

Automatic stops. Automatic stops can be successfully used on compound dies. These stops are thoroughly described in the book "Basic Die-making."

Construction cost. It is sometimes stated that compound dies are more expensive to build. This statement is, of course, erroneous. The principles embodied in compound dies represent a design evolution necessitated by piece-part requirements. It is true that if the compound principle is misapplied both tool cost and production cost can be needlessly high. However, this is true for any type of die design if it is misapplied. In fact, for appropriate situations, a compound die may be the most economical type of die.

Figure **4·21** Compound pierce and blank die to pierce three holes and blank out the piece part shown.

Shedding pins. Either shedding pins or shedding vents must be considered to be a vitally essential feature of shedder construction for compound dies. The shedding-pin principles discussed earlier for inverted dies are directly applicable for compound dies.

Figure **4·22** A two-gang compound pierce and blank die which produces two piece parts per press stroke. The die is shown set up on a Moore die flipper for doweling purposes. The piece parts are ejected to the rear by means of air jets. Ejection air is provided via the manifolds A, each of which vents through three air-jet tubes, as shown. The ejected piece parts are directed out through the rear of the die by the baffle plates B.

CHAPTER 5

PROGRESSIVE DIES USING THE BLANK-THROUGH PRINCIPLE

By definition, to progress means to advance toward completion. A progressive die is a die in which the stock strip is advanced through a sequence of operations which work toward completion of the piece part.

The successive positions into which the stock strip is registered are the basic divisions of a progressive die. These basic divisions are called "stations." In many respects, each station is individually similar to a single-station die, except, of course, that each station affects and is affected by the other stations in the progression.

The distance from any given point in one station to the equivalent point in the next station is an exact dimension. This dimension is identical for all adjacent station-to-station relationships in the progression. This dimension is also precisely equal to the advance distance.

The advance distance is the exact distance at which the stock strip is relocated (registered) for each successive press stroke. Generally, in the interests of simplified description the word "distance" is dropped from the term. This distance is usually specified simply as the "advance."

The feed distance is the distance the stock strip is moved, either manually or mechanically, between sequences. In a very few special circumstances, the feed distance is equal to the advance distance. For the great majority of progressive dies, however, the feed distance is either slightly longer or slightly shorter than the advance distance, whichever is appropriate for the specific application.

A FUNDAMENTAL PROGRESSIVE PIERCE
AND BLANK DIE

Figure 5·1 depicts a simple piece part. It is a rectangular blank which has tangent radii at the four corners and which is pierced as shown. A number of different procedures could be used for producing this piece part, of which the following are those most often used:

1. *Two dies.* The first operation die would be a single-station blank-through die which would produce the plain blank without the pierced openings. The second operation die would be a pierce die to pierce the openings into the plain blank. In production, the plain blanks would be produced by the first die and then fed individually into the pierce die. Production time would obviously be higher than for the following procedures.
2. *Compound die.* A compound die would produce the pierced piece part complete, as illustrated. It would also produce the flattest and most accurate piece part.
3. *Progressive die.* A progressive die would also produce the pierced piece part complete, as illustrated. The piece part would not be as flat or as consistently accurate as it would be if produced by a compound die. However, in this instance the progressive die could be less expensive to make and would be faster in operation.

It is the function of the tool engineer and die designer to determine the type of die best suited to the occasion. It is not always obvious that a certain type of die will be the most appropriate for a given piece part in relation to the circumstances under which it will be produced.

In the case of the piece part of Fig. 5·1 it would appear that it should be produced either by a compound die or by a progressive die. The illustration includes a representative stock-strip layout, and the layout indicates that the die is a two-station progressive die (Fig. 5·2). The progressive die was decided upon because it will be faster in operation, thereby minimizing production costs.

Operating sequence

1. Lead end of the stock strip is fed into the tunnel and past the pusher (21). Primary stop (19) is activated to enter the required distance into the

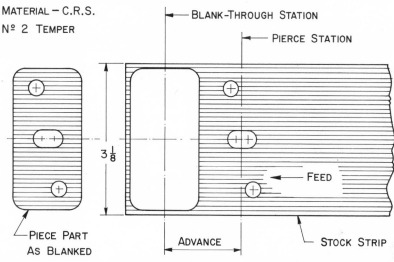

Figure **5·1** A piece part and its representative stock strip, with a blanked-out piece part shown alongside.

2.995 ±.005

1 1/16

1 1/16

1/4

5/8

1/4

1.495 ±.005

Fractional Dimensions ± 0.010
Material — C.R.S.
N° 2 Temper

.375 ±.002

11/32 DIA.

.040 ——(T)

1/4 R.

Blank-Through Station

Pierce Station

3 1/8

Feed

Piece Part
As Blanked

Advance

Stock Strip

tunnel. Lead end of the strip is then fed into contact with the primary stop. The press is now activated to produce the piercings in the stock strip.

2. Feeding is resumed. Lead end of the strip is fed against the final stop (18). This stop allows the strip to overfeed a slight amount, which will permit the pilots to register the strip without interference from the stop. The press is then reactivated to produce a completed piece part in the blanking station while simultaneously performing the piercing operation for the succeeding piece part in the first station. This cycle is then repeated until the stock strip is consumed. (Refer to Chap. 8, *Pilots,* and Chap. 14, *Die Stops,* in "Basic Diemaking.")

Dowels for the lower die assembly. This die employs a total of four dowels to position the

lower die assembly. The dowels are paired, each pair sharing common holes. This procedure should not be construed to be a universally desirable doweling procedure. However, it is well suited to the application illustrated in Fig. 5·2 and may be appropriate for many similar applications. The dowels are installed in the manner shown. Two dowels (9) position the die block (2) on the die shoe. These dowels should normally engage in both the die block and the die shoe a distance ranging from D to $2D$, where D is the diameter of the dowel. The length of dowel engagement should be in proportion to the die-block thickness, with the longer dowel engagements in thicker die blocks and the shorter engagements permissible for thinner die blocks. Two additional dowels (16) position the entire stripper assembly, (7), (4), (5), and (17) to (21), on the die block. For these dowels the engagement distance in the die block may

53

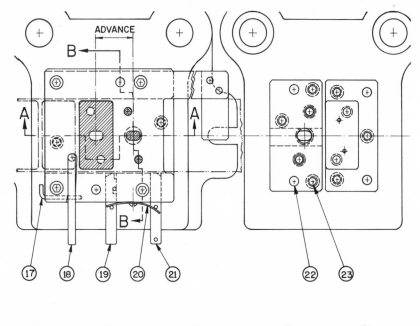

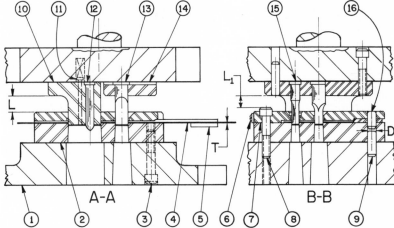

A-A

B-B

Figure **5·2** Progressive pierce and blank die: two stations. The die components and the number of each required are:

1. Back-post die set (one)
2. Die block (one)
3. Socket-head cap screw (two)
4. Guide rail (back gage) (one)
5. Shelf (one)
6. Button-head screw (one)
7. Stripper (one)
8. Socket-head cap screw (four)
9. Dowel (two)
10. Blanking punch (one)
11. Spring-pin assembly (two)
12. Pilot (two)
13. Pierce punch (one)
14. Punch plate (one)
15. Perforator (two)
16. Dowel (two)
17. Pivot pin (one)
18. Auto stop (one)
19. Finger stop (one)
20. Spring (one)
21. Pusher (one)
22. Dowel (four)
23. Socket-head cap screw (six)

have to be reduced to an entry distance approximating ¼D. Note that the rear dowel stabilizes the back gage (4) against the offset ledge in the stripper, thereby positioning the back gage in relation to the stripper. For thinner die blocks it may be more practical to use only two dowels instead of the four dowels shown. Each dowel would then extend all the way through the stripper assembly and the die block and into the die shoe.

The above doweling methods represent minimal doweling procedures adequate for average die conditions. They apply especially to constructions which are similar to the die shown. They may not be well suited for large dies and would generally be inappropriate for dies equipped with guiding strippers.

Screw attachment for the lower assembly. The lower die assembly is secured to the die shoe by four screws (8) (Fig. 5·2). These are the prime fasteners, necessary for attachment of the lower die assembly to the die shoe. They are installed with their heads uppermost. They are threaddedly engaged in the die shoe and cleared through the stripper, back gage, and die block. The screw heads are counterbored into the stripper plate as shown in order to provide die-life space at L, in the illustration. As a matter of diemaking expedience the counterbores should be omitted if the construction provides adequate die life without the counterbores.

Two auxiliary screws (3) assist in securing the die block to the die shoe. In this die these auxiliary screws are not actually essential to the security of the assembly. They were installed primarily as a convenience for the diemaker. Auxiliary mounting screws, installed as shown, can very definitely facilitate diemaking. These auxiliary screws can also serve a third purpose: they can make it possible to sharpen the die block without removing it from the die shoe, if and when this is desirable.

Dowels for the blanking punch. The blanking punch (10) (Fig. 5·2) is positioned by two dowels [refer to (22)]. The dowel holes were lapped to a very light force fit in the punch and reamed to a slightly heavier force fit in the punch holder. (Respectively, these fits are commonly referred to as a "tap" fit and a "drive" fit. Sometimes the latter fit is called a "light press" fit.) The above dowel-fitting procedure is in accordance with the practice of making the tighter fit in the soft member when a hardened component is being doweled to a softer component. Another factor which influences this dowel-fitting procedure is the fact that the dowel is installed from the punch side. It is driven through the punch flanges to enter into the punch holder. Because of this it is desirable to use a slightly lighter fit for the hole in the flange than for the mating hole in the punch holder.

Occasionally, owing to specific individual job requirements, it may be desirable or necessary to depart from this procedure by reversing the fits or by using a common fit in both members. However, it will be best to adhere to this procedure whenever possible. All dowel fits can be considered to be exacting. They are especially critical for dowels incorporated in the upper assembly, since the dowel fit must be tight enough to retain the dowel securely under running conditions. If a dowel were to drop out of the upper assembly, it would obviously create a safety hazard and a potential for severe damage to the die.

Screw attachment for the blanking punch. This blanking punch is secured in position by three screws (23) (Fig. 5·2). The screws are shown installed in the manner normally preferred, heads uppermost. That is, the punch holder is counterbored from the top to receive the screw heads, and the tapped holes are located in the punch flange. This method of installing mounting screws in the upper assembly will be best for the majority of applications. It will generally facilitate diemaking procedures by simplifying the process of mounting the punch in assembly. Screws should, of course, be securely tightened to prevent their loosening and backing out of the assembly. However, if looseness should occur, a screw will not back out and fall into the die assembly during operation if it is installed as shown in the figure.

Mounting screws for the upper assembly should be installed as described above in all cases where it is practical to do so. Keep in mind, however, that for some applications it will be more practical to install the screws in the opposite manner (threaded end uppermost). For example, it becomes necessary to invert the screws when it is desired to be able to remove and/or install the punch without removing the die from the punch press.

Spring pins for the blanking punch. In this die, the pilots (12) (Fig. 5·2) are contained in the blanking punch. Spring pins (11) are also included in the blanking punch. The spring pins prevent the blank from being sucked up from the die opening when the punch ascends. Spring pushoff pins (or their equivalent) can be considered to be mandatory in blanking or equivalent punches which contain pilots. (See "Pilots in Punches" in "Basic Diemaking.")

Screws and dowels for the pierce-punch unit. The three pierce punches (13) and (15) (Fig. 5·2) are assembled into the punch plate (14). This assembly is thereby unitized and can be mounted as though it were a single punch. The unit is positioned and fastened by two dowels (22) and three screws (23). The procedure for the screws and dowels is the same as that described for the blanking punch.

Die Life. Die life is a significant factor which influences the proportions of the various die components. Before proceeding with the analysis and study of the die components it will be helpful to consider the life potential of this die. The die design is predicated on the following.

Probable Life. The probable life requirements were estimated in advance to be ⅜ in. for the die block and 9/16 in. for the punches. The design is intended to provide the above amounts without rework.

Maximum Life. In order to provide a safety factor, the die is designed to provide additional life beyond the probable life. Maximum practical life for this die is considered to be ½ in. for the die block and ¾ in. for the punches. To attain these figures, some rework of the upper punch assembly will be necessary. For example extra clearance would be made in the blanking-punch flange and the punch plate for the screw heads (at L_1). Procedures of this kind are good diemaking practice, since die proportions are made as strong as possible, yet with some extra life available as a safety factor.

Note that the above life provisions are 50 percent greater for the punches than for the die block. This, too, is good diemaking practice. (See "Rela-

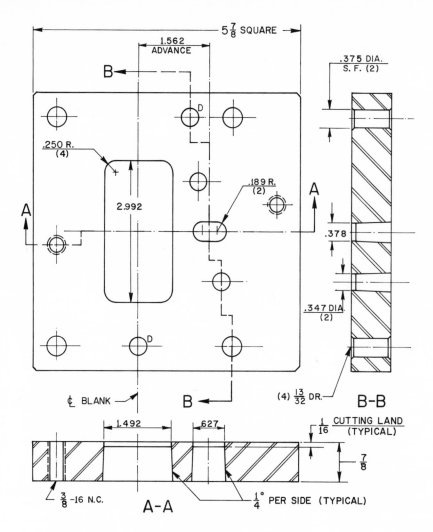

Figure **5·3** Die-block detail.

(4) $\frac{13}{32}$ DR.

B-B

$\frac{1}{16}$ CUTTING LAND (TYPICAL)

$\frac{7}{8}$

$\frac{3}{8}$ -16 N.C.   A-A $\frac{1}{4}°$ PER SIDE (TYPICAL)

② 1 REQ. O-1 T.S. R.C. 60-62

tive Life: Punches and Die Blocks" as described in "Basic Diemaking.")

The die block. Figure 5·3 is a detail drawing showing the die block as it would appear when finished and ready for mounting. The dimensions can be considered to be the optimum target dimensions for the diemaker. Dimensions for the die are, of course, derived from the piece-part dimensions (refer to Fig. 5·1). These dimensions must be related to the manner in which they are produced by their corresponding die functions. That is, is the dimension produced by a pierce punch, or is it produced by the blanking-die opening, etc.?

Consideration should be given as to how the particular type of die may influence the resulting piece-part dimensions. For example, if it were intended to produce a given piece part in a compound die, the size of the blanking-die opening might be made slightly larger than if it were intended to produce the same piece part by means of a blank-through die.

In addition to the above, due consideration should be given to the choice of dimensions in relation to practicality for diemaking. This involves permissible dimensional adaptions to permit maximum use of standard or available cutters, reamers, etc. This also involves minimizing the dimensional exactitude to which the diemaker must work. Most commonly, this last means taking advantage of permissible tolerances in order to provide maximum dimensional leeway for the diemaker.

In association with the above considerations the following factors contributed to the establishment of the diemaker's target dimensions specified in the detail illustrations.

Cutting Clearance. The piece-part drawing (Fig. 5· 1) specified the material to be cold-rolled steel, No. 2 temper, with a thickness of 0.040 in. For this material, an initial cutting clearance of

4 percent T per side is appropriate for the outer periphery of the blank. In this case, $.04T = 0.0016$ in. For the sake of convenience this is rounded off to 0.0015 in. per side. For the pierced openings, because their contours are round and nearly round, the cutting clearance is made smaller. This is done because round and/or nearly round contours are more susceptible to slug pulling than irregular contours. The use of a smaller cutting clearance tends to eliminate potential slug pulling. Consequently, an initial cutting clearance of 2½ percent T per side is appropriate for the pierced openings. In this case, $.025T = 0.001$ in. Actually, any clearance ranging between 2 and 3 percent T per side should be satisfactory for these openings. However, the 2½ percent clearance is a nice compromise, convenient for the diemaker.

For this die, then, the optimum cutting clearances are established as 0.0015 in. per side for the blanking station and 0.001 in. per side for the piercing station.

Advance Distance. For this kind of blank contour, the advance distance is equal to the blank width plus the width of the desired scrap web between blanks. For a blank of this size and shape, the scrap bridge should closely approximate 1¼T or ¹⁄₁₆ in., whichever is largest. In this case 1¼$T = 0.050$ in., which is less than ¹⁄₁₆ in. Therefore, a scrap bridge width of ¹⁄₁₆ in. is chosen. The blank width is specified 1.495 ± 0.005 in. From the point of view of tolerance, the widest acceptable blank is 1.500 in. This dimension is then added to the scrap-bridge dimension to determine the approximate advance distance. Thus, the approximate advance distance is $1.500 + 0.0625 = 1.5625$ in. Since this is a so-called "standard" dimension, rounding off is simply a matter of eliminating the fourth-decimal-place-digit. The resulting advance distance is 1.562 in., as shown on the detail drawing (Fig. 5·3).

Blanking-die Opening. The outer periphery of the blank is sized by the die opening. Consequently, the cutting clearance is not a factor in selecting the optimum dimensions for the blanking-die opening. Conventional blank-through dies cannot be expected to produce truly flat piece parts. Some dishing of the blanks can be considered normal for these dies.

The dishing tendency is due to unopposed compressive cutting forces. Softer grades of stock material tend to dish more than harder grades. The dishing tendency is also directly related to fenestration. That is, a blank which contains a previously pierced opening tends to dish more than a blank which is not previously pierced, a blank which contains a greater number of piercings tends to dish more than a blank with fewer piercings, etc. Dishing tends to be milder when the cutting edges are sharp and to increase as the edges become dull. Thus, the dishing tendency does not improve during a die run. There may, however, be some improvement later in the life of the die, when the die block has been sharpened away enough to produce an increase in the cutting clearance because of the die taper. The increase in cutting clearance tends to lessen the cutting force which, in turn, lessens the dishing tendency.

It should be understood that the above discussion concerns conditions that are subject to a wide and variable range of circumstances. There is no cut-and-dried procedure for precise predetermination of dishing tendencies. However, reasonably accurate predictions can be made by association with similar dies for similar blanks.

If precisely true plane flatness is required for a piece part, this fact should be specified on the piece-part drawing. If it is not so specified, it is commonly assumed that the blank will be acceptably flat as produced by a blank-through die.

The target dimensions for the die opening illustrated in Fig. 5·3 approach the low end of the limits set by the piece-part tolerances. This is done for the following reasons:

1. The target dimensions will produce an acceptable piece part "as blanked" throughout the entire life of the die.
2. If the blank should dish and be flattened later (by virtue of a deliberate flattening operation or as a result of assembly to another part, for example), the probable increase in size (0.001 to 0.003 in. overall) would be within the specified limits even when die-life factors have been accounted for.

    Actually, dishing effects probably are not important for this piece part. However, dishing is cited and discussed here because it does occur in operations of this kind and it must be understood that dies of this general nature should not be expected to produce piece parts which are precisely flat in their plane surfaces. Also, this kind of knowledge is an important factor in diemaking proficiency: if it is properly understood, doubt and hesitancy can be eliminated from diemaking procedures and better final results can be ensured.
3. The target dimensions provide an entirely adequate allowance for the increase in die-opening size which will be the eventual result of sharpening attrition. The detail drawing specifies cutting lands of ¹⁄₁₆ in. along with die

tapers (angular clearance) of ¼° per side. This combination, after the die-block thickness has been reduced ½ in. (as a result of sharpening attrition), will have produced an increase in die-opening size of 0.0019 in. per side.

4. The target dimensions provide maximum practical working leeway for the diemaker.

When all the pertinent factors are considered, the target dimensions shown should yield a probable blank size of 1.493 × 2.993 in. initially, with an increase to 1.497 × 2.997 in. as the die life is expended. These are "as blanked" dimensions. They provide a maximum margin which should be adequate for any normal eventuality which might be associated with this operation.

Pierce-die Openings. The pierced openings in the blank are sized by their respective piercing punches. As a consequence, the cutting clearance must be reckoned with in determining the dimensions of the die openings which are required for the piercings. A punch size of 0.345 in. diameter was chosen for the two round holes which are specified 11⁄32 in. diameter on the piece-part print (Fig. 5·1). It was decided to use a cutting clearance of 0.001 in. per side for the piercings. Therefore, these die openings are made 0.347 in. diameter at the top. They are tapered ¼° per side, leaving a cutting land of 1⁄16 in. at the top as specified *typical* on the detail print. For the oblong punch, the selected sizes are 0.376 × 0.625 in. Consequently, the respective die dimensions are 0.378 × 0.627 in. This die opening is, of course,

provided with cutting land and taper the same as the other die openings.

The blanking punch. The blanking punch is detailed in Fig. 5·4. It is an offset pedestal punch. This type of punch configuration was necessitated by the proximity of the piercing unit, which is in the preceding station. The punch sizes are equal to the respective die-opening sizes minus the cutting clearance. These are 1.489 × 2.989 in., with a corner radius of 0.2485 in.

Holes for the spring pins should be strategically located to provide effective stripping action for the pilots. These holes can be simply made as shown, smoothly drilled 1⁄64 in. larger in diameter than their respective spring pins.

The pilot-installation holes are provided in the manner shown. The fitted depth is 15⁄16 in. measured from the face surface of the punch. The balance of the hole is relief-drilled to 23⁄64 in. diameter. The presence of the relief minimizes the amount of precise fitting work required of the diemaker. In appropriate situations, such as this one, relief drilling is a very practical procedure which facilitates diemaking. In this case the fitted length is 15⁄16 in. This will provide as much as ¾ in. for sharpening attrition and still leave a fitted length of 3⁄16 in. at that stage of wear. The idea is to make the fitted length as short as possible without detracting from the necessary life potential of the punch.

The counterbores for the pilot heads are shown as 31⁄64 in. diameter minimum. This is the mini-

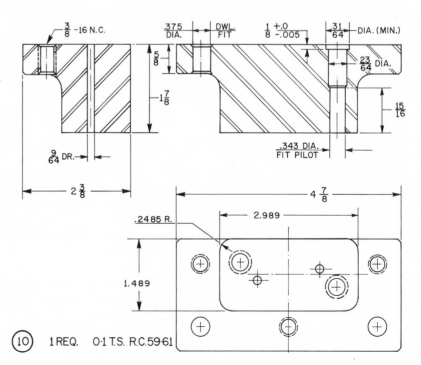

Figure **5·4** Blanking-punch detail.

mum diameter which will provide a satisfactory clearance for the pilot-head diameters. For practical reasons, such counterbores are not generally made to the minimum diameter. For example, a counterbore diameter of ½ in. would probably be more practical for the punch illustrated, since it is more likely that suitable cutting tools will be available for the ½ in. diameter. Depth of the counterbore is specified as ⅛ in. plus zero, minus 0.005 in. The tolerance is negative in order to ensure that the counterbore will not be made too deep.

It is generally much more practical to work the pilot head to suit the counterbore depth than it is to grind off the base surface of the punch to suit the pilot head. Ideally, the pilot heads should be fitted precisely flush with the base surface of the punch. To accomplish this, the mounting holes are made a snug tap fit for the pilots. The pilots are then tapped into place. The pilot heads should protrude very slightly above the punch-base surface. They are then ground off (while in assembly) until they are flush with the base of the punch.

However, for a punch-pilot assembly of this kind, the following approach may be more expeditious: After the punch is finished and ready to mount, accurately measure the counterbore depth. Then rework the thickness of the pilot head to 0.0002 to 0.001 in. less than the counterbore depth. Assemble the pilot into the punch, and check to be certain that the head does not protrude above the base surface of the punch. With this method, the pilot-mounting hole may be made a close slip fit for the pilot, since the pilot hole is not required to retain the pilot for flush-grinding purposes. When using this method, be certain that it is suitable for the particular application. Also, in any case, the pilot heads must not protrude above the punch base for constructions of this type.

The pilots. These are made as pictured in Fig. 5·5. The piloting size is 0.343 in. diameter, which is 0.002 in. smaller than the respective piercing punches. During the tryout procedure the blanks may show evidence indicating that the 0.343 in. diameter is slightly too large. If so, the pilots should be removed and stoned or lapped 0.001 to 0.002 in. smaller (on the diameter), as required. This reduced diameter should be limited to a suitable length A along the piloting length. Length A must be limited to some dimension which will not detract too much from the fitted length of the pilot in its mounting hole.

The piloting sizes described above could be as much as 0.004 in. smaller than the respective perforators. This is quite typical for pilots which are mounted in blanking punches. To analyze these sizes for the potential error of registry,

Perforator size, 0.345 in. diameter
Probable pierced-hole size, 0.3444 in. diameter
Possible pilot diameter, 0.341 in. diameter
0.3444 − 0.341 = 0.0034 in. diametral difference
$\dfrac{0.0034}{2} = 0.0017$ in. radial difference

Thus, the potential registry error for this construction is ±0.0017 in.

It should be understood that pilots mounted in blanking (or equivalent) punches cannot be expected to register the work as accurately as pilots which operate in the stock strip away from die openings.

The effective piloting length should extend beyond the punch face a distance B. Distance B must, of course, be long enough to ensure registry. For this kind of die, and where T represents the stock-material thickness, the initial dimension for B may generally be made

$$B = T \qquad \text{where } T > \tfrac{1}{32} \text{ in.}$$

or

$$B = \tfrac{1}{32} \text{ in.} \qquad \text{where } T < \tfrac{1}{32} \text{ in.}$$

These lengths can normally be considered optimum. Occasionally it may be desirable to make length B slightly longer, and quite often it may be necessary to make length B slightly shorter. If, in

Figure **5·5** Pilot detail, showing installation in punch.

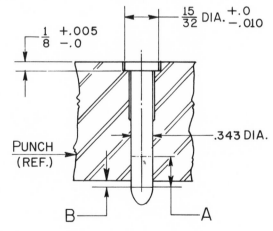

tryout, the blanks tend to lift up from the die opening, it may be necessary to decrease the B length to

$$B = \frac{T}{2} \qquad \text{where } T > \frac{1}{32} \text{ in.}$$

or

$$B = 0.005 \text{ in. to } \frac{1}{64} \text{ in.} \qquad \text{where } T < \frac{1}{32} \text{ in.}$$

This pilot has a head diameter of $\frac{15}{32}$ in. plus zero, minus 0.010 in. The tolerance is specified negative in order to ensure radial clearance in the counterbore. Head thickness is $\frac{1}{8}$ in. plus 0.005 in., minus zero. Here, the tolerance is positive in order to ensure that the pilot is the component which will be reworked instead of the blanking punch.

For most applications it will be economically desirable to purchase commercially available pilots.

The piercing punches. The two round perforators (pierce punches) appear in Fig. 5·6. They are conventional step-head perforators, typically standardized and available as commercial items. The shank diameter is normally furnished slightly oversize. The precise amount oversize may vary slightly, depending upon the source of supply. One practice is to make the shank equal to the nominal dimension plus 0.0002 to 0.0005 in. This minimizes fitting when standard-size reamers are used to size the perforator-mounting holes in the punch plate.

Since the perforators for this application are relatively sturdy, the vertical dimensions are se-

lected to provide the maximum life of $\frac{3}{4}$ in. without reworking. The head diameter of $\frac{1}{2}$ in. plus zero, minus 0.010 in., is a standard head size for the shank diameter. The tolerance is negative for the same reason as that described earlier for the pilots. Tolerance for the head thickness is plus 0.005 in., minus zero. This tolerance is positive for the same reason as that given earlier for the pilot head thickness. The cutting portion is 0.345 in. diameter which is consistent with the accepted practice of making the perforator 0.001 in. larger (overall) than the intended pierced hole size.

The oblong (oblate) pierce punch is pictured in Fig. 5·7. The width of the cutting portion is 0.376 in., which is a logical punch size for producing this dimension of the pierced opening adequately within the tolerance specified on the piece-part print (Fig. 5·1). The 0.625-in. cutting dimension is assigned on the basis of making the punch shank with a nominally standard $\frac{5}{8}$-in.-diameter shank. The head of this perforator is not installed in a counterbore. Consequently, the $\frac{3}{4}$-in. diameter does not require a negative tolerance. The head thickness should, of course, have a positive tolerance as shown.

This punch, too, is a proportionately sturdy punch. Therefore the vertical dimensions are such that they provide the maximum anticipated life of $\frac{3}{4}$ in. The shank length is shorter than that of the round perforators because of the larger fillet required at F. This punch is keyed to achieve and maintain its proper position. Keying is accomplished by providing a flat on one side of the head. The flat is matched to the corresponding slot provided in the punch plate.

The punch plate. Figure 5·8 is a detail drawing of the punch plate for this die. The screw and dowel provisions are made as previously described. Openings for the perforators are specified at 0.375 in. and 0.625 in. diameter. These openings must, of course, be precisely located, and the perforator shanks must fit nicely in the openings. The optimum fit for most applications can best be described as a light tap fit. For the two round holes in this application one approach would be to finish-ream the holes to 0.0002 to 0.0005 in. undersize on the diameters. Both holes should be precisely the same diameter. The perforator shanks can then be lightly polished until the desired fit is achieved.

Another approach is, of course, to size the mounting holes to provide the desired fit for the perforator shank, as furnished. For the oblong punch, the largest punching dimension is 0.625 in. Its shank diameter is 0.6252 to 0.6255 in. diam-

Figure **5·6**   Pierce-punch detail.

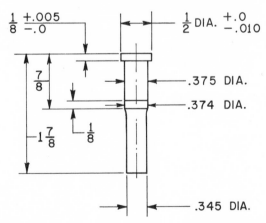

$\frac{1}{8} \begin{array}{c} +.005 \\ -.0 \end{array}$ $\frac{1}{2}$ DIA. $\begin{array}{c} +.0 \\ -.010 \end{array}$

$\frac{7}{8}$

.375 DIA.

.374 DIA.

$1\frac{7}{8}$ $\frac{1}{8}$

.345 DIA.

⑮   2 REQ.   O-1 T.S.   R.C. 59-62
HEAD   R.C. 40-50

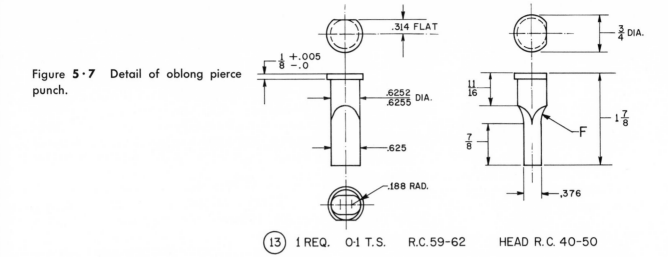

Figure **5·7** Detail of oblong pierce punch.

.314 FLAT

$\frac{1}{8}$ +.005 -.0

$\frac{6252}{6255}$ DIA.

.625

.188 RAD.

$\frac{3}{4}$ DIA.

$\frac{11}{16}$

$1\frac{7}{8}$

$\frac{7}{8}$

F

.376

⑬ 1 REQ.   O-1 T.S.   R.C. 59–62   HEAD R.C. 40–50

eter. Consequently, there is very little leeway for polishing this shank to suit the mounting hole in the punch plate. Essentially, therefore, this mounting hole should be sized to suit the perforator shank. For this particular piercing, if it had been felt that it was especially desirable to polish the shank to fit the hole, the punching size could have been made 0.624 in. for the long dimension. This would have been permissible because the dimension is specified as a fractional dimension on the piece-part drawing (Fig. 5·1). Still another approach would have been to use a larger shank diameter, etc.

Many variations in method are possible in fitting punches into punch plates. The decision as to which is the optimum method depends upon the specific application, including the diemaking and production circumstances pertaining to that application. As shown, a slot is machined laterally through the punch plate to receive the head of the oblong perforator. One side of the slot provides the keying surface which aligns the perforator. It is generally easier to make the slot first and then finish-grind the perforator head to the desired key fit. Be meticulous when making key fits. If the fit is too tight, the punch will tilt. If the fit is loose, the punch can rotate out of position.

Material for this punch plate is low-carbon steel, specified HRS (hot-rolled steel). The presence of the key slot is the reason for this choice.

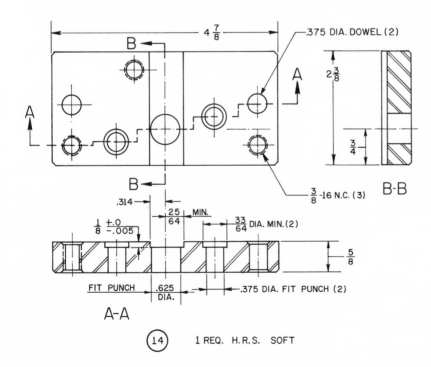

$4\frac{7}{8}$

B

.375 DIA. DOWEL (2)

A

A

A

B

B

$2\frac{3}{8}$

$\frac{3}{4}$

$\frac{3}{8}$-16 N.C. (3)

B-B

Figure **5·8** Detail of punch plate.

.314

$\frac{1}{8}$ +.0 -.005

$\frac{25}{64}$ MIN.

$\frac{33}{64}$ DIA. MIN. (2)

$\frac{5}{8}$

FIT PUNCH   .625 DIA.

.375 DIA. FIT PUNCH (2)

A-A

⑭   1 REQ. H.R.S. SOFT

If cold-rolled steel were used, there would be danger of excessive warpage as a result of machining the key slot.

Cold-rolled steel is produced from hot-rolled by removing outer rough scale and creating a smooth finish by rolling cold. This process of cold rolling stretches the outer fibers of steel against the inner fibers in compression. When the outer tension fibers are machined away, the steel piece warps. The amount of warp varies with the degree of stress involved. If the cold-rolled piece is heated red hot and slowly cooled, the strains will be relieved or normalized. If this is done, the steel will again have a scale resembling hot-rolled. Hot-rolled does not have these strains because they are immediately relieved in the process of being rolled red hot.

The stripper assembly. This assembly is composed of the details shown in Fig. 5·9. This is not a guiding stripper. The opening for the blanking punch should be made 0.005 in. to 1/64 in. per side larger than the blanking punch. Clearance openings for the pierce punches may be made to the suggested optimum sizes shown in the illustration. The above sizes (for all the punch clearance openings) are based upon this stock-material thickness, which is 0.040 in. as specified on the piece-part

drawing (Fig. 5·1). Optimum stripping clearance for punches is relative to the thickness and hardness of the stock material. Thin, soft stock material necessitates the use of smaller clearances between punch and stripper. Thicker and/or harder stock material permits the use of larger stripping clearances.

The stripper plate (7) (Fig. 5·1) may be made from low-carbon steel. The use of hot-rolled steel will alleviate warping tendencies associated with machining the double-stepped configuration (section *B-B*). The first step, which is shown as $\frac{1}{16}{}^{+.010}_{-.0}$, creates the tunnel roof, which is the surface against which the stripping action takes place. The target dimension of 1/16 in. is limited by a negative tolerance of zero to ensure that the step will be made not less than 1/16 in. A lesser tunnel height would probably offer objectionable resistance to feeding. The positive tolerance for this step is indicated to be +0.010 in., which limits the tunnel height to less than 2T. The limited tunnel height will preclude the possibility of feeding one stock strip on top of another. This procedure, although logical, is limited in application. It does not lend itself to long dies or to applications involving light-gage stock material.

The second step is made, as shown, to provide a space of 0.145 to 0.150 in. for the back gage (4) (Fig. 5·1). This permits the back gage to be made from standard 5/32-in.-thick gage stock, providing 0.006 to 0.009 in. for grinding the back-gage top and bottom to suit the step. This back gage was made 1 1/4 in. wide in order to use a standard and minimum width of gage stock. This second step is machined in the stripper at a dimension of 1.560 in. from the center of the blank, as shown. The back gage is aligned against the resulting ledge. The back-gage location was determined as follows:

Distance from center of blank to back edge of blanking punch, 1.4945 in.

Recommended minimum back scrap web for a blank of this size and shape, 1/16 in.

Adding these,

$$1.4945 + 0.0625 = 1.557 \text{ in.}$$

This sum was then rounded off to 1.560 in., as shown in Fig. 5·9.

The distance from the center of the blank to the front edge of the stripper tunnel is specified as 1 19/32 in. plus 1/64 in., minus zero. This dimension provides the edge clearance necessary for feeding the stock strip through the tunnel. The edge clearance also provides for normal variations in stock width.

Figure **5·9**   Details of stripper assembly.

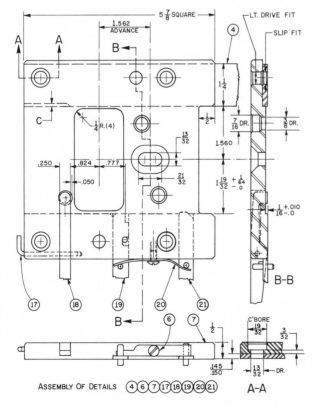

The above description is of normal construction for blanking-die stripper tunnels: the stock strip is guided accurately against the back gage, and edge clearance is provided at the front.

Further aids to feeding are the starting notch, which is shown ½ in. deep in the illustration, and the offset *C* in the back gage, which will accommodate possible bulging of the stock strip due to blanking. In this particular die an offset *D* of 1⁄32 in. will be ample.

The dowels should be fitted as specified in Fig. 5·9, a light drive fit through the stripper plate and a slip fit through the back gage. Counterbores for the screw heads are held to ¼ in. deep to provide a minimum land of 3⁄32 in. under the screw heads as shown in section *A-A*. The counterbore is shown to be 19⁄32 in. diameter, which is the minimum diameter consistent for the 13⁄32-in.-diameter screw clearance hole. The counterbore can be made 39⁄64 in. diameter, and it would then provide an allowance for eccentricity of the screw head.

The construction shown in Fig. 5·9 employs one spring (20) (Fig. 5·1) to actuate both the pusher (21) and the finger stop (19). Because the pusher requires more spring pressure than would be desirable for the finger stop, the spring is contoured in order to exert a lighter action for the finger stop. In fact, this particular finger stop does not actually need a return spring. The spring is a convenience rather than a necessity in this case. However, it should be remembered that return springs can be absolutely necessary for some finger-stop applications. In any application where there is a possibility that a finger stop can cause interference, the stop should be equipped with a return spring. For example, if the front edge of the stock strip is previously notched or otherwise altered, the finger stops should have adequate return springs.

Locating the stops. This die has only one finger stop. It functions as a primary stop. It acts only against the lead end of the strip. Its purpose is to properly locate the lead end of the strip for the initial press stroke when starting the strip. The optimum primary stopping position must be decided for any given application on an individual basis. There is no blanket rule for deciding the precise dimensional location of the primary stopping position. The optimum primary stopping position is often a matter of judicious compromise in relation to a number of possible factors. The following factors can affect the primary stopping position:

Feeding method. For hand-fed dies the primary stop must be considered in relation to the succeeding stops in the die. For automatic feeds, the feeding cycle must be considered in relation to the punching cycle.

Feed-qualifying allowance. This is the overfeed or underfeed increment (whichever is required) which allows the pilots to register the stock strip accurately and without interference.

Stock material. Thicker and/or harder materials permit larger feed-qualification allowances than are practical for thinner and/or softer materials.

Pilot size. Larger pilots permit feed-qualification allowances which are larger than those practical for smaller pilots.

Lead-end condition. The primary stopping dimension should permit as much variation in the condition of the lead end of the stock strip as is practically possible.

Partial blanking. Avoid the production of partial blanks whenever practicable. In all cases where feasible the first blank produced in the strip should be a complete blank.

Nipping. Preclude, to the fullest practical degree, the possibility that a punch may nip the lead end of the stock strip.

The manner in which the stops function, how they are constructed, their relationship to piloting, etc., are described in Chap. 14, *Die Stops,* and Chap. 8, *Pilots,* in "Basic Diemaking."

The following conditions exist specifically for the assembly under discussion at this time:

1. The die is intended for manual feeding.
2. Thickness and temper of the stock material will permit a relatively large feed-qualifying allowance.
3. The pilot diameters are proportionately large enough to permit a relatively large feed-qualifying allowance.
4. It was ascertained that it would be most desirable to provide for a ±1⁄32-in. out-of-square condition at the lead end of the strip (measured from the front edge to the back edge).

In order to provide the maximum plus or minus angular variation for the lead end of the stock strip, the primary stopping position would coincide with the center of the scrap bridge (between blanks). In this die the scrap bridge is equal to the difference between the advance distance and the width of the blanking punch, or

$$1.562 - 1.489$$
$$= 0.073 \text{ in., scrap bridge between blanks}$$

For this scrap bridge, the maximum out-of-square

63

condition for the lead end of the strip could be

$$\frac{0.073 - 0.003}{2} = 0.035 \text{ in.}$$

The figure of 0.003 in. above is subtracted from the bridge width to allow for a minimum of 0.0015 in. clearance against the possibility of nipping the lead end of the strip. Thus, if the primary stop is set to coincide with the center of the scrap bridge, it will satisfy the $\pm\frac{1}{32}$ in. tolerance for the lead end (specified in condition 4 above), with 0.004 in. to spare. However, the relationship of the finger stop to the sidewinder stop (18) (Fig. 5·1) must be considered. If the scrap web at the lead end of the strip (which we will call the lead scrap) is narrow in proportion to the bridge scrap, the sidewinder stop may not function automatically when working against the lead scrap. In the case of the die under discussion it was decided to locate the primary stopping position where shown, that is, 0.777 in. to the right of the vertical center line of the blanking station. This location provides the widest lead scrap feasible for this specific set of circumstances.

The next and final stop in this die is a pivoted automatic stop (18) (Fig. 5·1). In die-shop parlance stops like this one are often very appropriately referred to as "sidewinder" stops. This sidewinder stop is located (see Fig. 5·9) to provide a stopping position for the strip which is 0.824 in. from the center of the blanking station. The stopping position then provides an overfeed of 0.0065 in. when the stop is acting against the scrap bridge between blanks. For the first blank in the strip, when the stock is acting against the lead end of the strip, the overfeed will be 0.039 in. In the illustration, the horizontal swing distance for the stop is specified 0.050 in. After the nose of the stop has swung back through this swing distance, the nose drops onto the scrap web as a necessary part of its action cycle. The ledge portion of the scrap web on which the stop nose rests during this phase of the cycle is equal to the horizontal swing distance minus the overfeed. Therefore, for this die the size of the scrap ledge available for this phase of the stop action is

$$0.050 - 0.0065 = 0.0435 \text{ in.}$$

when the stop is acting on the bridge scrap (between blanks) and

$$0.050 - 0.039 \text{ in.} = 0.011 \text{ in.}$$

when the stop is acting on the lead scrap.

Thus, for this die it is possible to feed stock strips which are as much as $\frac{1}{32}$ in. out of square

at their lead ends and simultaneously to achieve automatic action for the sidewinder stop when it is acting upon the lead end of the stock strip.

The stop relationships assigned for this die and described above should be considered as approaching the functional limits practical for this particular set of circumstances. The feed-qualifying overfeed dimension of 0.0065 in. for the bridge scrap is minimal. The overfeed dimension of 0.039 in. for the lead-end scrap is of necessity larger than might normally be considered desirable (but it is definitely feasible for the given conditions). The out-of-square tolerance for the lead end of the stock strip is maximum on a plus-or-minus basis.

This die, because it is a simple die and because of the manner in which the stops are applied, is an excellent example for the study and comprehension of the relationships involved. It should not be inferred that this procedure is directly applicable to other applications. However, it should be emphasized that a genuine understanding of the relationships involved and as associated in the foregoing description is absolutely essential to the development of adequate relationships for other applications.

Situations may be encountered where it is not practical to secure automatic stop operation on the lead end of the stock strip. In these situations it will be generally acceptable to manually trip the automatic stop for purposes of starting the strip. Also, for many applications it will be better to restrict the out-of-square tolerance for the lead ends of the stock strips. This is often much more practical than expecting the die construction to accommodate excessively inaccurate lead-end conditions on the stock strips.

Locating the sidewinder stop. Refer to Fig. 5·9, and note the following dimensions:

A, stopping position = 0.824 in.
B, horizontal swing distance = 0.050 in.
C, stop width = 0.250 in.

Add;

$$B + C = 0.050 + 0.250 = 0.300 \text{ in.}$$

Round this off to the next larger standard drill size, which is $\frac{5}{16}$ in. diameter in this case. Call this diameter D. This will be the size of the drilled hole to be provided for the stop nose as shown in Fig. 5·10A. Subtract:

$$A - B = 0.824 - 0.050 = 0.774 \text{ in.}$$

This is the swing position of the stop E. Add:

$$E + \frac{1}{2}D = 0.774 + 0.156 = 0.930 \text{ in.}$$

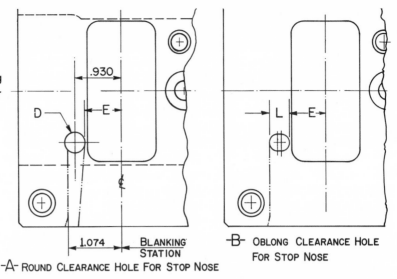

Figure **5·10**   Two methods for installing nose of sidewinder stop through stripper plate.

-A- ROUND CLEARANCE HOLE FOR STOP NOSE

-B- OBLONG CLEARANCE HOLE FOR STOP NOSE

This is the center location for the nose opening, as shown in Fig. 5·9. To locate the stop for the stopping position, add:

$$A + C = 0.824 + 0.250 = 1.074 \text{ in.}$$

As specified in the illustration, this is the dimension at which the far wall of the stop lever slot must be located in order to provide the desired stopping position for the strip.

The above dimensions are, of course, specifically for the die we have been discussing. However, the method of procedure may be applied in an associative manner to many different stop applications. For further information in regard to stop construction and stopping procedures refer to Chap. 14, *Die Stops,* in "Basic Diemaking."

Alternative Method. With this method an oblong hole is milled to receive the stop nose. The oblong hole is made as shown in Fig. 5·10B. It is located with one edge tangent to the swing position E. Length of the opening, L, is made equal to the swing distance B plus the width of the stop, C:

$$L = B + C$$

For this specific die

$$L = 0.050 + 0.250$$

$$= 0.300 \text{ in.}$$

This last method is probably the one most commonly employed, just because it is simplest in concept and most obvious in execution.

The die-shoe openings. These openings, illustrated in Fig. 5·11, should provide interference-free passage through the shoe for the blanks and/or slugs. They should be made in the simplest practicable manner. They should not detract any more

than necessary from the supporting strength of the shoe.

On occasion, it may be necessary to match these opening sizes closely to the die-opening sizes. However, such occasions can be considered exceptional. For average situations the openings may be made to provide relatively large clearances for the blanks and/or slugs. For this specific die the blank clearance opening is dimensioned as shown to provide a minimum nominal clearance of ⅟₃₂ in. per side with a tolerance which permits an additional ⅟₃₂ in. per side in order to facilitate die-making. This opening also has the corner radii offset in order to eliminate sawing (or machining,

Figure **5·11**   Passage openings through die shoe for blanks and slugs.

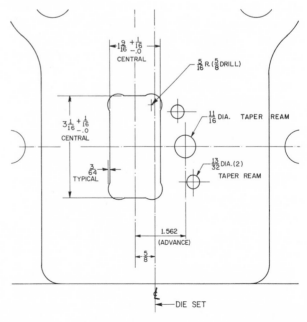

or filing) to a tangent condition at the corners. For the round slugs the clearance holes are specified as ¹³⁄₃₂ in. diameter, which is larger than necessary but which will do no harm and will minimize the degree of exactness required for their location. For the oblong slug, the clearance opening is simply a round hole, ¹¹⁄₁₆ in. in diameter. Providing round clearance holes for other than round slugs whenever feasible will facilitate diemaking.

The back-gage assembly. Details (4) and (5) (Fig. 5 · 1) compose a conventional assembly, typical for this kind of die (see "Basic Diemaking"). This back gage (4) should be hardened to resist erosion caused by the back edge of the stock strip. Remember that back-gage erosion is noticeably increased when dies are equipped with pushers at the front edge of the strip.

THREE-STATION DIE

The die which is described and discussed in Figs. 5 · 1 to 5 · 11 is a two-station progressive die. From the point of view of design it is the minimum progressive die for the application. As such, and as described, it is somewhat limited in regard to its potential for producing highly precise piece parts. The source of the limitation is the piloting method. The pilots operate within the die opening. Such pilots are inherently less accurate in function than pilots which operate outside a blank-through (or equivalent) die opening. The above two-station die will, of course, adequately produce the specified piece part. However, a three-station progressive die would be capable of producing the piece part to a higher degree of precision, and more consistently as well (this is largely because the pilots can be much more

closely fitted to their respective openings in the stock material).

Figure 5 · 12 depicts a representative stock strip as it would appear for the same piece part if it were produced in a three-station progressive die. This die could be very similar in construction to the previous die except for the addition of the piloting station between the pierce station and the blank station, as indicated in the illustration. On the assumption that this die, too, is intended for manual feeding, an additional finger stop will be necessary to position the lead end of the strip in relation to the piloting station. This stop is actuated only for the second press stroke when starting the stock strip. It operates only against the lead end of the strip. In function, it is a secondary stop and is located accordingly. The distance from the first stopping position to the second stopping position should be equal to one advance plus an overfeed allowance. Thus, for the situation illustrated, the second stop position is located 0.761 in. from the center of the blanking station, as shown. This dimension provides an overfeed allowance of 0.016 in. for feed qualification in the second station. It is readily apparent that the second-stop-location dimension is simply the overfeed allowance of 0.016 in. subtracted from the equivalent location dimension for the first stop (0.777 in.).

In Figure 5 · 12, the dimensions showing the stop locations are depicted in a logically consistent manner. However, other methods of presenting these dimensions may be encountered by the diemaker as he works with different designs. Or, on occasion, the stop locations may not be dimensionally specified on the design drawings at all—in the expectation that the diemaker alone will determine these locations. Therefore, it will be a

Figure **5 · 12** Blanked-out piece part with representative stock strip from three-station die.

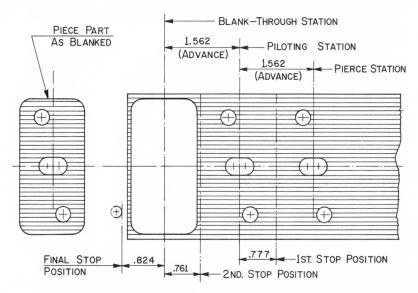

good idea to review the actual derivation of the stop-location dimensions shown in this illustration. A thorough understanding of the derivation of these dimensions will enable the diemaker to apply the underlying principles to the development and derivation of stop locations for other applications.

To locate the primary stop and the final stop, proceed as described earlier for the two-station die. Then, locate the second stop a distance equal to the overfeed plus one advance in the direction of feed from the primary stop. If the die has more than three stations and more secondary stops are required, then locate these incrementally a distance equal to one advance in the direction of feed from each preceeding secondary stop.

The 0.761 in. dimension for the illustrated secondary stop was derived as follows: The overfeed allowance of 0.016 in. was interpolated from the table presented in Chap. 14, *Die Stops,* in "Basic Diemaking." This allowance plus the advance distance is

$$0.016 + 1.562 = 1.578 \text{ in.}$$

The distance from the primary-stop position to the center of the blanking station is

$$0.777 + 1.562 = 2.339 \text{ in.}$$

Then

$$2.399 - 1.578 = 0.761 \text{ in.}$$

This difference is the required distance from the center of the blanking station to the second stop, as shown in the illustration.

PROGRESSIVE DIE, SPRING STRIPPER

The piece part pictured in Fig. 5·13 requires the piercing of two long, narrow slots. The space *W* between the slots is quite small. If these slots were to be pierced together within a single die station, their proximity would make it necessary for the die section between the slots to be relatively fragile. In order to maximize die strength, it will be necessary to pierce each slot individually, in separate piercing operations. To accomplish this, the following procedures are valid:

1. For low production. Use two dies. The first die would be a single-station blanking die. It would produce the plain blank without pierced openings. The second die would be a single-slot piercing die through which the blanks would be fed twice, piercing one slot each time. Dimensional location of the slots would derive from a nest gage, which would act upon the outer contour of the blank.

2. For other than low production. Use a pro-

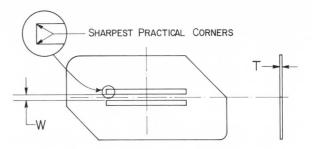

Figure 5·13 A piece part in which there are two long, narrow slots.

gressive die in which the slots can be pierced individually, in separate stations. To accomplish this, at least three stations will be required in the progression, two for piercing and one for blanking.

Stripper requirements. Separating the piercings into two operations has a decisive effect upon the choice of stripper type. The cutting forces imposed in piercing the second slot will create a pronounced tendency to distort the web *W* of the piece part. To alleviate this tendency, the stripper should act as a true pressure pad, strongly clamping the stock material against the die face, in order to prevent both vertical and lateral reactions in the stock material at *W*. Generally, the most logical stripper choice for this and similar applications would be a clamping-type spring-actuated stripper.

Sequence of progression. Assume that production requirements are other than low-production and that the stock strip will be fed by a mechanical feed. A process layout of the stock strip and piece part could then appear as shown in Fig. 5·14. As mentioned earlier, the progression will require at least three stations. The strip layout confirms this and makes it readily apparent that

Figure 5·14 The piece part and a representation of the stock strip from which it is produced.

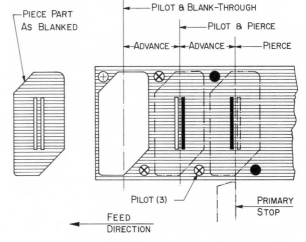

only three stations are required. For this particular die, extra (idle) stations will not be required in order to ensure adequate registry or adequate die construction, etc. As indicated in the illustration, the sequence of progression is as follows.

First Station. Pierce one slot, and pierce two holes to be used for piloting. The pilot holes are located out in the scrap area of the stock strip. Pilots located in this manner are commonly called "scrap" pilots. Note that the contour of the piece part has been exploited in order to achieve optimum effective registry with a minimum of die construction while the most favorable die strength proportions are ensured.

Second Station. Pilot in the two previously pierced scrap-pilot holes, and pierce the other slot. The presence of two pilots in this station is a distinct asset. Whenever a stock strip permits two pilots per station, the fact should be taken advantage of by using both pilots in the second station, if at all possible.

Third Station. Pilot (using front pilot hole only), and blank through. The rear pilot is omitted because of its proximity to the blanking-die opening. In order to incorporate the rear pilot in the third station, it would be necessary to change its location. This could be accomplished by increasing the stock-strip width and/or the advance distance. However, for a die of the proportions indicated by the strip layout, three pilots should be entirely adequate. In fact, it would require some exceptional circumstance to justify the additional stock-material consumption which would be required in order to incorporate the rear pilot in this station.

Stop location. It was stated earlier that this die is intended to operate in conjunction with a mechanical feed. In order to be certain of the optimum primary stopping position, it is necessary to ascertain the desired relationship of the feed cycle to the press stroke cycle and the desired starting procedure as well. In this case it is assumed that the feed will be set to feed one half the feed distance on the upstroke of the press and the remaining half on the downstroke. It is further assumed that it is desired to position the lead end of the strip for starting when the press is stopped at its top-dead-center position. Therefore, the primary stop is located where shown, at the center of the first station.

Starting procedure. The press is stopped, and the ram is at the top of its stroke. Actuate the finger stop, and hand-feed the lead end of the stock strip into position against the stop. Engage the

feeder. When the press is started, the lead end will feed to a position approximating the center of the scrap bridge between blanks while the press ram is stroking downward. Thus, the cyclic relationship of the feed to the press is established, and the strip will be fed to the desired stopping position during each press cycle. The pilots then act to qualify the feed in the same manner as they do for manual feeding, but in the opposite direction. That is, for automatic feeding the stock strip should be underfed instead of overfed (refer to "Basic Diemaking"). Feed-qualification allowances for underfeeding will be dimensionally the same as the overfeed allowances desirable for manual feeding.

The above discussion describes a specific cyclic relationship and starting procedure, one which is very commonly employed. However, many variations of both the cyclic relationship and the starting procedure are possible and often desirable. Therefore, to determine the stop location it is necessary to know the circumstances desired for the specific application. Nevertheless, if the above discussion is thoroughly understood, it can be associatively applied to the other situations.

The diemaker should also know that automatic feeding devices may be employed which are not intended to operate in conjunction with die pilots. Such devices may not permit the registration of the stock strip by means of pilots in the die. Therefore, the use of these devices should be restricted to those applications to which they are suited.

THE DIE CONSTRUCTION

In the foregoing discussion the following factors pertaining to design and construction of the die have been decided upon:

1. The die will be a progressive die.
2. The die will have a spring-actuated clamping-type stripper.
3. The primary stop will be located at the center of the first station.
4. The stock strip will be registered by means of scrap pilots.

The die which was designed with these factors in mind is shown in Fig. 5·15.

Assembly description. The lower die assembly is composed of details numbered (2) to (10). This assembly is fastened by the various screws and dowels numbered (21) through (26). The upper assembly is composed of details numbered (11) through (20). This assembly is mounted and fastened by a combination of the stripper bolts

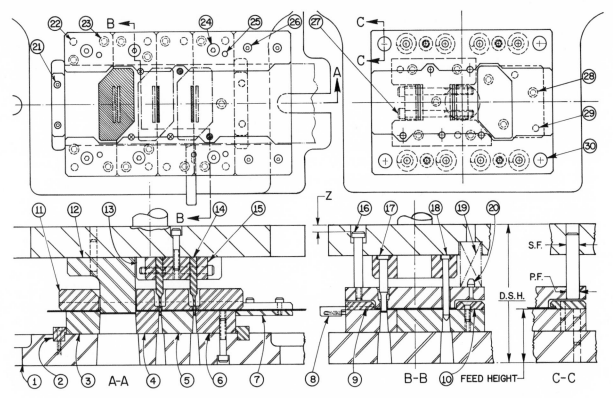

Figure 5·15 Progressive pierce and blank die with spring-actuated stripper. The pilots operate in the scrap portion of the stock strip. The components of this die and the number of each required are:

1. Back-post die set (one)
2. Key (two)
3. Die-block section (one)
4. Die-block section (one)
5. Die-block section (one)
6. Die-block section (one)
7. Shelf (one)
8. Finger stop (one)
9. Front guide rail (one)
10. Rear guide rail back gage (one)
11. Stripper (one)
12. Blanking punch (one)
13. Punch plate (one)
14. Pierce punch (two)
15. Clamp pad (two)
16. Stripper bolt (four)
17. Perforator (two)
18. Pilot (three)
19. Spring (eight)
20. Spring locator (eight)
21. Socket-head cap screw (four)
22. Dowel (eight)
23. Socket-head cap screw (thirteen)
24. Flat-head screw (six)
25. Dowel (four)
26. Socket-head cap screw (four)
27. Socket-head cap screw (two)
28. Socket-head cap screw (eight)
29. Dowel (four)
30. Guide pin (four)

(16) and the screws and dowels numbered (27) through (29).

The assembled die block is made up of the individual die-block sections (3), (4), (5), and (6). These are fastened to the die shoe by means of dowels (22) and screws (23). Dowel fits in the die sections may range from a close push fit to a very light drive fit. Dowel fits in the die shoe should be slightly tighter—a light drive fit will be optimum. For the kind of die typified in Fig. 5·15, the die-block screws should be installed as shown in the cross section view *A-A* with the threaded end of the screw entering the die block from the bottom. This method is generally the soundest and the easiest for the diemaker as well. To prevent the possibility of lateral displacement from cutting forces, the die sections are confined between two end keys (2).

The guide rails (9 and 10) are assembled to the die blocks by means of dowels (25) and flat-head screws (24). These dowels should be drive-fitted in the rails and slip-fitted in the die blocks. Flat-head screws were used here because the guide rails are too low to receive counterbored cap screws. Flat-head screws are proportionately strong and are generally satisfactory for this kind of application. However, it should be mentioned that they can be a source of alignment problems. For other dies where the stock-guide requirements are more critically accurate, button-head screws may be more desirable. The ledges on the stock guides extend over the strip to create a partial tunnel, which prevents the strip from lifting out from between the guiding edges. The ledges are profiled as shown in the plan view to permit the stripper face to contact the necessary areas on the stock strip. These ledges also act as hook strippers, ensuring that the pilots will be withdrawn from the stock strip on the upward stroke. The entry shelf (7) is an asset in that it makes it easier and safer to enter the lead end of the stock strip into the partial tunnel. This shelf is attached to the guide rails by four screws, as shown. Dowels are not usually required for mounting an entry shelf.

The combined height of the complete lower assembly must conform to the limits imposed by the vertical setting and adjustment range of the feeding unit. This height is the feed height, as indicated in Fig. 5·15.

The blanking punch (12) is a typical offset-pedestal punch. It is fastened to the punch holder by three screws (28) and two dowels (29). Fits and procedures for these screws and dowels should be the same as those described earlier (refer to Fig. 5·2).

The punch plate (13) is fastened to the punch holder by five screws (28) and two dowels (29). Fits and procedures for these screws and dowels would also be the same as those described earlier in this chapter (refer to Fig. 5·2).

The pierce punches (14) are integrated in the punch plate by means of clamp pads (15) and tie bolts (27). This permits the entire unit to be assembled together and then mounted to the punch holder as though it were a single component.

The stripper (11) is retained in suspension by the stripper bolts (16) and actuated by the springs (19). The springs are retained in spring pockets provided in the punch holder and by spring locators (20) provided in the stripper. Minimum dimension for clearance Z above the stripper bolts should be $5/16$ in. when the die is in the closed position, as shown. This is to permit stripper-bolt replacement (when required as the result of sharpening attrition) in standard increments of $1/4$ in.

The die-block sections. For this die, the individual die-block sections were made as pictured in Fig. 5·16. The sections were finished by grinding. Naturally enough, this procedure is commonly specified as "sectional-ground construction." Die taper (angular clearance) may be applied in the die openings as shown in the cross-section views and where shown (dotted lines) in the plan views.

If a constant taper is applied to the entire periphery of the blanking-die opening [in (3) and (4)] it will create a mismatched condition at the junction of the die sections. The mismatch will develop progressively as a result of sharpening attrition. When necessary, the mismatch can be eliminated by reducing the degree of die taper where indicated at b in the illustration. For most applications, the die taper at b can be compensated as

$$b = a \sin L$$

Since b is proportionate to L, b will increase or decrease as L increases or decreases. For conditions where angle L is a small angle, it may be desirable to blend the taper from an amount equal to a at point c to an amount equal to b at the junction of the sections.

The pierce-die openings are contained in (5). For these and similar openings, the simplest and most common method of applying the die taper is that which is depicted in the illustration. This method requires a matching tapered portion on the mating components (4) and (6) in the manner shown.

Figure **5·16** The die-block sections.

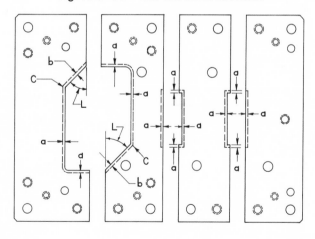

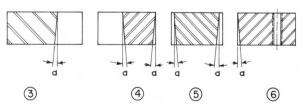

Other methods of incorporating die taper in openings of this kind are, of course, possible and practical for some more or less specialized circumstances. For the majority of applications, however, the above-described method will be most generally satisfactory.

The manner in which this example is divided into sections at the pierce-die openings produces the condition shown in Fig. 5·17. One end of the pierce-die opening between sections (5) and (6) is shown enlarged in order to illustrate normal diemaking practice for this kind of opening. The die-opening corner at C_1 is created by the intersection of the die-block sections (5) and (6). As a result, C_1 is absolutely sharp. It is not generally practical to produce an absolutely sharp corner in the solid die block at R. Consequently, this corner has a minute fillet R. Neither is it generally practical to make the punch corners absolutely sharp. Thus, the punch profile is made with a minute radius r at each of its corners. The normal cutting-clearance condition is indicated as C. A minuscule discrepancy in cutting clearance occurs at C_1 due to the difference in punch profile and die-opening profile. This discrepancy is generally acceptable.

The above is a description of practical diemaking procedure which is valid for many situations. It is based on the following assumption: for most piece parts stamped from light- to medium-gage stock material, a corner radius of 0.005 in. is customarily acceptable instead of an absolutely sharp corner.

If absolutely sharp corners are mandatory for a pierced opening, it may be necessary to resort to additional operations such as shaving, broaching, etc. And it should be remembered that these additional operations are not cure-alls, since they, too, are subject to practical limitations.

In actuality, if a sharp-cornered piercing is indicated on the piece-part drawing and there is doubt as to the feasibility of producing the corner by normal procedures, the condition should be checked and verified before building the die. In many cases it will be found that some fillet is permissible in the corners of the pierced opening.

Alternative sectioning method. It should be kept in mind that for many applications the condition shown at C_1 (Fig. 5·17) is not advisable. For these applications the die block should be sectioned in the manner illustrated in Fig. 5·18. This alternative method applies especially to:

1. Dies for piece parts which are required to be especially burr-free.

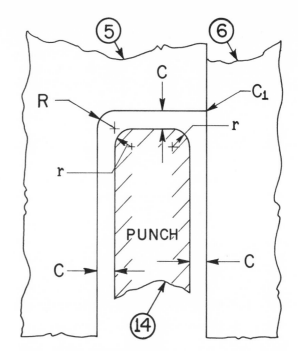

Figure **5·17** Enlarged plan view showing pierce punch and die-opening profiles.

2. Carbide dies: sharp corners on carbide components are highly susceptible to chipping.
3. Dies where the stock material is relatively thick. "Relatively thick" can mean 0.010 in. thick for tough and/or abrasive materials or for materials which are susceptible to burring. It can also mean $\frac{1}{16}$ in. thick for free-cutting materials.

Figure **5·18** Alternative method of sectioning the die blocks.

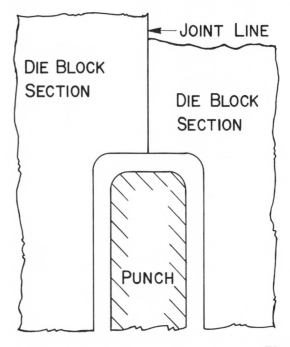

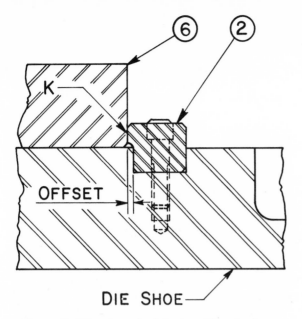

Figure 5·19   A method for installing the keys.

4. Dies in general where truly high production of quality piece parts is required.

The keys. One method for making and install-ing confinement keys is shown in Fig. 5·19. This method permits the key (2) (Fig. 5·15) to be fit-ted to the key slot in the die shoe while allowing extra stock for fitting purposes on the offset por-tion of the key. The key can then be ground at K to produce the desired fit against the die block (6). If interchangeable keys are desired, it will be necessary to locate and size the key slots in the die shoe more accurately than otherwise and/or it may be necessary to allow extra stock on either or both of the two end die-block sections for pur-poses of fitting. If the keys are not intended to be interchangeable, they should be foolproofed in order to ensure absolute compatibility with the required die-block positions.

Piercing and piloting unit. (Fig. 5·20). The per-forators (17) and the pilots (18) are assembled into the punch plate (13) (all shown in Fig. 5·15) in the same manner as that described earlier in this chapter for the die of Fig. 5·2. In addition to this, the punch plate is contoured to provide fit and location for the two pierce punches (14). These are held in position and retained in assem-bly by clamps (15) and crosswise screws (27).

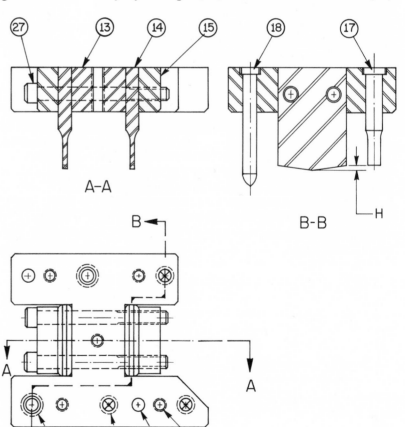

Figure 5·20   Unitized assembly con-taining the piercing punches and the pilots.

These punches are provided with a gable-type shear as depicted in section *B-B*. The purpose of the shear is to minimize the punching forces in the area of these pierced slots, which tends to facilitate the pressure-pad function of the spring stripper (11), by reducing the distortive effects of the piercing operation. When shear is provided for this described purpose, optimum height *H* for the shear (if stock material thickness is *T*) will be

$$H = T \qquad \text{where } T > \tfrac{1}{32} \text{ in.}$$
$$H = \tfrac{1}{32} \text{ in.} \qquad \text{where } T < \tfrac{1}{32} \text{ in.}$$

For some applications, this type of punch plate can be left soft. For other applications, however, it will be necessary to harden the punch plate. If hardening is required, the degree of hardness will generally be in the range Rockwell C50-58. Whether hardening is required depends upon the punch proportions, the anticipated incidence of punch replacement, interchangeability, etc. These factors are, of course, related in turn to piece-part quality, production requirements, etc.

The stripper. Figure 5·21 illustrates the stripper. The manner in which the punches (12), (14), and (17), pilots (18), and stock-strip guides (9) and (10) are associated with the stripper is also depicted. This stripper is a nonguiding stripper. Its functions are to strip the stock material from the punches and to clamp it against the die face in order to prevent distortion of the material. It is not intended to guide or support the punches. Therefore, the stripper openings are sized to provide clearance *S* for the various punch members in the manner described earlier for the box-type stripper (refer to Fig. 5·9). Keep in mind, however, that the clearance at S_1 should be minimal. This is the area of the narrow web in the piece part. The stripper face should clamp the stock material in this area to the maximum practicable extent.

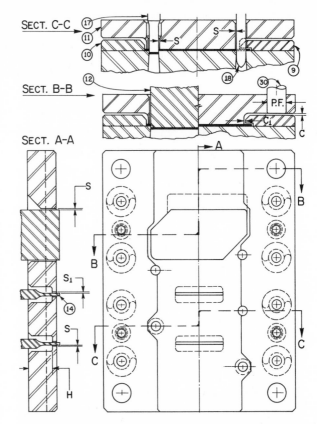

Figure 5·21 Stripper, showing its relationship to the stock guides and the punches.

As stated above, this is not a guiding stripper. It is, however, a guided stripper. It is guided by four guide pins (30) which are press-fitted in the stripper and slip-fitted in the punch holder. This procedure is adequate for many applications of this type if the punch holder is made of cast iron (semisteel). For steel punch holders it will be better to install bushings (either bronze or hardened steel) in the punch holder to receive the guide pins. The purpose of the guide pins is to ensure lateral stability for the stripper, thereby preventing possible deflection of the smaller punches. This per-

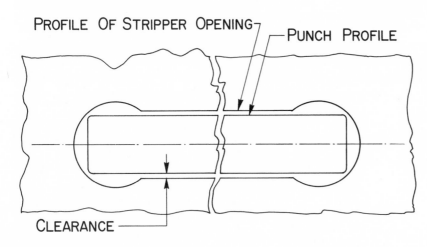

PROFILE OF STRIPPER OPENING

PUNCH PROFILE

CLEARANCE

Figure 5·22 Enlarged plan view showing stripper clearance opening for pierce punch.

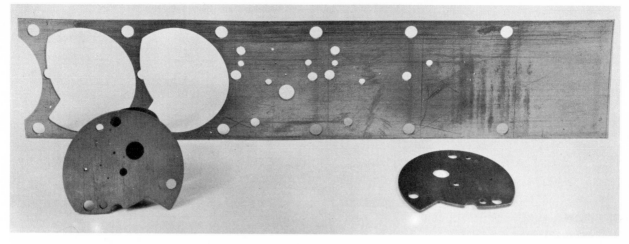

Figure **5·23**   The sequence of operations is readily seen in this picture of a stock strip from a progressive pierce and blank die. Two of the piece parts produced appear in the foreground.

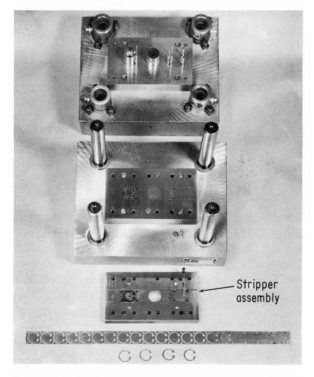

Stripper assembly

Figure **5·24**   A progressive pierce and blank die. The stripper has been removed and placed in the foreground in order to better illustrate construction. A stock strip and four of the piece parts produced by this die also appear in the foreground.

mits smaller clearance at S (and especially at S_1) than would otherwise be practical.

For other guiding and guided stripper constructions refer to "Basic Diemaking."

Generally, there are no stringent requirements for the size of clearance C_1 between the stripper face boss and the guide rails. However, clearance should be judiciously applied and, in the area of the punches, carefully controlled. The stripping face boss must extend entirely around the periphery of the punches, as shown in the cross-section views.

Clearance C between the stripper ledges and the guide rails is necessary to the pressure-pad function of the stripper. However, when the lead end of the stock strip is being started through the die, it creates an unbalanced condition which tends to cause the stripper to tilt. For the stripper shown, clearance C is limited in order to provide a leveling effect for the stripper against the guide rails. Clearance of 0.002 to 0.006 in. at C is commonly suitable for average die constructions where it is desired to level the stripper in this manner.

Relief and clearance for the stripper openings. The stripper openings for the pierce punches (14) (Fig. 5·15) are relieved as shown in Fig. 5·21 to the maximum practical depth H. This relief permits the punch body to be longer than otherwise, creating a sturdier punch configuration. The relief also considerably facilitates making the opening. In addition, diemaking can be further facilitated by making the peripheral contour of such openings in a manner similar to that pictured in Fig. 5·22.

PROGRESSIVE DIES USING THE CHOPOFF PRINCIPLE

CHOPOFF FUNDAMENTALS

The term "chopoff" is employed to indicate a specific kind of cutting operation, one in which complete severance of the stock material is accomplished in a scrapless manner. Most typically, chopoff operations sever the stock strip in a way which is functionally the same as that which is shown in Fig. 6·1. This illustration depicts a version of a chopoff die which is quite fundamental in concept. Its purpose is to produce rectangular pieces of required length by severing them from the stock strip in the scrapless manner typical of chopoff operations.

This die is shown mounted on a "no-guidepost" die set. That is, there are no guideposts to align the punch holder with the die shoe. Such die sets are sometimes called "plain" die sets or "open" die sets. However, these terms can cause confusion (especially the term open). Therefore, in the interests of more accurate communication, it is better to refer to these sets as no-guidepost die sets.

One procedure for setting up this die in the press would be:

1. Close the die as far as possible.
2. Insert a shim equal in thickness to the desired cutting clearance (C, inset view) between the punch sidewall and the die-block sidewall.
3. Clamp the punch laterally to the die block with the shim between them.
4. Place the die in the press, and clamp the shank in the ram.
5. Bolt the die shoe to the bolster
6. Remove the clamp which is clamping the punch-shim-die sandwich.
7. Adjust the press ram to the desired shut height, and remove the shim.

FOR DIES USING GUIDEPOST-EQUIPPED DIE SETS

If this die were mounted on a guidepost-equipped die set, the setting-up procedure would obviously be simplified. For a die which employs a guidepost die set, the amount of cutting clearance C (Fig. 6·1) may be changed, if desired, by shimming or by grinding the punch at C_1. A guidepost die set is a distinct asset to die setting. It is also obvious that guidepost die sets can greatly facilitate diemaking procedures. However, keep in mind that die sets are not intended to absorb lateral forces to any large degree, such as those which can occur in chopoff operations. For such applications, the design and construction of the die should eliminate as much as possible the transfer of heavy lateral forces to the guideposts (and to the bearing ways of the punch-press ram also). The above applies, of course, to any type of die operation where strong and unbalanced lateral forces are engendered.

Figure **6·1** A fundamental chopoff die.

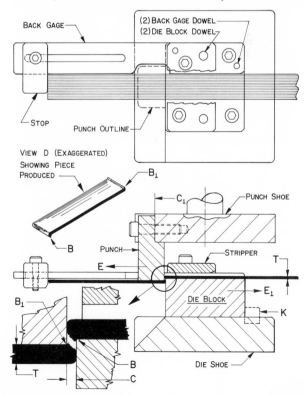

75

CHOPOFF CUTTING CHARACTERISTICS

The chopoff cutting action causes reactions in the stock material which are identical to the shearing action of blanking and/or piercing operations (refer to "Basic Diemaking"). For blanking and/or piercing operations, larger cutting clearances are commonly used for cutting irregular contours than for round contours. For chopoff operations, optimum cutting clearance C (Fig. 6·1, inset view) will be the same percentage of T as that which would be optimum for an irregularly contoured blanking operation.

Burr side. Piece parts produced by the conventional type of chopoff die will inherently have two burr sides, as shown exaggeratedly at B and B_1 in view D (Fig. 6·1). Thus, these dies cannot be used per se to produce piece parts which have a unidirectional burr-side requirement. The opposing burr-side condition is created by the basic cutting action which produces the burr side on one end of the piece as shown (B in the inset view), and on the other end of the piece as shown (B_1).

Cutting-force reactions. In reaction to the cutting forces the piece part tends to be displaced

Figure **6·2** Chopoff die: yoked and heeled. In this die, the lateral cutting forces are contained by the yoked-die unit assembly.

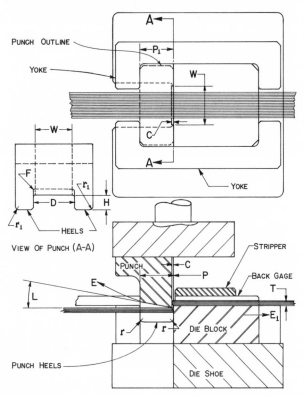

VIEW OF PUNCH (A-A)

laterally in the direction shown (E, Fig. 6·1). The stop, of course, resists this tendency. The effectiveness of the stop for this purpose depends upon the relative thickness, length, and strength of the piece part, in addition to the security of the stop fastening. The stock strip tends to be displaced in the opposite direction (E_1). For simple chopoff operations (such as this one) these tendencies are generally ignored, although spring-actuated strippers are quite often employed instead of the box-type stripper shown in the illustration. The spring stripper then clamps the strip against the die face, tending to resist lateral displacement of the stock strip.

The cutting forces also act upon the die in the manner shown. The forces tend to displace the punch laterally in the direction E and the die block in the direction E_1. Lateral force E is transmitted to the punch shoe by way of the punch and its mounting screws. Force E_1 is transmitted to the die shoe via the die-block dowels and screws. With this construction some lateral "breathing" is likely to occur, depending upon the magnitude of the lateral forces. The lower die assembly could be made rigid by installing a key such as that indicated at K. Remember, however, that the lateral forces must not be too great to be safely absorbed by the equipment by which the operation will be performed. Actually, the die illustrated should be considered to be a relatively light-duty die. The die construction in Fig. 6·2 is more appropriate for performing heavier work.

FORCE-BALANCED CHOPOFF DIE

Another version of a plain chopoff die appears in Fig. 6·2. The plan view depicts the die with its stripper and back gage removed in order to show the construction more clearly. In addition to the stripper and back gage, the lower die assembly consists of the die block and two yoke blocks, mounted on the die shoe. The die block fits between the yokes as shown, providing a space which receives the punch when the upper assembly descends. Punch dimension P is made a slip fit to die dimension P_1. Cutting clearance is provided in the punch as shown (C). As described for the previous die, C will be the required percentage of T for the type of stock material being severed. The cutting clearance extends a width W, which is slightly wider than the stock strip and is equally disposed in relation to the strip. (It should be obvious that cutting clearance $C \times W$ may be installed on the die block instead of the punch—if circumstances are such that this is easier or otherwise more desirable.)

The punch configuration provides two heels,

as shown. Distance D between the heels must be wider than the stock strip, wide enough to provide slight fillets (for strength) at F and to facilitate diemaking. Height (H) of the heels beyond the cutting edge is related to the thickness of the stock material T. Minimum height H must be great enough to ensure adequate entry depth into the die opening before the cutting action begins. Small lead-in radii are provided on the heels were shown (r). If necessary, lead-in radii are also made at r_1. Matching lead-in radii should also be provided on the noncutting edges of the die opening. These lead-in radii are, of necessity, made quite small. This is because they detract from the effective supporting height of the punch heels. They are commonly made

$$r = \frac{1}{64} \text{ to } \frac{1}{16} \text{ in.}$$

proportionate to specific job requirements. Lead-in radii outside the above range may be appropriate for some applications but are not the general rule. Remember that matching lead-in radii on the punch heels and the die edges subtract an amount equal to $2r$ from the supporting heel engagement in the die opening. An angle, similar to L, may be ground on the cutting face of the punch. Such an angle may tend to reduce lateral forces on the punch at the time of initial impact against the stock material.

Lateral-force compensation. Lateral forces E and E_1 (Fig. 6·2) are produced by the cutting action in the same manner as described for the previous die. Force E, acting on the punch, is transmitted to the yokes. Force E_1 is also transmitted to the yokes, but in the opposite direction. As a result, these lateral forces tend to compensate. The compensating effect minimizes the transfer of objectionable lateral forces to the die set and/or the punch press. The above discussion applies, of course, to any die in which lateral forces are developed. If such forces are of any consequence, the die should be constructed in a manner that will provide a self-compensating condition within the die.

Keep in mind that the normal die set is not a device which is intended to absorb lateral forces of any consequence.

To return to the die construction, this die design employs a no-guidepost die set. However, compared with the previous die, this die will be easier to set up in the press because of the manner in which the punch is fitted to the die opening. Depending upon the application, construction methods other than the yoked construction illustrated may be employed to compensate for

undesirable forces. Some of these are "set-in" die blocks, cross-bolted dies, side-clamped dies, etc., which are described in "Basic Diemaking."

PROGRESSIVE PIERCE AND CHOPOFF DIE

A simple progressive die which incorporates the chopoff principle is illustrated in Fig. 6·3. It is a semiscrapless die. The only scrap produced intentionally is the pierced-out slug.

Operation. This die would be said to have a "sight stop." The primary stopping function for the lead end of the stock strip is accomplished by visual reference to the cutting edge of the chopoff-die block (7).

Phase 1. The operator feeds the lead end of the strip to a position just short of the cutting edge. He determines this position visually, by sighting along the cutting edge. He then trips the press to produce the first perforation in the strip.

Phase 2. He next feeds the lead end of the strip to the stopping face of the stop-and-heel block (2). This block is positioned to act as an approximation gage, providing the necessary overfeed condition. On the downstroke the pilot enters the previously pierced hole and qualifies the feed as described in Chap. 14, *Die Stops,* in "Basic Diemaking." This second phase is then repeated until the stock strip is consumed.

The above description assumes that the die is hand-fed. If this die were to be used in conjunction with an externally mounted automatic feeding device, dimension F would have to be within the range of the feeder. If dimension F is suitable, the die could be run "as is." If, however, the feeder is of the type which is mounted on the die set, a larger die set than the one shown (1) would be necessary in order to provide mounting space for the feeder. The shelf (8) would be removed and the guide rails (9) shortened in order to eliminate the need for an unreasonably large die set.

The construction. Die dimension P_1 equals the piece-part length plus the overfeed allowance. Punch dimension P is made $P_1 - C$, where $C =$ cutting clearance. The punch (13) is mounted to provide a sliding fit against the heel block (2). Matching lead radii are made on the punch and on the heel block where shown (r). The discussion pertaining to equivalent radii for the previous die will naturally apply for this die also. The heel block is made high enough to provide adequate thrust-support area for the punch in order to alleviate unbalanced lateral cutting-force reactions (this height also creates the final stop for the stock strip). With this construction, lateral

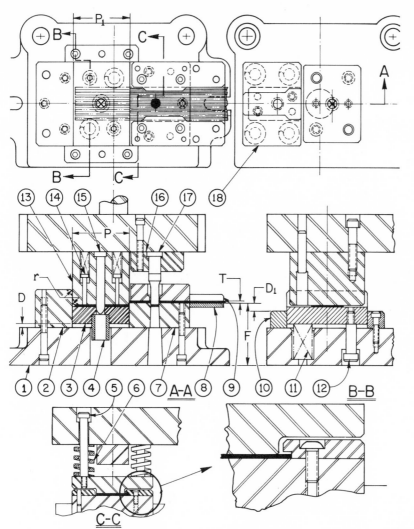

Figure **6·3** A pierce and chopoff die equipped with spring-actuated stripper and chopoff pad. Major components of this die and the number of each required are:

1. Back-post die set (one)
2. Stop and heel block (one)
3. Spring pad (one)
4. Slug tube (one)
5. Stripper bolt (four)
6. Spring (four)
7. Chopoff-die block (one)
8. Shelf (one)
9. Guide rail (two)
10. Guide block for pad (two)
11. Spring (two)
12. Stripper bolt (two)
13. Chopoff punch (one)
14. Spring pin (assembly) (two)
15. Pilot (one)
16. Punch plate (one)
17. Perforator (one)
18. Stripper (one)

forces are self-compensating within the limits that the mounting screws and dowels will contain. Consequently, this construction is suitable only for relatively light lateral forces. For truly heavy work the construction would have to be changed to yoked, or set-in, or tie-bolted construction, etc.

Space D under the chopoff pad (3) is a die-life provision. An amount equal to D may be removed, by successive sharpenings, from the die block (7) before it will become necessary to rework the pad thickness. Another maintenance provision appears at D_1. The pad guide blocks (10) are made lower than the die face by some practical amount (D_1). This eliminates the necessity for grinding the guide blocks each time the die is sharpened.

In the event of a misfeed, the pilot (15) may pierce a slug into the opening in the pad. If this occurs, it is essential that the slugs do not lodge between the pad and the die shoe. To ensure that such slugs will be eliminated through the die

shoe, this die has a slug passage tube (4) installed in the pad. In this die the slug tube is made of seamless tube which is sweated (soldered) into the pad. The pilot hole in the pad should be reamed to taper in the normal manner. The tube should also be taper-reamed.

The stripper (18) is a clamping stripper, actuated by springs (6). The contour of the stripper face boss is made as shown in the inverted plan view of the upper assembly. The contour provides full stripping action across the width of the stock strip at the chopoff line. The guide rails are, of course, contoured to clear the stripper in this area (refer to section *C-C*). When in its extended position, the stripper face must be flush with, or very slightly beyond, the face of the chopoff punch. The pilot (15) must be long enough to ensure proper registration of the stock strip before the stripper clamps the strip against the die face. Two spring pins (14) are installed to strip the piece part from the pilot.

The perforator should be shorter than the chopoff punch in order to eliminate lateral deflection of the perforator which can be caused by lateral forces originating at the chopoff. This is especially necessary where:

1. Perforators are relatively small.
2. Perforators are close to the chopoff punch.
3. Chopoff dies are equipped with box strippers.

For most applications the difference in punch heights may be made equal to T or to $\frac{1}{32}$ in., whichever is greater. Naturally, the practice of employing differential punch heights is not restricted to chopoff dies. The practice can be advantageous for many different applications where the size and proximity of the punches are such that lateral deflection is likely. Obviously, when differential punch heights are required, the punches which are most likely to be deflected should be made shorter than their stronger neighboring punches.

Before proceeding with the actual making of a die, always check to be certain that the die-set guideposts will not interfere with disposal (ejection) of the piece part from the die. This is especially important where die sets are of the back-post type.

DIMENSION RELATIONSHIPS

For progressive chopoff dies, the manner in which piece-part dimensions are related to punch and die dimensions is presented in the schematic of Fig. 6·4. The leading end of the piece part (in relation to the feed direction) derives its size from the chopoff punch as shown (A). The trailing end of the piece part derives its size from the chopoff die edge as shown (B). The overall length of the piece part is

$$A + B$$

The cutting clearance is designated C in the illustration. Note that the advance distance is shorter than the overall length of the piece part by an amount equal to C. Therefore,

$$\text{Advance} = A + B - C$$

The above conditions are quite obvious at the simplified level of this presentation. However, they are probably not so obvious in the normal course of more advanced die work, to judge by the hesitation and errors that have often resulted because these conditions were not adequately considered. Consequently, they should be thoroughly comprehended at this level in order that they may be logically associated with more complex situations.

LEAD-END TRIMMING

In starting the stock strip in the previous die, the lead end of the strip is intended to be sight-stopped just before it reaches the chopoff-die cutting edge. This method is acceptable for many applications. However, there are also many applications where it may be more desirable to trim the lead end of the stock strip with the chopoff punch as pictured in Fig. 6·5.

Leveling. Trimming in this manner can cause an objectionable tilting of the pad. This condition can be alleviated by incorporating leveling heels on the punch in the manner illustrated in Fig. 6·5. The levelers must permit a very small gap between the punch and the pad where shown (G). The gap is necessary in order to ensure effective pad pressure against the piece part. Therefore, height of the heels (H) will be

$$H = T - G$$

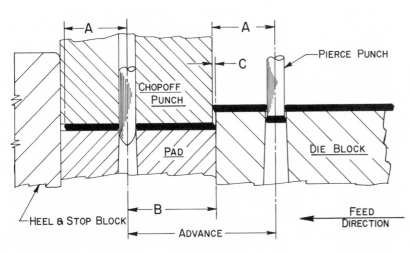

Figure **6·4** Schematic showing piece-part size derivation in chopoff die.

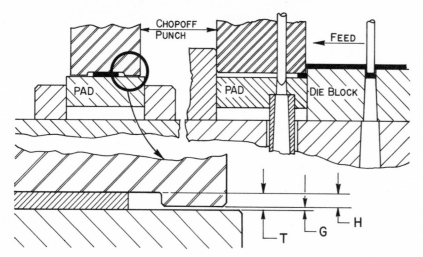

Figure **6·5** Leveling heels provided on punch to prevent objectionable tilting and/or binding of the pressure pad.

The specific tolerance which applies to the thickness of the stock strip must be considered. For the purpose of determining H, the thickness T should be considered at its minimum, tolerance-wise.

If gap G is too large, the heels will not serve the desired purpose. A gap G of 0.002 will generally be optimum for average conditions, with somewhat larger gaps appropriate for heavy stock and/or cruder work.

It is readily apparent that this method does not absolutely eliminate the tilting effect. However, it does reduce pad tilting to an amount that is practical for most applications.

Another method of leveling for lead-end trimming is depicted in Fig. 6·6. The operator places a small piece of the proper stock material (s) on the pad, which then acts as a leveler. Leveling heels are not required and should not be present on the punch when this is done.

COMBINED CHOPOFF AND FORM

Figure 6·7 pictures an elemental progressive die for producing the piece part which appears in

Figure **6·6** A procedure for lead-end trimming.

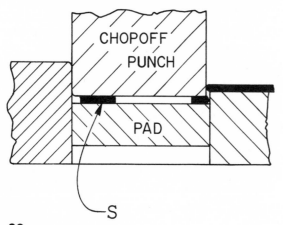

the inset view. This die produces completed piece parts, pierced and formed as shown.

Operating procedure for this die is the same as that described for the preceding pierce and chopoff die. The washer and nuts which retain the pad spring (14) are not shown. These are also the means of adjusting the spring for suitable pad pressure. Pressure-pad assemblies and construction factors are thoroughly described under "Pads, Pressure" in "Basic Diemaking." Actually, this book treats detailed basic constructions which may be associatively applied to every component of this die and to many different dies also.

The construction. The die blocks (3) and (5) with the spacer blocks (11) between them are confined between the end clamps (9). This assembly creates the chopoff- and form-die opening in which the pressure pad (4) operates.

Detail 2 is a dual-purpose component. It acts as a final stop when required for hand feeding and serves as a skyhook to strip the finished piece part from the punch and pilot (16) and (17). Height H under the skyhook must be equal to the overall height of the piece part plus sufficient clearance to facilitate ejection of the piece part. The amount of clearance needed will vary in accordance with specific job requirements. The amount of clearance will tend to be proportionate to the general size of the piece part. For smaller piece parts, a minimum gap H of ⅛ in. plus the overall height of the piece part will probably function adequately. Remember, however, that trouble can result if the height of the gap (H) is inadequate.

Note that the use of a diagonal-post die set provides ample ejection area at the rear of the die set. This die-set configuration eliminates the likelihood that a guidepost may interfere with ejection disposal of the piece part.

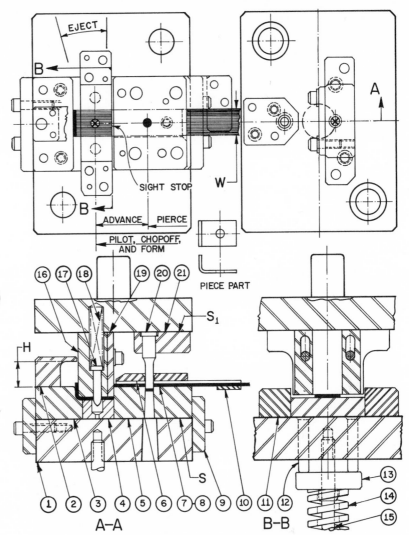

Figure **6·7** A progressive pierce, chopoff, and form die. Major components of this die and the number of each required are:

1. Diagonal-post die set (one)
2. End stop and skyhook (one)
3. Form-die block (one)
4. Pressure pad (one)
5. Cutting-die block (one)
6. Stripper (one)
7. Front guide (one)
8. Rear guide (one)
9. End clamp (two)
10. Shelf (one)
11. Pad guide and spacer block (two)
12. Transfer pin (two)
13. Spreader plate (one)
14. Spring (one)
15. Stud (one)
16. Form-punch section (one)
17. Pilot (one)
18. Spring (one)
19. Chopoff punch (section) (one)
20. Pierce punch (one)
21. Punch plate

The perforator and punch-plate assembly (20) and (21) is conventional, made and assembled as described earlier. The stripper-and-stock-guide assembly, too, is conventional, and is made and mounted as described elsewhere (earlier) in this book.

The pilot (17) is a retractable one. In the event of a misfeed, it retracts upward and does not pierce a hole in the stock material. This type of pilot was selected in order to eliminate the need of considering slug disposal through the pad and die shoe. The pilot actuation spring (18) is critical. It must be strong enough to assure adequate piloting, but it must not drive the pilot through the stock material. The most commonly encountered design errors are springs which are too small and, especially, too short. The spring must be long enough to permit pilot retraction without exceeding its optimum service deflection range.

The chopoff-and-form punch is a combined unit (16) and (19). The unit is made this way in order to enhance punch life and to facilitate

maintenance, as explained in the following text under "Maintenance Consideration." On occasion, it may be necessary to install a hardened thrust plate above the chopoff blade (19) to prevent it from setting into the punch shoe. Whether the thrust plate is needed or not needed depends upon the area of the base surface of the blade in relation to the cutting force. A thrust plate will be required if the blade is small in relation to the severity of the work. It will not be required if the base area of the blade is adequate in proportion to the severity of the work it performs.

Maintenance considerations. One procedure applicable in sharpening the lower die assembly is as follows:

1. Grind (sharpen) the face of the cutting-die block (5), removing only the amount of material necessary to restore the cutting edges.
2. Grind precisely the same amount from the face surface of the pad (4).
3. Grind the base (bottom) surface of the form-

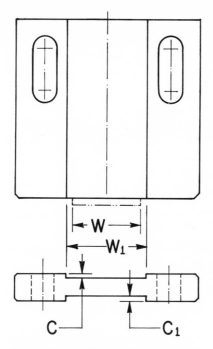

Figure **6·8** Chopoff-punch detail.

die block (3), removing precisely the same amount as above.

4. Grind the base surface of the spacer blocks (11), if and when required.

Figure **6·9** Lateral forces in a chopoff and form die.

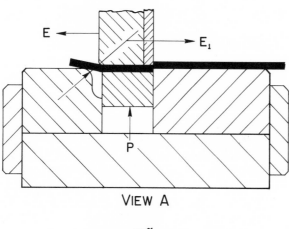

VIEW A

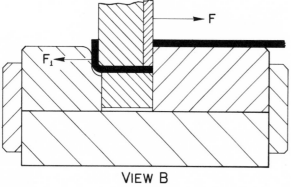

VIEW B

Another procedure for this lower assembly is to sharpen the cutting face of the die block (5) and raise it to its proper height by inserting a shim between the die block and the die shoe (see S in Fig. 6·7). This last method is the one actually used for the die from which this illustration was derived.

Both procedures may in fact be used. In the course of the total life of the die, it may be desirable to use one procedure during one sharpening and the other procedure at another time. This can depend upon individual conditions and situations which may be subject to change from time to time.

To facilitate maintenance of the upper punch assembly, the chopoff-punch section (19) is provided with elongated clearance holes for the cross screws which secure it to the form punch. These slots permit differential maintenance grinding. It would not be practical to rework the form radius on the forming punch at each sharpening. The above-described elongated slots permit the following sharpening procedure:

1. Separate the two punch sections (16) and (19).
2. Grind (sharpen) the necessary minimum amount from the cutting face of (19).
3. Grind precisely the same amount from the base surface of (16) to restore the desired, exactly flush relationship.

The perforator is, of course, conventionally sharpened.

In the case of this specific die construction, however, there is another maintenance factor which must be taken into account: the reduction in spring space (lengthwise) which occurs as a result of grinding off the base surface of (16). For many applications this condition can be compensated for by shimming between the punch assembly and the punch shoe as in maintaining the lower assembly. But in this case, it was felt that it would be better to avoid shimming this punch assembly if possible (because of the adverse effects that might be caused by lateral forces acting on the unit). As a consequence, the chopoff component (19) is provided with cutting clearance on both sidewalls as shown (C and C_1, Fig. 6·8). This allows the component to be assembled two ways, thus providing two edges alternately available for the chopoff cutting. Therefore, it is necessary to sharpen the cutting face of this component at alternate sharpenings only. This effects a 100 percent increase in the life potential of the pilot spring (18) when compared with more conventional differential sharpening procedures. To compensate for the fact that the overall punch height is reduced only at alternate sharpenings, it is necessary to shim between the perforator-punch-plate assembly at these alternate sharpenings (S_1, Fig. 6·7).

Lateral forces. Side thrust induced during the cutting action produces the characteristic reactions which are apparent in Fig. 6·9, view A. The cutting force tends typically to displace the punch in the direction E. Resistance to this displacement develops through E_1 as the bending (forming) action begins. This is a transitory stage in the work cycle of the die. As the work progresses, the lateral forces develop as shown in view B. Here, side thrust acts on the punch in the direction F and on the die assembly in direction F_1. At this stage the lateral forces compensate each other through the die structure. Naturally, if the structure is inadequate, the lateral forces may displace some or all of the components instead of compensating each other. To return to view A, it becomes apparent that pad pressure P acts to stabilize the punch unit and also tends to hold the piece part from skidding in direction E as well. It follows, then, that relatively strong pad pressures are normally required for actions of this kind. As described above, there is a possibility that some slight punch vacillation may occur during this transitory work phase (view A). However, dies of this kind can successfully perform surprisingly heavy work.

The manner in which these forces and reactions are above described and pictorially represented is especially suitable for the diemaker. If he comprehends them in the above manner, he will be able to treat with them in a competent manner when the occasion requires.

MORE COMPLEX COMBINATIONS

The trend in design and construction of the preceding dies has been toward increasing complexity. This is the result of the specified work requirements and, practically speaking, can be continued almost indefinitely. (This applies, of course, to all types of dies.) For example, a piece part may require additional piercings. Or it may require other operations such as semipiercing, notching, side trimming, etc. Or it may require other forming or de-forming procedures. Such conditions will require that the dies become more complex, both in concept and in execution. This is naturally reflected in the operational and maintenance aspects, also.

The preceding chopoff dies did not require side trimming: the width of the piece parts coincides

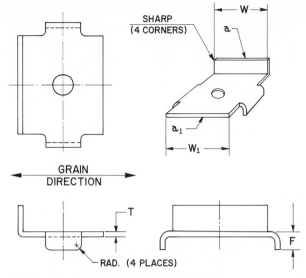

Figure 6·10   Piece part.

entirely with the width of the respective stock strips from which they are produced. Chopoff dies (and parting dies also) are fundamental die types for producing piece parts in this manner. Where applicable, this production method is very desirable from the standpoint of stock-material consumption.

Figure 6·11   Strip layout for piece part in Fig. 6·10, showing front edge view and cross sections.

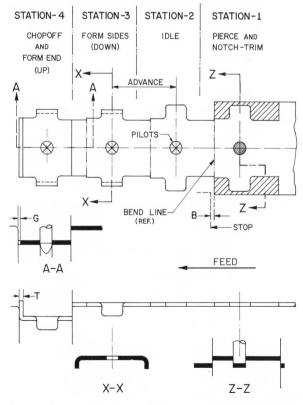

A MORE COMPLEX PIECE PART

Complexity is a matter of degree. The piece part which appears in Fig. 6·10 is not actually difficult in any way, but it is more complex than the preceding piece parts. This piece is inherently suitable for production in a progressive die which employs the chopoff method, because:

1. Contour of ends a and a_1 is such that they may be cut by the chopoff method (no scrap required between them).
2. Width W is the same as width W_1.
3. The grain direction coincides with the feeding direction required for producing this piece in a progressive die which incorporates the chopoff method.
4. No burr-side specification. Thus, the opposing burr-side condition (which is typical for chopoffs) is permissible.

The die in concept. The concept of a die for producing this piece part is shown in Fig. 6·11. The operations performed in each station are specified in the plan view. They are further clarified in the front edge view and in the cross-section views X-X and Z-Z.

The position and configuration of the notch-trim operation is conducive to sound and practical die construction. The notch trim coincides with the bend line of the piece part. Thus, the mismatch occurs at the bend line, where it will be least discernible on the piece part. This condition is quite desirable as far as piece-part appearance is concerned. Keep in mind, however, that it is not desirable enough to justify a weak or otherwise risky die construction. In other words, the condition is desirable within practical limits only.

This location for the notch trim also provides a desirable stopping position for the lead end of the stock strip. When the lead end of the strip reaches the final station, its relationship to the die will exist as shown in the inset section A-A. Gap G will be equal to T minus the overfeed allowance B. Gap G permits the lead end of the strip to be out of square by this amount before it could touch the sidewall of the forming die block. This condition will be thoroughly satisfactory for the great majority of applications. If, on occasion, it is not, then another stop can be added at the rear edge of the strip. The presence of two stops will prevent either corner of the lead end from extending beyond the stopping position.

Mismatching. Conditions as they exist for the first station are enlarged and exaggerated for illustrative purposes in Fig. 6·12. The front and rear cutting contours are made with offsets as shown (M). These offsets greatly facilitate die-making by providing a mismatch for the necessary cutting overlap at B. Mismatch steps may be made as small as 0.0005 in. (smaller than this is not generally practical except possibly for very fine, small work). Or they may be made considerably larger if circumstances permit and if it is really desirable. One practical method which may often be employed in the absence of other criteria is

Where C = cutting clearance, make $M = C$ or 0.0005 in. (whichever is larger)

For further and more detailed information refer to "Trim Stops" in "Basic Diemaking."

The die design. The die which produces this piece part is illustrated in Figs. 6·13 to 6·16. Figure 6·13 is the assembly drawing. The die components are numbered in the assembly drawing, and the corresponding numbers appear in the cross-section views in order to facilitate association.

Construction and operation. In this die it is assumed that it is necessary to make the tunnel height (E, section Z-Z) lower than the overall height of the first forming operation (refer to F in the piece-part illustration, Fig. 6·10).

Figure **6·12** Notch-trim conditions; stock-strip and punch relationship.

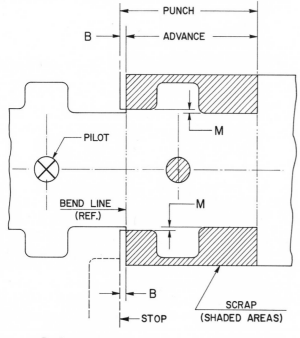

B = OVERFEED

PUNCH SIZE = B + ADVANCE

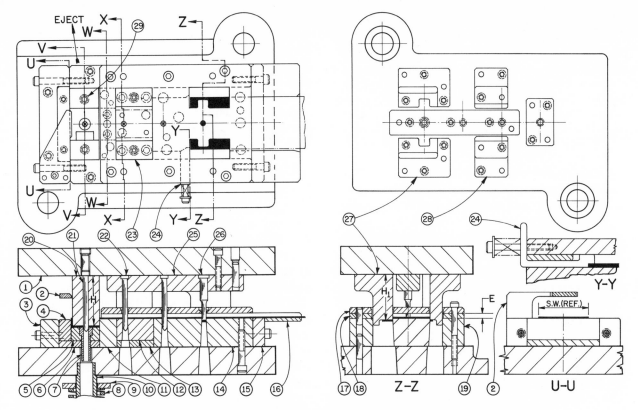

Figure **6·13** Progressive die to produce the piece part shown in Fig. 6·10. Die is designed in accordance with the strip layout shown in Fig. 6·11. The major components of this die and the number of parts required are:

1. Diagonal-post die set (one)
2. Skyhook (one)
3. End clamp and yoke (one)
4. Form-die insert block (one)
5. Pressure pad (one)
6. Height-compensator plate (one)
7. Slug tube (one)
8. Spring (one)
9. Spreader (one)
10. Spring stud and slug tube (one)
11. Chopoff-die block section (one)
12. Form block (one)
13. Height-compensator plate (one)
14. Cutting-die block (one)
15. End clamp (one)
16. Shelf (one)
17. Stripper (one)
18. Stock guide rail (two)
19. Yoke block (two)
20. Chopoff and form punch (one)
21. Pilot (one)
22. Pilot (two)
23. Lift pad (two)
24. Stop (one)
25. Punch plate (one)
26. Perforator (one)
27. Notch-trim punch (two)
28. Form punch (two)
29. Tube-and-screw assembly (two)

The stop (24) (Fig. 6·13) is a conventional finger stop, made and installed as shown in section *Y-Y*. For a die of this kind, the retractable stop can be a distinct asset to die operation. The presence of the bending (forming) operations on the stock strip may prevent it from being withdrawn from the stripper tunnel in the direction opposed to the feed direction. The retractable stop will permit the strip to be pulled through the tunnel in the feeding direction. When the tail end of the stock strip reaches the die, the operator can retract the stop and pull the strip through the die.

The skyhook (2) must be made and installed in a manner which will permit the strip to be pulled through. The skyhook for this particular die is as pictured in section *U-U*. Mounted as shown, it provides ample clearance to provide free passage for the full stock width. The value of the above construction is emphasized in the event of a misfeed. If a feeding mishap should occur (and it will), the operator can sever the stock strip at the die entrance. He can then pull the mutilated section of the strip out of the die in the manner described above for the tail end of the strip. This can very often eliminate the need to remove the stripper or even to remove the die from the press, which might otherwise be necessary in the event of a mishap.

The pilots (22) are made long enough to engage in the stock strip before the chopoff punch begins its cutting action. They are intended to resist lateral skidding of the stock strip due to the cutting action, but in some applications they may be inadequate for this purpose. One solution for such a situation is to make height H_1 of the notch-trim punches (27, section Z-Z) longer. For conditions of this kind, make

$$H_1 = H + \tfrac{1}{2}T$$

Figure 6·14 is a cross-section view through the chopoff-die block (11) (Fig. 6·13). This view, unlike the rest of the illustrations for this die, shows conditions as they exist when the die is open and during the feeding act. The view is self-explanatory, showing how this component is contoured to provide clearance for the previously formed piece-part projections on the stock strip. Die-block width W_2 must of necessity be wider than width W shown in the piece-part illustration. This component (11) has lifters installed in it, as shown. The lifters elevate the stock strip, permitting the formed-down projections to feed through without interference. Die life is provided at J to eliminate the need for maintenance grinding at surfaces K.

Figure 6·15 is a cross section through the first forming station (section X-X). This drawing shows the contour of the forming punches (28) (Fig. 6·13). These punches set the form by spanking the outer surface of the bends in the manner described in "Basic Diemaking". Another feature of the punch contour is the heel bosses, which contact the lift pads (23) at N. These bosses depress the pads in advance of the forming action in order to prevent them from interfering with the forming action. For this particular bending application the actual need for this procedure is

possibly somewhat dubious. However, many applications will be encountered where it can be of great value. The lift pads are actuated by internal springs. This construction is desirable in that it is convenient, especially for die-setup purposes. However, many situations will be encountered where the method will not be applicable because of insufficient die space, either horizontal space or/and vertical space. For applications where strong stripping forces and/or long pad travels are required it will be necessary to substitute an external spring construction.

Detail (13) is a compensator plate—so called because this plate is ground lower during maintenance to compensate for the lowering of the cutting faces, which is the natural result of sharpening attrition. It is simpler to grind the required amount from a plain flat plate than it is to rework the other components of the forming station. Further consideration will reveal that compensator plates can also be a definite asset to the original making of the die.

Compensators could have been supplied under the punches (28). However, they were omitted in order to illustrate another procedure. In this case the base surface of the punches is ground during maintenance (where shown, S in section X-X).

Figure 6·16 depicts a cross section through the chopoff-and-form station (section V-V). The slug tube (7) (see also Fig. 6·13) is a hardened tool-steel bushing, taper-reamed. Its head should be high enough to permit some rework of the pad's upper contour if this should become necessary. However, sufficient space should exist under the head to permit the bottom of the pad (5) to be reground if necessary. These two conditions will almost automatically ensure a strong construction under normal conditions.

The pad is externally actuated. It is driven by the spring (8). Spring resistance is transmitted to the pad via the tube-and-screw assemblies (29),

Figure **6·14** Cross-section view through die at W-W. In this view, conditions are shown as they exist when the die is in open position (at top of press stroke).

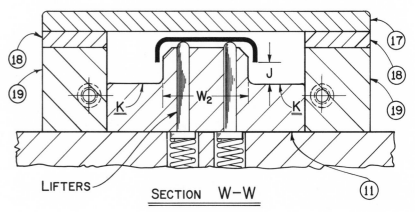

SECTION   W—W

LIFTERS

86

which act as pad retainers as well as transfer pins.

This station, too, has a compensator plate (6). It is apparent by examination that the compensator is even more desirable in this station than it is in the preceding station.

The stud (10) is installed directly under the pilot. Consequently, the stud is also a tube providing egress for any slugs which may descend through the slug tube (7).

A beveled notch is incorporated in the front of the pad as pictured in the three-dimensional view. This ramp serves two purposes. It permits the ejecting air blast to get under the piece part. It also ensures that the formed-down lug on the piece part will not catch on the pad.

CHOPOFF CONTOURS

The cutting of mating contours is a natural and inseparable feature of chopoff dies. Most typically (for dies operating on stock strips) the contours of chopoff-type cutting edges are reproduced on the piece part in the manner shown in Fig. 6·17. One end of the piece part is contoured (and sized) by the punch. The opposite end of the piece part is contoured (and sized) by the mating die block. Consequently, these dies are restricted to the production of piece parts whose contour relationships are typified in the illustration.

In views A and B the lead end and the tail end of the piece parts are produced with completely mating contours. In views C and D the end contours of the piece part are not completely mating. However, the fact that these end contours are partly mated permits the piece parts to be produced by progressive dies which incorporate a chopoff station to cut the mating portions of the end contours. In these two views C and D it is readily apparent by examination how other operations (such as piercing and notching) may be employed in conjunction with the chopoff method in order to produce piece parts which have dissimilar end contours. Combining operations in this manner can greatly increase the production range of dies which use the chopoff principle. Keep in mind that one end of the piece part will have two burr sides when produced in dies of this kind.

A chopoff die with sidewinder stop. The die shown in Fig. 6·18 is not pilot-equipped. A pusher is employed to push the stock strip against the rear stock guide. Right-to-left gaging depends solely upon the sidewinder stop, which acts in the pierced hole A. Obviously, this die cannot be expected to produce piece parts which require consistently accurate outer-edge dimensions. Therefore, the design of this die should be considered to be atypical rather than typical. In fact,

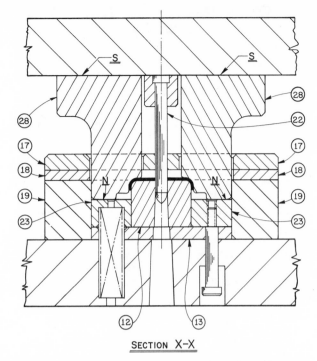

Figure **6·15** Cross-section view through die at *X-X*. Die is in closed position (bottom of press stroke).

Figure **6·16** Cross-section view through die at *V-V*. Die closed (bottom of press stroke).

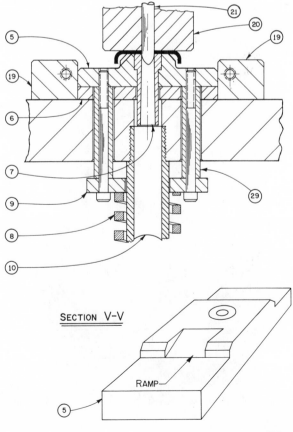

SECTION V-V

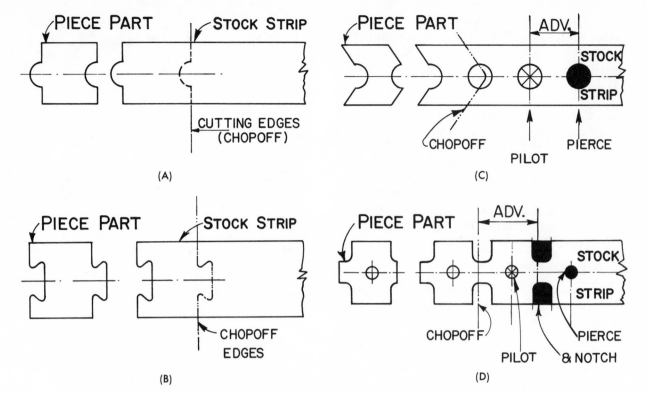

(A)

(C)

(B)

(D)

Figure 6·17   Contour relationships indigenous to chopoff type of cutting.

Figure 6·18   In this pierce and chopoff die, the piece parts drop through the opening which has been made in the die shoe.

it should be emphasized that it is rarely practical to make nonpiloting progressive dies.

Diemaking procedures for this die could have been facilitated by inverting the mounting screws

Figure 6·19   A more complex progressive die which produces two piece parts per press stroke.

88

S, which fasten the punch plate and the chopoff punch to the punch shoe. Inverting these screws would also preclude the possibility that one or more of them could work loose and drop out, which could create a hazard to die operation.

A two-row chopoff die. In the die that is shown in Fig. 6 · 19, final severance of the piece parts from the stock strip is accomplished by chopoff-type cutting action, which, in this die, is parallel to the feed direction. Piece-part disposal is through the die via the openings shown (A). Note that the chopoff punches are equipped with shedding pins B. This die is, of course, equipped with pilots (11 of them).

CHAPTER 7

PROGRESSIVE DIES USING THE PARTING PRINCIPLE

PARTING OPERATIONS

In the nomenclature of diemaking, the term "parting" is used to indicate another specific kind of cutting operation, one in which complete severance of the stock strip is achieved by punching out a piece of stock material from between the piece parts.

Contour relationships. In contrast to the chopoff method of cutting, parting operations are not restricted as to contour relationships. As pictured in Fig. 7·1, each contour is produced by its own individual set of cutting edges. Consequently, one end of the piece part will be contoured (and sized) by one side of the punch. The other end of

the piece part will be contoured (and sized) by the opposite side of the punch. *Note:* Both ends of the piece part derive their respective contours and sizes from the punch. Normally, the stock material which is punched out from between the piece parts is scrap. Therefore, for this kind of operation, only the scrap is sized by the cutting edges of the die opening. The manner in which contouring and sizing are accomplished is readily discernible by examining Fig. 7·2.

It should be mentioned that on occasion the punched-through piece of stock material may also

Figure **7·2** Relationship of parting punch and die opening to stock strip and piece part.

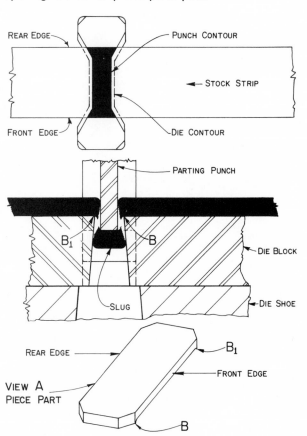

Figure **7·1** Some piece-part end contours typically produced in parting dies.

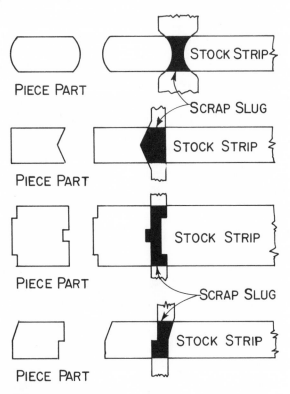

90

be a piece part (instead of scrap). If this is the case, the die would not be called a parting die. It would be considered to be a tandem die, as described in the discussion on scrapless and semi-scrapless operations in "Basic Diemaking"

Burr side. The exaggerated drawing (Fig. 7·2) illustrates the burr-side condition which is inherently typical for parting operations. The tail-end burr side B_1 and the lead-end burr side B are on the same side of the stock strip. Both burr sides are toward the die opening. Consequently, parting operations produce a common burr side on the piece part. That is, burr sides B and B_1 will be on the same side of the piece part, as pictured in view A.

In conventional parting dies of the progressive type, the parting punch operates in the same direction as any of the other punches such as those for piercing, notching, trimming, etc. It follows, then, that the respective burr sides resulting from any combination of these operations will be common to one and the same side of the piece part produced by a die of this type. *Caution:* Keep in mind that this does not necessarily guarantee the burr-side direction for the entire perimeter of the piece part—only for those portions of the piece part which have been produced (cut) by the various operations performed in the die. For example, in the illustration (Fig. 7·2), only the end contours are produced by the cutting action of the die. Therefore, in this case only the end contours are considered to have a consistently predictable burr side. Condition of the front and rear edge portions of the perimeter will depend upon the edge condition of the stock strip, as furnished and as oriented with respect to the die.

A NONPILOTING PIERCE-AND-PART DIE

Two piece parts are pictured in Fig. 7·3. They are simple flat straps. Each has two elongated holes whose location is equidistant from the ends. These piece parts are identical in all respects except for lengths A and A_1. Width W is equal to a standard stock-strip width dimension. The end radii R are greater than $W/2$. Therefore, the end radii are not tangent to the sides of the piece parts. This type of end radius on a piece part supplies a favorable cutting condition for producing the piece part in a parting die. In fact, these piece parts were designed with this in mind. The parts were designed to a standard width at W and with $R > W/2$ in order to facilitate producing them in a parting-type die. Consequently, tool

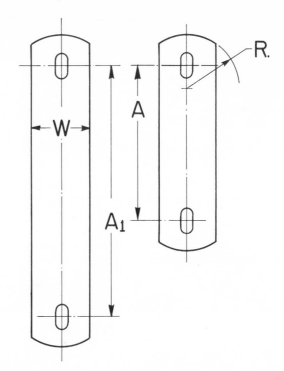

Figure **7·3** Piece parts with different length dimensions (A, A_1) which were produced by the die shown in Fig. 7·4.

costs can be minimized, and stock-material consumption will also be minimized.

The die which was employed to produce these straps is shown in Fig. 7·4.

Construction and operation. Both piece parts (dimensioned A and A_1, respectively) are made by this die. This is accomplished by means of the two-position end stop (7). The stop is mounted at gage position G to produce piece parts to dimension A. After a desired number of parts have been made to this dimension, the stop is moved to gage position G_1, which permits the parts to be made to dimension A_1.

Since this die is not equipped with pilots, it should be thought of as a somewhat unconventional die construction. For accuracy, it depends upon the press operator. He must feed the lead end securely against the stop at each press stroke. There is no safety factor as far as registry is concerned. Nevertheless, simple dies of this type, on suitable occasion, have been made in this manner and have been satisfactory. The well-informed diemaker should be aware of this. However, before making such a die he should ascertain that it will be acceptable.

For applications of this sort it may be practical to install a microswitch (or equivalent device)

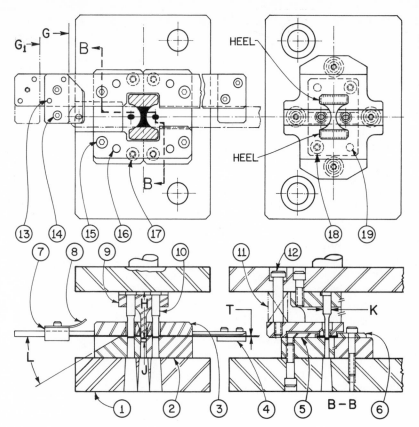

which will operate in conjunction with the end stop. Then, if the stock strip is fed short of the stopping position, the switch will not allow the press to operate. This will ensure piece-part accuracy within the limits imposed by the action range of the switching device. On the debit side, tool cost will be increased and the die may also be slower in operation.

Another approach is to operate the die in conjunction with an automatic feeder. The initial accuracy of the piece parts depends upon how precisely the feeder setting is made. The consistency with which the accuracy is maintained will depend upon the capabilities of the feeder. In other words, the degree of accuracy to which the piece parts can be produced is limited to the capabilities of the specific feeder. Also, the advance distance cannot be longer than the maximum stroke of which the feeder is capable. This, of course, imposes its limit on the overall length of the piece parts which can be produced by this method. Do not forget—the advance distance includes the scrap in addition to the overall length of the piece part.

This die is mounted on a back-post die set (1) (Fig. 7·4). With respect to the die, the die set is oriented at 90° to the conventional mounting orientation. Doing this locates both guideposts toward the in-feed side in order to provide max-

imum clearance on the out-feed side, which simplifies disposal of the piece parts.

The die block on the out-feed side [refer to (2)] is provided with an angular channel L which permits the piece parts to slide clear of the die. The parts may drop through a bolster opening if one is provided, or they may be allowed to accumulate on top of the bolster to be cleared away by the operator from time to time. Or off loading may be accomplished by means of an air blast, if feasible.

The stripper (3) is actuated by springs (11), which are installed around the stripper bolts (12). Its outer peripheral contour as shown in the plan view provides clearance for the mounting screws (15) as shown in section *B-B*. (It would probably have been cheaper to eliminate this contour sawing and use a plain rectangular plate with four clearance holes drilled through it to clear the heads of these lower mounting screws.) The cross-sectional profile of the stripper is also shown in section *B-B*. The stripper is a clamping-type stripper in order to help alleviate the tendency of the stock material to skid while being parted.

On the in-feed side, the front and rear stock-strip guides (5) and (6) are provided with ledges to prevent the strip from lifting out of the channel. Ledges are not provided on the out-feed side, since their presence here would prevent the piece parts from dropping out via the angular chute. The deflector and rake-off (8) substitutes for the missing ledges on the out-feed side, since it serves the equivalent function which is to prevent the piece part from being lifted out of the die. It also prevents the lead end of the strip from being fed over the top of the stop. The presence of this component (8) eliminates the need for a shedding pin in the stripper.

The parting punch (9) is a pedestal-type punch. Height of this punch at the cutting face is shown (H). Height of its heel is shown (J). Overall height of this punch is $H + J$. The punch is fitted to the die opening with normal cutting clearance at the cutting portions of the contour. The heels are a slip fit in their corresponding part of the die opening. The perforators (9) are mounted in the flange area of the parting punch. They are keyed by flats ground on both sides of their heads to match the slot, which is ground in the base of the parting punch as shown at K in view B-B. Overall height of the perforators is made $H - T$ (T is the stock-material thickness). This is done to protect the perforators from lateral displacement, which can occur as a result of the cutting forces engendered by the parting punch.

For more detailed information, especially in regard to the fitting of heeled punches and the keying of perforators, see "Basic Diemaking."

A PILOTING PIERCE-AND-PART DIE

Figure 7·5 depicts one version of a pierce-and-part die in which the stock strip is piloted. The mounting screws and dowels are not shown in the stock list. When this die was designed, it was left to the diemaker to determine the location, size, and quantity of screws and dowels, as well as the manner in which they were to be installed. The serious reader will find it good practice to make these determinations himself, just as though he were a diemaker who is making the die according to this design drawing.

The construction. The diagonal-post die set (1) provides maximum clearance for ejecting the piece parts to the rear, as indicated in Fig. 7·5. This particular die-set configuration is supplied as a standardized die set by at least one die-set manufacturer, Superior Steel Products Corporation (Milwaukee, Wis.).

The die block (3) is one-piece. In it are two air channels machined as shown on the off-loading side of the die. These permit the ejection air blast to get under the piece part, lifting it and ejecting to the rear, as indicated. These channels may be renewed by grinding them deeper, if and when required.

A channeled box-type stripper (4) is installed on the in-feed side of the die. The stripper on the

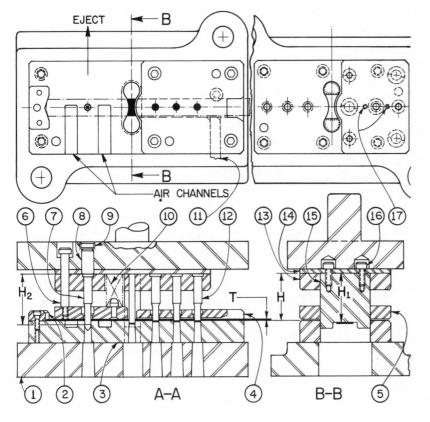

Figure **7·5** A two-station die to pierce and part the stock strip. In this die, the second station is equipped with a spring-actuated stripper (5) in contrast to the first station, which incorporates a box-type stripper (4).

1. Superior diagonal-post die set (one)
2. End stop (one)
3. Die block (one)
4. Box stripper (one)
5. Spring stripper (one)
6. Stripper bolt (three)
7. Pilot (one)
8. Spacer plug (one)
9. Setscrew (one)
10. Spring (three)
11. Pusher assembly (one)
12. Perforator (three)
13. Punch plate (one)
14. Thrust plate (one)
15. Parting punch (one)
16. Socket-head cap screw (two)
17. Standard shedding pin (two)

out-feed side (5) is a spring stripper, in order to clear this area on the upstroke to permit ejection of the piece part. It is a clamping-type stripper in order to minimize lateral thrust against the pilot. This stripper includes two shedding pins (17), which act to strip the piece part from the pilot.

The pilot (7) is removable through the punch holder. This will permit the punches to be sharpened in assembly, if desired.

The punch plate (13) is one-piece. In it are fitted (in addition to the pilot) the perforators (12) and the parting punch (15). The parting punch is shear-fitted into the punch plate and is retained in assembly by two screws (16), which secure it against the thrust plate (14). Remember that the punch heels must be nicely fitted to the die opening in order to ensure stability for this punch.

Height of the perforators is indicated as H. Height of the parting punch at its cutting face is shown as H_1. Effective piloting length is shown as H_2. Height H_1 is made equal to $H + T$, to alleviate lateral-thrust effects. Piloting length H_2 must be long enough to ensure registry of the strip before the spring stripper contacts the stock material.

ASSOCIATION OF PARTING OPERATIONS

On rare occasions a die may be required in which the parting operation is the only operation. However, most dies which employ parting operations will also include other operations. For example, piercing operations are included in the last two dies which we have described in the foregoing text.

The nature of parting operations is such that they are inherently well suited to operate in conjunction with other types of operations in progressive dies. These other operations include piercing, notching, trimming, forming, etc. In fact, parting operations are very commonly associated with progressive dies which include forming (especially bending) operations.

A DIE TO TRIM-PART, PIERCE, AND FORM DOWN

The die in Fig. 7·6 combines a trimming operation with the parting operation. This die also includes a piercing operation (two holes) and a forming (specifically bending) operation.

Die action and operation. For registry, this die depends upon the trim-stop principle. A hard insert (9) is brazed into the stripper (3) to provide a stopping face.

In operation, the lead end of the stock strip is fed to the stop. The trimming operation then produces an offset on the strip at A. Next, the strip is advanced until offset A contacts the stop. When the press ram descends, the forming punch (6) is the first punch to contact the stock material. The forming action tends to pull the strip in the same direction as the feed direction, but offset A (on the strip) is against the stop, which prevents the strip from pulling. Thus, the forming action tends to ensure that the strip is properly registered against the stop. As the ram continues to descend, the perforators (8) and the trim-and-part punch (10) contact the strip to complete the cutting operations at the bottom of the press stroke. When the press ram rises on its upstroke, the form pad (5) acts as a spring stripper, causing the finished piece part to remain on the face of the die block (2). As the press ram continues its ascent, pressurized air is injected into the passage hole shown in the die shoe. This air jet blows upward through the air-lift hole shown in the die block, lifting the piece part clear of the die face. This ensures that the conventional open air blast (directed horizontally across the die face) will eject the part out the rear, as indicated in the illustration.

NOTE

This die causes the burr sides to be produced on the inner surface of the piece part, which was a factor in designing the die to form downward.

Cutting relationships. Punch and die relationships for this die are shown in the exaggerated drawing (Fig. 7·7). In this drawing, C represents normal cutting clearance, and C_1 is equal to C. The cutting clearance at C_2, however, is less than C. Reducing the cutting clearance at C_2 alleviates burring tendencies, which occur whenever cutting edges approach a condition of tangency with an edge of the stock material. A tangent (or nearly tangent) condition produces a shaving action which necessitates a reduction in the amount of cutting clearance in the vicinity of the tangency.

Note especially that cutting clearance C_1 is provided in the die block—*not* on the punch. This is done in order to minimize the tendency to produce a noticeable burr or even a whiskered condition at B. For further and more detailed information concerning trim stops refer to "Basic Diemaking."

An alternative construction. The die we have discussed above is not equipped with pilots. This might not be acceptable for many applications. For such applications, the design of this die could easily be modified to one which includes pilots.

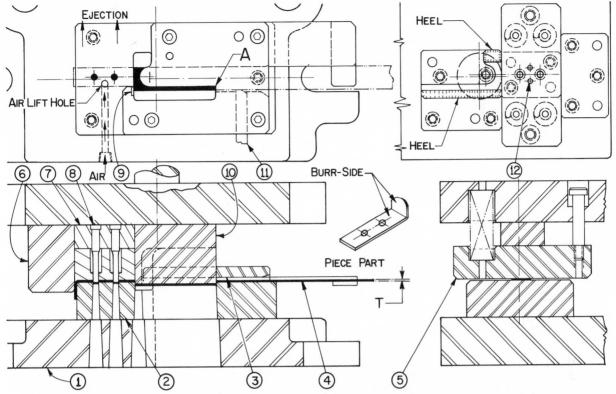

Figure **7·6** A die to trim-part, pierce, and bend. The trimming operation is integrally combined with the parting operation. The major components of this die and the number of each required are:

1. Back-post die set (one)
2. Die block (one)
3. Stripper (one)
4. Back-gage assembly (one)
5. Form pad (one)
6. Forming punch (one)
7. Punch plate (one)
8. Perforator (two)
9. Stop insert (one)
10. Trim-and-part punch (one)
11. Pusher (one)
12. Shedding pin (two)

To accomplish this, the following changes would be necessary:

1. In the second station, replace the perforators (8) (Fig. 7·6) with pilots.
2. Relocate the piercing operation to the first station.
3. Increase the distance from ledge *A* to the stop (9) in order to provide a normal overfeed. This will require a compensatory increase in the length of the trim-and-part punch (10).

A DIE TO PIERCE, PART, AND FORM UP

The nature of parting operations is such that they are inherently well suited to applications of the kind pictured in Fig. 7·8. Here, the piece part is formed upward. The actions, in forming upward in conjunction with parting (as shown here), are innately compatible. Consequently, this relationship is a most typical one for progressive part-and-form dies.

Construction and operation. In this die the forming punch (23) is stabilized laterally by virtue of a sliding fit with the heel block (2). The heel block is made high enough to adequately engage with

Figure **7·7** Punch and die opening relationships for the combined trim-part operation. (Drawing is exaggerated.)

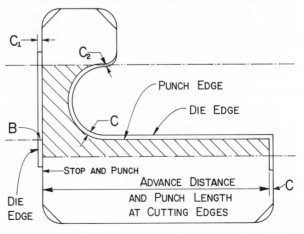

95

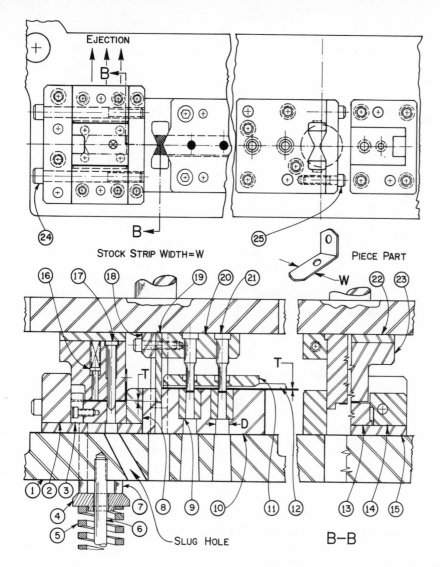

STOCK STRIP WIDTH=W

PIECE PART

SLUG HOLE

B-B

Figure **7·8** Progressive die to produce the right-angled bracket shown. The bending action is upward in this die. The major components of this die and the number of each required are:

1. Back-post die set (one)
2. Heel block (one)
3. Stop insert (one)
4. Spreader plate (one)
5. Spring (one)
6. Stud (one)
7. Transfer pin (four)
8. Forming-die block (one)
9. Pierce-die bushing (two)
10. Die block (one)
11. Box stripper (one)
12. Back-gage assembly (one)
13. Forming pad (one)
14. Pad retainer (two)
15. Compensator plate (one)
16. Spring pin (one)
17. Pilot (one)
18. Clamp bar (one)
19. Parting punch (one)
20. Punch plate (one)
21. Perforator (two)
22. Compensator plate (one)
23. Forming punch (one)
24. Socket-head cap screw (two)
25. Socket-head cap screw (two)

the form punch before the forming action begins, in order to eliminate possible entry interference between these two components. The heel block, together with the forming block (8) and the pad retainers (15), is constrained laterally by tie bolts (24). This combination makes a self-contained unit of the forming station to support the punch and eliminate any lateral displacement due to the one-sided bending (forming) forces. Upper and lower compensating plates (22) and (15) permit vertical compensation when the die is sharpened in maintenance, which can also be a distinct asset when the die is being constructed originally. The stop (3) necessitates a clearance notch in the forming punch, as shown.

The parting punch (19) is clamped into the punch plate (20) and further retained vertically by means of head tabs, one of which is shown in section B-B. Height of the parting punch at its cutting face must extend beyond the face of the forming punch a minimum distance equal to T

(T = stock-material thickness). This is compulsory: the stock strip must be completely severed before the forming action begins. It follows, then, that effective piloting length of the pilot (17) must extend beyond the cutting face of the parting punch a minimum distance of $\frac{1}{2}T$, in order to register the stock strip. The clamp bar (18) is angled as shown in the front section view, in order to provide adequate clearance for the leg of the piece part to swing upward during the act of forming.

The pierce-die bushings (9) do not extend through the die block. When this construction is used, be sure that diameter D of the slug clearance hole is adequately large. Diameter D must be large enough to permit entry of a drift which is big enough to seat adequately against the bottom of the bushing. This will greatly facilitate bushing removal, if and when required.

A slug clearance hole is installed at an angle, as shown in the front section view. If the pilot inadvertently pierces the stock strip, the resulting slug will be carried clear of the spreader plate by the angled hole. This slug clearance hole, like the others, should be taper-reamed.

NOTE

The burr side typically produced by the cutting actions in this die is toward the outer surfaces of the piece part.

A PARTING AND U-BENDING DIE

The die pictured in Fig. 7 · 9 combines a U-bend-ing operation in conjunction with the parting operation.

Construction and maintenance. Since width W of the piece part is constant, the bending forces at both bends are equal. The balanced forces tend to center the forming (bending) punch in relation to the forming station. These forces, and others, are described in Chap. 3, *Bending*, in "Basic Diemaking."

Perpendicularity for the legs of the piece part is achieved by corner setting. This is accomplished

Figure **7 · 9**   Progressive die to pierce, part, and bend the U-shaped piece part shown. The major components of this die and the number of each required are:

1. Back-post die set (one)
2. Socket-head cap screw (two)
3. Form-die block (one)
4. Form pad (one)
5. Slug tube (one)
6. Spring (one)
7. Die-block insert (one)
8. Die-block insert (one)
9. Pierce-die bushing (two)
10. Die block (one)
11. Thrust plate (one)
12. Back-gage assembly (one)
13. Skyhook plate (one)
14. End step and spacer (one)
15. Forming punch (one)
16. Pilot (one)
17. Compensator plate (one)
18. Parting punch (one)
19. Pad retainer (two)
20. Pilot (one)
21. Punch plate (one)
22. Punch plate (one)
23. Finger stop (one)
24. Perforator (two)
25. Thrust plate (one)
26. Socket-head cap screw (two)
27. Thin locknut (two)

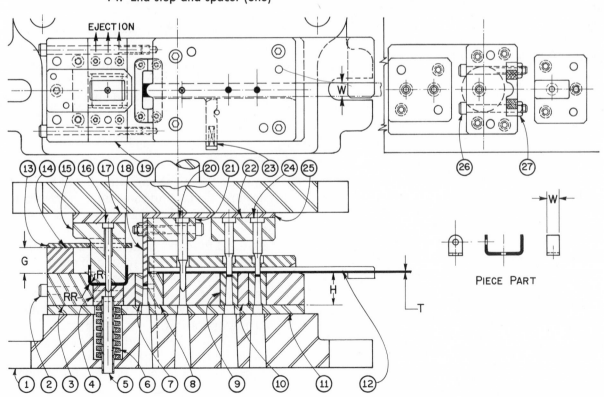

PIECE PART

by a slight squeeze between the bend radii (refer to R) and radii RR which is provided on the die blocks (3) and (10). To develop the required size for these setting radii, use the formula

$$RR = R + \tfrac{5}{4}T$$

Then check and decrease radius RR, if necessary.

The two die blocks (3) and (10), together with the pad retainers (19), are unitized by means of tie bolts (2). This was done to resist the bursting-type strains which are characteristic of this kind of bending operation.

The forming-die block (10) also creates a yoke for the cutting-die inserts (7), (8), and (9). The manner in which this die is constructed makes it necessary to install shims under these inserts to compensate for sharpening attrition: only the inserts are ground for normal maintenance purposes.

A different approach to maintenance could be applied to this same basic design:

1. Sharpen the required amount from the top face of the inserts (7), (8), (9).
2. Grind exactly the same amount from the bottom surface of (3), (4), (10), and (19) to restore the necessary vertical-height relationship.

This last procedure would necessitate an increase in thickness H for the lower die assembly to provide grinding life. Actually, this is necessitated by the vertical proportions of the form pad (4) in this particular die. Therefore, a third approach could be to provide a separate compensator plate under the form pad. Sharpening procedure would then be the same as in items 1 and

2 above, except that the compensator plate would be ground instead of the bottom of the pad (4). This third approach would obviate the need for thicker die blocks. The die could be made to the original H thickness, as shown.

The upper punch assembly can be conventionally sharpened. The compensator plate (17) is ground thinner to compensate for the shorter punch heights caused by sharpening the face of the cutting punches (18) and (24). For more information concerning die life, punch life, and relative punch and die life refer to "Basic Diemaking."

In this die construction the parting punch (18) is fitted into a slot in the punch plate (21). It is secured by two cross screws (26). The holes in the parting punch are threaded and the screws are threadedly engaged in these tapped holes. The locknuts (27) are added as a safety factor.

Operation. This is a three-station die. On the first cycle, the strip is fed to the finger stop (23), and the holes are pierced. For the second cycle the strip is sight-stopped at the parting station. It is then fed to the final stop (14), and the cycle is repeated until the strip is consumed.

Detail (13) is assembled to the end stop, creating a skyhook type of stripper which strips the piece part from the form punch. An air blast then ejects the piece part to the rear, as indicated in Fig. 7·9.

PRACTICE PROBLEM: NOTCH, PART, AND FORM DIE

In addition to the foregoing progressive parting dies, the reader will encounter more complex dies, which will require that forming operations are performed on the in-feed side of the parting operation. A piece part which could be made in such a die appears in Fig. 7·10.

PROCEDURE

1. Compare this piece part with that of Fig. 6·10. They are similar, but they differ in ways which critically affect the type of progressive die required.
2. List the differences, and note why they dictate the use of a parting operation to make the new piece part in a progressive die.
3. Using Fig. 6·11 as a guide, make a strip layout for the new part which incorporates the parting operation.
4. Using Fig. 6·12 as a guide, make a relationship layout for the cutting operations.
5. Make a design layout. For guidance refer to Figs. 6·13 and 6·25.

Figure **7·10** The bending operations required to produce this piece part are directionally opposed.

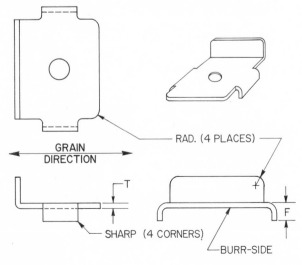

GRAIN DIRECTION

RAD. (4 PLACES)

T

SHARP (4 CORNERS)

BURR-SIDE

F

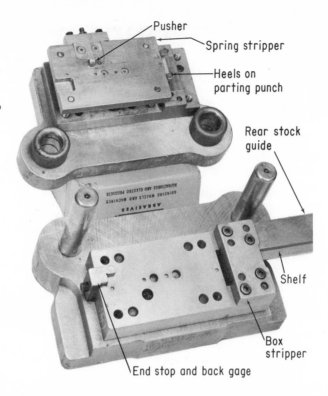

Figure **7·11** A parting die which also pierces six holes in the piece part.

Pusher

Spring stripper

Heels on parting punch

Rear stock guide

Shelf

Box stripper

End stop and back gage

The serious reader will find the above exercise to be of great value in the understanding of die relationships. The effort involved is a bargain price to pay for the increase in diemaking proficiency which results from working out problems of this sort.

FURTHER PRACTICE EXERCISES

Obviously the piece part in Fig. 7·10 could be produced by a means of a series of separate dies instead of a progressive die. From the viewpoint of practice for proficiency, it will be very much worthwhile to process this piece part to determine the optimum number of dies (this can vary, depending upon the equipment in which the production run is to be made). It will also be necessary to determine the die type best suited to each purpose in order to proceed with the design layouts.

In Fig. 7·11 note that the stock-strip pusher is a type which is mounted as part of the upper assembly. The use of this kind of pusher in conjunction with the spring stripper facilitates unloading the piece parts from the die.

SECONDARY OPERATIONS: DIES TO PIERCE, SEMIPIERCE SHEARFORM, FORM

A SMALL PIERCE DIE FOR A LARGE PIECE PART

The piercing die which appears in Fig. 8·1 is a very simple one. However, it represents a practical approach to a specific production situation. It is an economically desirable die, in both con-

cept and construction. It is worth studying and remembering for association with other applications in the future.

The piece-part requirements. The workpiece

Figure **8·1** A pierce die which is incorporated in a no-guide post die set. Setup pins (5) are used to facilitate installing this die in the punch press. The major components of this die and the number of each required are:

1. Punch shoe (one)	8. Perforator (four)
2. Die shoe (one)	9. Rest button (four)
3. Die bushing (four)	10. Stripper (one)
4. Pilot (one)	11. Thumbscrew (one)
5. Setup pin (two)	12. Cover plate (one)
6. Setscrew (four)	13. Stripper spring (eight)
7. Locknut (four)	14. Stripper bolt (four)

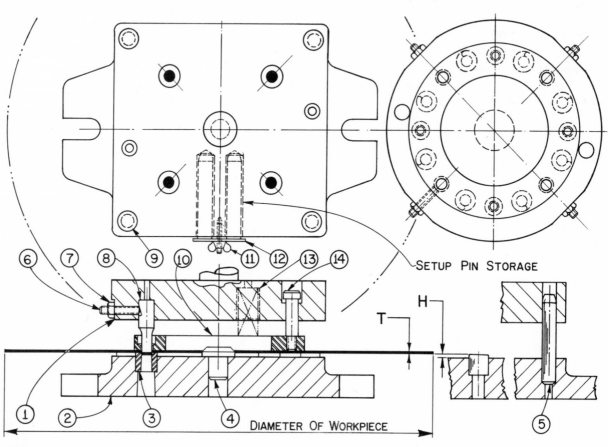

SETUP PIN STORAGE

DIAMETER OF WORKPIECE

(piece part) on which this die operates has had its center hole pierced and the outer diameter blanked in a previous operation. The piercing die illustrated represents one of a series of piercing dies which were used to pierce a number of different hole patterns and sizes in these workpieces. In addition, it was anticipated that new hole patterns and shapes would be required from time to time. Consequently, separate piercing operations were a logical procedure for producing this piece part.

The die construction. The die set is a no-guidepost die set, employing a standardized punch shoe (1) and die shoe (2). This choice was made because the relatively large outer diameter of the workpiece would require a guidepost-equipped die set to be inordinately large. The size of the workpiece also dictated the use of a spring-actuated stripper (10). It should, of course, be remembered that this is only one of a number of reasons for using spring strippers.

A die which employs a spring stripper in combination with a no-guidepost die set will require special setup procedures and/or provisions. This die is equipped with setup pins (5), which are installed as shown in the section view for press-setup purposes. After the die is set up, the pins are removed and stored in the storage holes provided in the die shoe, as shown in the plan view of the lower die assembly.

The pierce-die bushings and the perforators (3) and (8) are standardized, commercially available components. The perforators are retained by set screws (6), which are secured by locknuts (7). The pierce bushings are press-fitted in the die shoe. These protrude above the die shoe (H) to provide a sharpening land, as described and discussed in "Basic Diemaking." When the face of these bushings is sharpened down to the face of the die shoe, the bushings are meant to be replaced with new bushings, which will restore the original sharpening land condition. The slug holes through the die shoe are made large enough to facilitate removal of these bushings for replacement. Rest buttons (9) are installed to increase the seating area for the workpiece, which prevents tilting, thereby facilitating loading and production. These leveling buttons are simple cold-rolled steel plugs. They are, of course, ground down in sharpening and replaced along with the pierce-die bushings. Knockout holes are provided under the rest buttons to facilitate their removal.

A PIERCE DIE WITH POSITIVE KNOCKOFF

A piece part and a piercing die appear in Fig. 8·2. Except for the pierced holes, the piece part has been produced by a series of previous die operations. The die illustrated pierces the large hole in the cupped portion of the piece part and the three smaller holes as shown in the flange area.

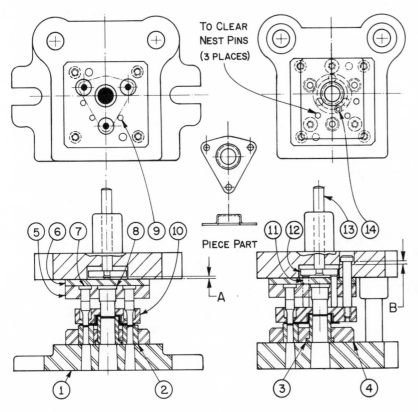

Figure **8·2** A piercing die equipped with a positive knock-off arrangement. The major components of this die and the number required are:

1. Back-post die set (one)
2. Pierce-die bushing (three)
3. Pierce-die bushing (one)
4. Die yoke block (one)
5. Punch plate (one)
6. Thrust plate (one)
7. Perforator (three)
8. Perforator (one)
9. Nest-gage pin (three)
10. Stripper plate (one)
11. Transfer pin (three)
12. Spreader plate (one)
13. Knock-off shaft (one)
14. Shedding pin (one)

The die construction. The die bushings (2) were press-fitted into the yoke block (4). They protrude above it, to provide the sharpening-land condition. The yoke block was not hardened. Because of its relatively thin wall, the center die bushing (3) was made a wring fit to its yoke opening and provided with a head for security. The head also provides a larger base area for this bushing, which disperses the cutting force over a larger die-shoe area, thereby preventing the force from sinking the bushing into the shoe. The larger base area can also make it easier to install the slug hole through the die shoe.

This die is equipped with three nest pins (9). The two pins which are located toward the front of the die act as gage pins, fixing the radial relationship of the holes to the outer periphery of the piece part. The third pin acts as a "foolproofer," to prevent the workpiece from being loaded in a position other than the required one.

The knock-off arrangement is a conventional assembly, with the stripper plate (10) suspended by stripper bolts. The functional relationship of the stripper plate to the perforators (7) and (8) is the same as that of a positive shedder to its die opening. Remember that dimension B must be greater than dimension A and that dimension A must include the necessary safety factor. These relationships should be made in accordance with the recommendations given in "Basic Diemaking."

In order to complete this piece part, another separate piercing operation was required, which appears in the next illustration.

A HORN-TYPE PIERCE DIE

Here, the requirement is to pierce one hole where shown (A, Fig. 8·3). The position of this hole in the piece part requires the die to be either a horn-type die or a side-action die. To produce this piece part, a horn-type die is the more practical of the two.

The horn-type die is considerably more economical to make and maintain. And since only one piercing is required, a side-action die cannot offer any advantage as far as rate of piece-part production is concerned.

The die set. The die set (1) is a standard back-post type. It is called a "V-punch-holder" die set because of the plan contour of the punch shoe. This configuration affords more empty space in the vicinity of the die, which can be a convenient operating feature for dies which perform secondary operations.

The die construction. In this die the horn is a round boss which is turned on the die block (4). Diameter of the horn is the desired gage fit to the piece part. The horn then serves as a pilot to position one axis of the piece part. The small pilot (3) positions the piece radially about the horn. The toggle clamp (5) clamps the piece against the die-block face, which completes the gaging. The toggle clamp also ensures that the piece part is securely held in its totally gaged position.

The perforator (6) has a whistle notch ground in one side of its shank. A setscrew (7) acts in the notch to retain the perforator in the punch shoe. The setscrew is secured by a locknut (8). The perforator shank is made with a flat surface where shown (B) in order to clear the piece-part flange. The perforator is prevented from rotating by the setscrew acting against the whistle-notch flat, which ensures the necessary clearance at B.

This die does not require a stripper. The horn holds the piece part in place vertically. When the perforator ascends, it is withdrawn from the piece part without requiring further assistance from a specific stripping component. Keep in mind, however, that for light-gage and/or soft materials, it may be necessary to install a separate stripper in order to prevent distortion of the piece part.

Figure **8·3** This horn-type pierce die employs a toggle clamp (5) to secure the workpiece in position on the horn. The major components of the die illustrated and the number of each required are: (1) Back-post die set (one). (2) Pierce-die bushing (one). (3) Pilot (one). (4) Die block (horn) (one). (5) Toggle clamp (one). (6) Perforator (one). (7) Setscrew (one). (8) Locknut (one).

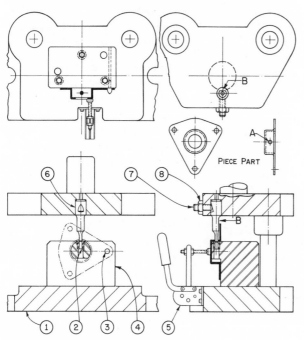

A PROGRESSIVE PIERCING DIE

A piece part and the die which produced it are illustrated in Fig. 8·4. The piece part is a long steel strip. The entire length of the strip is perforated as shown. The perforations are in groups of five holes, which have a center distance of B within the group. Each group is separated by the center distance C. The first and last hole groups are located distance D from each end of the strip.

The die construction. The stop (3) is a spring pin, which permits the stock strip to feed over it during the required number of piercing cycles. The stop is located as shown, tangent to distance D from the first piercing center.

One pilot (2) is located at the required C distance from the first piercing center and engages in the last hole of the pierced group. The other pilot is located a distance $E = 4B$ from C, which causes it to engage in the first hole of the same pierced group. Locating the pilots as shown, to engage in the two end holes of the pierced group, foolproofs the feeding of the strip. If the operator can engage the strip on both pilots, he knows the strip is in position to pierce the next hole group.

Operation. The lead end of the strip is fed against the stop pin (3). The first hole group is pierced at this position. Then, the strip is fed over the stop pin and engaged on the pilots (2), and the next hole group is pierced. This cycle is repeated until the required number of piercings are performed.

The stripper (7) is a flat plate mounted on the top surface of the back gage (6), creating an open-gap type of stripper. A rather strong pusher (10) forces the rear edge of the strip to ride against the back gage (6). Carbide inserts are installed in the back gage to resist the strong erosive condition created by the edge of the strip as it moves along the back gage. Various insert types and installation methods are described in "Basic Diemaking."

Strip growth. For work of this sort, if the strip is very long and requires a considerable number of piercings, growth phenomena should be taken into consideration. That is, if a given strip is measured before and after piercing, it may be found to be longer after it is pierced than it was originally. This can result from work strains induced by the piercing operations. The amount of growth will depend upon the length of the strip and the amount of work performed upon it. Relatively long strips on which a large number of work operations are performed may exhibit significant growth. The amount of growth can also vary

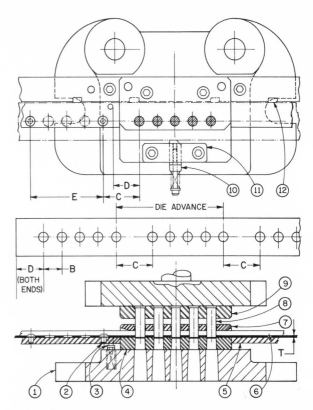

Figure **8·4** A progressive die to pierce a series of hole groups in a long stock strip. The major components of this die and the number of each required are:

1. Back-post die set (one)
2. Pilot (two)
3. Stop (one)
4. Die block (one)
5. Shelf (two)
6. Back gage (one)
7. Stripper (one)
8. Perforator (five)
9. Punch plate (one)
10. Pusher (one)
11. Pusher retainer (one)
12. Back-gage insert (six)

according to the type of stock material. For work of this kind, it may be necessary to determine the amount of growth and make appropriate compensatory allowances for it.

Growth phenomena are, of course, not restricted to piercing operations and are of particular concern in relation to continuous strip operations, especially when intermittent operations are performed in conjunction with continuous operations.

MULTILEVEL PIERCING

Many piercing operations must be performed on piece parts which are previously formed or drawn, creating surfaces which are at different

103

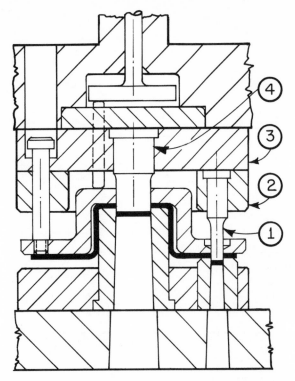

Figure **8·5** This bilevel piercing die incorporates an auxiliary punch plate (2). The result is a desirably sturdy die construction.

levels. If the difference between levels is relatively small, it can be disregarded as far as piercing punches are concerned (refer to Fig. 8·2). If, however, the difference between levels is relatively

Figure **8·6** A trilevel pierce die.

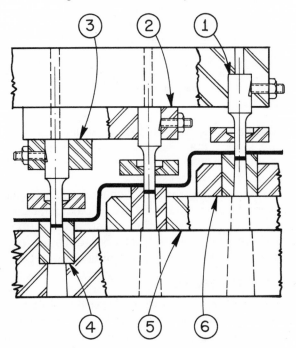

large, the die construction should compensate for the disparity.

Figure 8·5 shows a section through a piercing die which pierces a flanged drawn shell at two levels. To preclude the need for excessively long perforators (1), they are installed in an auxiliary punch plate (2). This plate is mounted to the master punch plate (3), which contains the pierce punches (4) required for the other level.

Construction for multilevel piercing is carried a step further in Fig. 8·6, where a composite construction is shown. One set of pierce punches (1) is mounted in the punch shoe. Another set is installed in a punch plate (2) and a third set in an auxiliary punch plate (3). The principle is also applied to the lower die members. One set of die bushings (4) is installed in the die shoe. Another set is installed in a die block (5) and the third set in an auxiliary die block (6).

If the various levels of the piece part contain identical pierced openings, it will be generally desirable to use construction proportions which will permit all punches to have the same overall height. This will be a convenience in diemaking and maintenance. It will not always be practical to do this, but it should be done when feasible. The foregoing applies also to lower die inserts—when practical.

PIERCINGS CLOSELY SPACED

When two or more punches are in proximity, the cutting forces cause the punches to tend to displace each other laterally and a large punch will displace a small punch. This condition can be alleviated by employing a differential (H) in punch heights as depicted in Fig. 8·7. The smaller punch is made shorter than the large punch.

The minimum theoretical dimension for H is a dimension equal to the shear-penetration depth attained by the larger punch: this is the stage at which the maximum cutting forces are developed. (Refer to "Shear Action" and to "Cutting Force" in "Basic Diemaking.") However, it must be remembered that the shear-penetration depth for any punch is a variable dimension, depending on the amount of cutting clearance, the sharpness of the punch, etc. Therefore, it has become accepted that the minimum practical differential for H should be $0.7T$, where T is the stock-material thickness.

For average conditions and on the assumption of normal cutting clearances, the following differentials are generally acceptable:

$H = 0.75T$ where $T > \frac{3}{16}$ in.
$H = T$ where $T = \frac{1}{32}$ to $\frac{3}{16}$ in.
$H = \frac{1}{32}$ in.   where $T < \frac{1}{32}$ in.

Obviously, the foregoing is not restricted solely to piercing dies. It also applies to any other die when similar conditions are encountered.

DIFFERENTIAL PUNCH HEIGHTS FOR LESS TONNAGE

Cutting-force requirements for a given operation can be lessened by making the punches as shown in Fig. 8·8. This method can be applied to as few as two punches, if necessary, but is far more often required for dies which contain a great number of punches.

If the punches are located close to each other, make the differential H to the dimensions recommended earlier for piercings in proximity. If, however, the punch spacing is adequate and the object of differential H is only to reduce the tonnage, the increment for H may be made smaller, if necessary.

There are three reasons why it may be desirable to make H equal to a smaller percentage of T for tonnage-reduction applications. One reason is to avoid the need for making the longer punches undesirably long and/or the shorter punches undesirably short. Another reason is to secure a smooth press action instead of incurring a series of jerks as each group of punches is driven into the stock material. This second reason applies especially to large work and/or a great number of punches. The third reason is to minimize, as much as possible, friction and wear on the longer punches. The farther a punch travels through the stock material, the greater the friction and wear. These reasons are all associated with the stock-material thickness T. Heavier (thicker) stock material tends to require that H is made a smaller percentage of T. For such applications the differential can be reduced to

$$H = \frac{T}{2}$$

with a practical minimum of

$$H = 0.4T$$

Remember that these percentages assume that the amount of cutting clearance is adequate for the application. Remember also that larger cutting clearances tend to reduce the cutting-force requirements, while smaller cutting clearances tend to increase the cutting-force requirements.

Important: The use of differential punch heights does *not* reduce the stripping-force requirement. In addition to this, a longer stripper travel distance is necessary in order to strip the stock material from the punches.

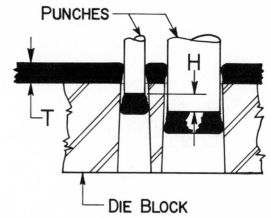

Figure **8·7**   Application of differential punch heights to eliminate possible breakage.

AN INVERTED HORN-TYPE PIERCE DIE

The die in Fig. 8·9 pierces through from the inner surface of the piece part.

Construction and operation. The punch (5) is part of the lower assembly. It is held in the yoke block (4) by the crosswise screw (9) and supported by the thrust block (6). The stripper (10) is guided by its guideposts and bushings (7). The stripper serves also as a horn on which the workpiece is loaded. The workpiece fits over the yoke and the thrust block which position it from left to right. It is held in place by snap springs (8). When the upper assembly descends, the wiper (14) acts to ensure that the piece is properly in place. The die block (11) contacts the levelers (16) to stabilize the stripper. When the ram ascends, the slug is carried up within the die opening. It is ejected at the top of the stroke by the shedder-knockout action (12) and (13) and blown clear by an air jet.

Figure **8·8**   Using differential punch heights to reduce the cutting-force requirement.

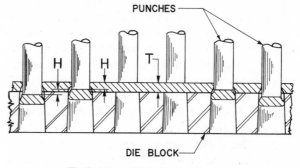

T= STOCK MATERIAL THICKNESS

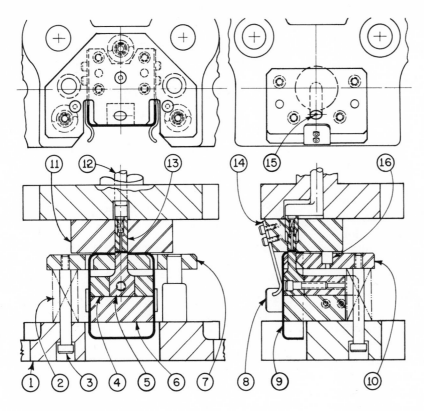

Figure **8·9** This horn-type die pierces an elliptical hole through one side of a rectangular drawn shell. The piece part specifications required the burr side of the pierced opening to be on the outer surface of the piece part. This requirement led to the inverted construction of this die. The major components of this die and the number of each required are:

1. Back-post die set (one)
2. Stripper spring (three)
3. Stripper bolt (three)
4. Yoke block (one)
5. Punch (one)
6. Thrust block (one)
7. Guide-pin and bushing assembly (two)
8. Snap-in spring (two)
9. Socket-head cap screw (one)
10. Stripper (one)
11. Die block (one)
12. Knockout (one)
13. Shedder (one)
14. Wiper (one)
15. Shedding pin (one)
16. Leveler (three)

SEMIPIERCING

Semipiercing is the process of displacing the stock material to create an integral boss on a piece part in the manner shown in Fig. 8·10. The constructions illustrated have proved to be generally satisfactory for semipiercing operations. The features shown here are, of necessity, exaggerated. The radii and angles will be quite small in actuality. In fact, they may be almost indiscernible for some applications.

The punch is made larger than the die opening and acts as a swedge, forcing the stock material to flow into the die opening. The swedge action prevents the initiation of cutting action, thereby producing a strong boss which will not easily be separated from the piece part. Radius R on the punch nose permits the stock material to flow easily. A slight angle L also contributes to smooth flow but is primarily an aid to stripping. The size of radius R_1 permissible on the die opening depends upon the piece-part requirements. It will usually be very small, in some cases almost nonexistent. The die opening should be made tapered —larger at the top. The amount of taper must not exceed the dimensional tolerances specified for the semipierced boss. The purpose of this taper is to facilitate shedding the boss from the die open-

ing. A very slight taper will serve this purpose. A common practice is simply to polish the opening to a very slight bell-mouthed condition at its top end.

At view A the shedding pin is installed in the die opening. At view B, externally located lifters perform the shedding act. Such lifters should be strategically located for balanced shedding and must not be situated too far from the die opening. At times it may be desired to set the height of the boss (H) as shown in view C. Here the shedder is made to bottom against a thrust plate in order to limit height H. A variation of this construction, using externally located lifters and a solid plug instead of a shedder, is shown in view D.

Semipierced bosses are sometimes produced in the manner depicted in Fig. 8·11. Here, the idea is to achieve a deeper boss D by displacing the stock material more effectively. The proportions indicated in the illustration are:

$$T = \text{stock-material thickness}$$
$$A = \text{diameter of die opening}$$
$$B = 1.3A$$
$$C = 0.5A$$
$$D = 0.8T$$
$$E = 0.7D$$
$$R = 0.5B$$

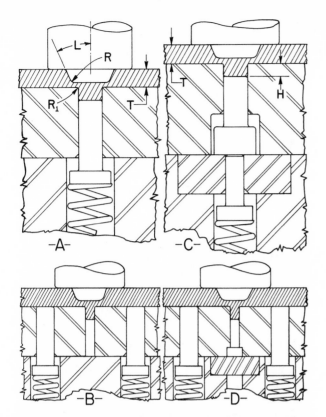

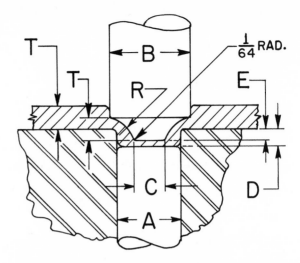

Figure **8·11** An alternative method for producing semipierced bosses.

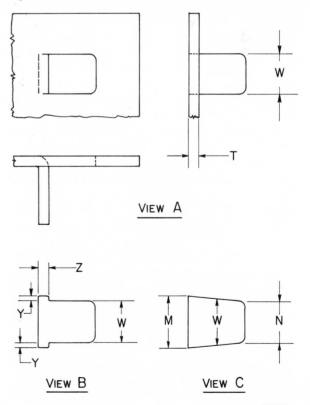

Figure **8·10** One method for producing semipierced bosses. Construction variations for shedding and height control are also shown.

SHEARFORMS

The term "shearform" is a very appropriate one: both cutting and forming functions are combined into a single action. The cutting and the forming are performed simultaneously by a single set of components (punch and die). Keep in mind that the forces engendered during the act of shearforming tend to stretch the stock material. As a consequence, normal bend allowances will not apply to shearforms.

SOME PROCEDURES FOR SHEARFORM DIES

A typical perpendicular shearformed lug is pictured in Fig. 8·12, view *A*. In this view, the specified width of the lug is indicated as *W*. The stock-material thickness is shown as *T*.

To produce this type of shearform, either of two proved diemaking approaches may be followed.

1. Stepped Opening (see view *B*). The cutting portion of the die opening is made the same width *W* as the desired lug. Two small opposing clearance steps *Y* are incorporated in the sides of the opening at the root of the shearform. The purpose of these notches is to facilitate shedding the lug from the die opening. Optimum notch sizes will vary according to the thickness and

hardness of the stock material. However, the following proportions will be generally satisfactory:

$$Y = \frac{T}{10}$$

$$Z = T + \frac{T}{10}$$

Figure **8·12** The die-opening contours in views *B* and/or *C* may be used to produce the shearformed lug shown in view *A*.

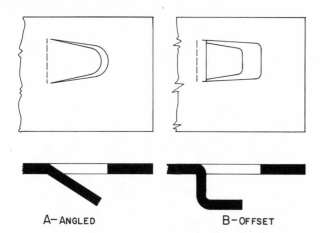

A—ANGLED   B—OFFSET

Figure **8·13**   Two very typical shearform profiles.

It is obvious that this procedure applies only for perpendicular shearforming.

2. Tapered Opening (see view *C*). The die opening is wider (*M*) at the root of the shearform than at the nose end *N*. Then, as the forming action progresses, the lug becomes correspondingly freer within the die opening. If desired, this method can often be employed for piece parts where the lugs are shown with parallel sides (refer to view *A*). This is done by taking advantage of the dimensional tolerance permissible for *W*.

EXAMPLE

W is specified 0.124 in., with a tolerance of ±0.005 in.

Make the root end of the die opening

$$M = 0.128 \text{ in.}$$

Make the nose end

$$N = 0.122 \text{ in.}$$

The above will produce a lug which is within tolerance and which has an included taper of 0.006 in., which is quite ample to facilitate shedding.

This type of die opening (view *C*) is not limited to perpendicular shearforms. It is employed for all practical shearform profiles (see Fig. 8·13).

It should be kept in mind that it may sometimes be desirable to have the shearforms cling somewhat tightly in the die openings. This could be desirable, for example, in an inverted shearform die equipped with a positive knockout. The clinging lugs would retain the piece part in order to permit it to be ejected at the top of the press stroke. An inverted shearforming die is depicted in Fig. 8·14.

A REPRESENTATIVE SHEARFORM DIE

Figure 8·15 is a partial cross-section view through a shearform die.

Construction and operation. To prevent rotation, the head of the shearform punch (6) is flatted and keyed (*K*) in a slot provided in the punch plate (7). A load-unload slot is indicated (*L*) in the die block (4).

Figure **8·15**   Cross section showing a typical shearforming operation. (1) Die set. (2) Lifter spring. (3) Lifter. (4) Die block. (5) Stripper. (6) Shearform punch. (7) Punch plate. (8) Stripper spring.

Figure **8·14**   An inverted shearform die.

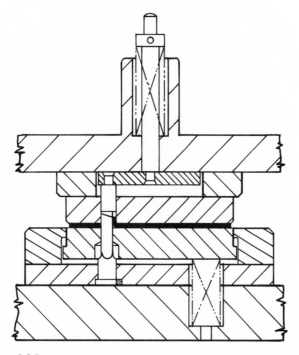

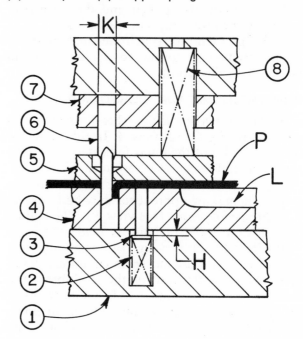

The die is shown in its closed position. During the upstroke, the spring-actuated stripper (5) and (8) will strip the workpiece (P) from the punches. This causes the workpiece to remain upon the face of the die block with its shear-formed lugs projecting into the die openings. The lifter (3) lifts the part some small distance H to overcome any slight sticking tendencies which may be present. (It is assumed here that the die openings have been either relieved or tapered as described earlier). This frees the workpiece, permitting it to be lifted out of the die.

A SHEARFORM DIE WITH PRESSURE PAD

The die design in Fig. 8·16 exhibits interesting construction features.

Construction and operation. Each die opening is created by a left-hand and a right-hand insert (4) and (5). Inserts of this kind are commonly called "split" die bushings. Each pair of inserts is contained in a yoke bushing (6) which makes the assembly a unit and prevents the inserts from separating when subjected to the cutting forces. These assemblies are mounted in a die plate (3) and keyed (10) in position.

In operation, the workpiece is loaded onto the pressure pad (2) and gaged between the pad guide blocks (7 and 8). The stripper (9) is actuated by greater spring pressure than is the pressure pad. On the downstroke, the stripper forces the pad downward until it is flush with the cutting faces of the die inserts. The stripper motion is arrested by the die-insert assemblies, and the shearform punches enter the die openings to perform the shearforming operation, as shown.

During the upstroke, the stripper causes the punches to withdraw from the piece part. (The stripper must be provided with a shedding pin to prevent the piece part from adhering to the stripper face.) As the pressure pad raises, it strips the shearformed lugs out of the die openings. The piece part then lies free on the pad face to be unloaded. A clearance step at the front of the die facilitates both loading and unloading.

SHEARFORM DIE: PRACTICE EXAMPLE

The die in Fig. 8·17 produces, by shearforming, a row of eight louvers in a formed panel. A detail number has been assigned to each of the predominant components of this die.

PROCEDURE

1. Assume that the illustration is one-fourth actual size. (Do not assume scales for any other illustrations unless specified in the text.)

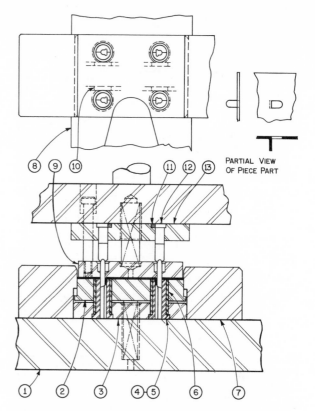

PARTIAL VIEW OF PIECE PART

Figure **8·16** Shearform die with pressure pad and split-bushing-type die inserts. The major components of this die and the number of each required are:

1. Die set (one)
2. Pressure pad (one)
3. Die plate (one)
4. Die insert, left hand (four)
5. Die insert, right hand (four)
6. Yoke bushing (four)
7. Keeper and guide block (two)
8. Guide block (two)
9. Stripper (one)
10. Key (four)
11. Key (four)
12. Shearform punch (four)
13. Punch plate (one)

Assume the stock material to be cold-drawn steel 0.048 in. thick.

2. Study and analyze the construction and action of the die.
3. Prepare a stock list, giving each component an appropriate name and stating how many of each are required.
4. Make an actual-size three-view drawing of the piece part, based on the views shown in the illustration.
5. Assign dimensions to the piece part showing the dimensions needed to produce it.

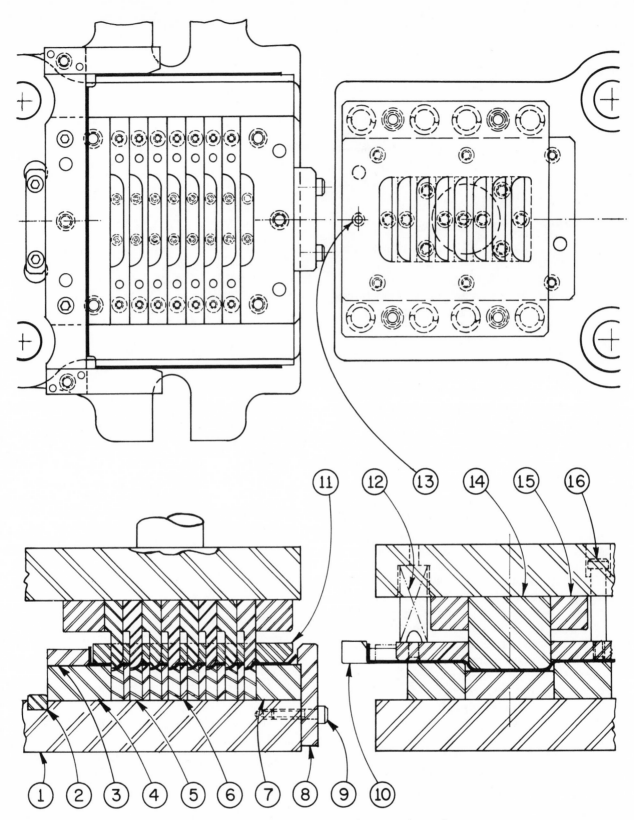

Figure 8·17   Shearform die to produce ventilation louvers.

110

Figure **8·18** The shearformed lug (*S*) is incidental to the primary piercing function of this die. This type of operation is sometimes called "stab piercing."

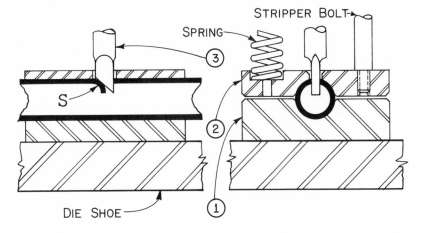

6. Make, to actual size, an assembly drawing of the die as it is shown in the illustration.
7. Make a full-size drawing of each component. Show as many views as needed.
8. Dimension the detail drawings—showing all dimensions needed in order to completely finish each detail ready for assembly. Also specify the kind of material from which you would ordinarily make each component. If the component is to be hardened, specify its hardness.

A SLUGLESS PIERCE DIE

The purpose of the die in Fig. 8·18 is to pierce a required slot in a tube. Instead of a slug, a curved lug is shearformed inside the tube as indicated (*S*). The curved lug results because of the natural curling tendency inherent in the shearforming action. This die does not have a female die opening for the cutting action. The punch cuts on air, so to speak. Actually, it is the resistance of the tube wall, supported by the die block (1) and the stripper (2), which causes the punch (3) to cut.

Do not assume that the work will be entirely undistorted. The tube may show some distortion in the area surrounding the pierced opening: the thinner the tube wall, the more pronounced the distortion. Remember, however, that piercing in this manner will be well suited for many applications.

OVERFORMS

For purposes of classification, some typical formed contours are pictured in Fig. 8·19. Those of the general type shown in view *A* can be considered as open forms, those in view *B* as closed forms, and those in view *C* as partly closed. The production of closed and semiclosed forms (views *B* and *C*) is commonly referred to as "overforming."

To produce overforms, it may be desirable or it may be necessary to preform the piece part before producing the final form.

A PREFORM DIE AND FINAL FORM DIE

The die in view *A* (Fig. 8·20) is a pad-type bending die. Its function is to preform angles *K* and *L* in the manner illustrated. The U-bending die shown in view *B* can then complete the piece part with angles *K* and *L* overformed as shown.

In view *A*, the pressure pad (1*A*) is retained by stripper bolts (2*A*). A spring plunger (4*A*) strips the workpiece from the punch (3*A*).

In view *B*, the pressure pad (1*B*) is a typical shouldered pad, retained by the keeper blocks (2*B*). The punch (3*B*) has a massive offset to

Figure **8·19** Some typical formed contours.

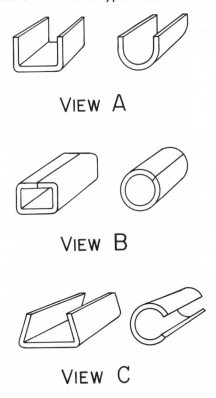

VIEW **A**

VIEW **B**

VIEW **C**

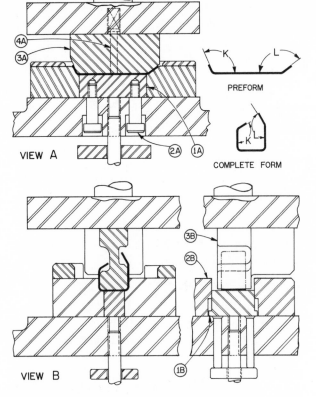

VIEW A

PREFORM

COMPLETE FORM

VIEW B

Figure 8·20   Two forming (bending) dies used to produce an overformed piece part, as shown.

provide strength and to supply an area in which adequate mounting screws and dowels may be incorporated. At its front end the punch is contoured as shown to provide the necessary clear-

Figure 8·22   A pierce die to pierce two angled slots, as shown.

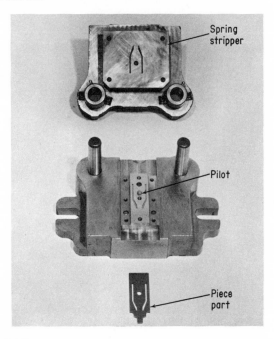

Spring stripper

Pilot

Piece part

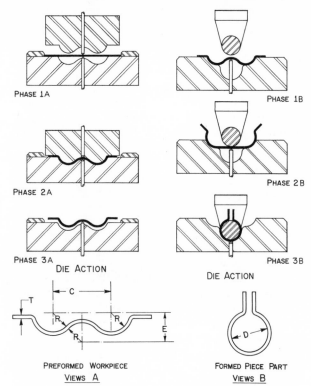

PHASE 1A

PHASE 2A

PHASE 3A
DIE ACTION

PHASE 1B

PHASE 2B

PHASE 3B
DIE ACTION

PREFORMED WORKPIECE
VIEWS A

FORMED PIECE PART
VIEWS B

Figure 8·21   Schematic, showing action of preform die and final-form die for cylindrical piece part. Dimensional relationship of preform to final form is also shown.

ance for the overforms. This die requires the operator to manually remove the formed piece part from the punch.

FORMING A CYLINDRICAL BAND

A two-operation procedure for preforming and finish forming a cylindrical band appears in Fig. 8·21. The views at *A* depict the preforming die, showing how its action produces the illustrated preformed workpiece.

In phase 1*A* the flat workpiece has been previously loaded in the die nest. The punch is descending, about to contact the workpiece.

In phase 2*A* the die is closed, at the bottom of the press stroke. The flat blank has been formed to the required preform contour, as shown.

In phase 3*A* the die is open. The stripping actions have been performed. The workpiece is ready to be unloaded.

The views at *B* depict working phases of the second forming die, which produces the cylindrically formed piece part illustrated.

In phase 1*B* the punch is descending, about to contact the previously loaded preformed workpiece.

In phase 2*B* the punch has entered the die, straightening the inversely preformed arc. Note that the ends of the workpiece have rotated up-

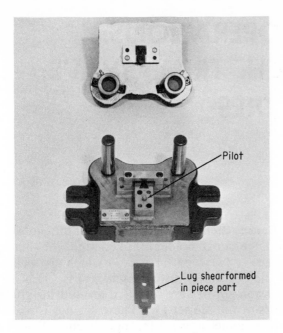

Figure 8·23 A shearform die.

Figure 8·24 A horn-type pierce die.

ward as the stock material slides along the concave arcs in the die block.

In phase 3*B* the die is closed, at the bottom of the press stroke. Forming is completed, as shown. After this phase, the punch ascends to its top-of-the-stroke position, carrying the formed piece part with it. The formed part can then be manually removed from the punch, or it can be ejected by a side-acting knockoff, whichever is appropriate.

Preform related to final form. The following relationships prevail for this type of forming:

T = stock-material thickness
D = inside diameter of final formed piece part
$R = D/2$ approx. (allow for spring-back).

To determine vertical center distance for R,

$$E = (D + T)0.707$$

To determine horizontal center distance for R,

$$C = (D + T)1.414$$

If $R = D/2$, radii will be tangent

If $R \neq D/2$, radii will require blending

For more detailed information pertaining to bending and forming allowances and construction practices refer to "Basic Diemaking."

The die shown in Fig. 8·22 has a spring-actuated stripper. The die block is composed of three sections which are fitted into the slot in the die shoe. This die is in the tryout stage. Its construction is not yet complete. Two gage blocks (to confine and align the workpiece) are yet to be installed.

Note that the workpiece of Fig. 8·23 is the same as the workpiece for the pierce die in Fig. 8·22. Thus, two different secondary dies are used to produce two different piece parts from identical workpieces.

The workpiece of Fig. 8·24 is a drawn cup which has a spherical bottom. This die pierces a small, round hole at an angle into the spherical portion of the drawn cup.

113

CHAPTER 9

SECONDARY OPERATIONS: DIES TO NOTCH, TRIM, SHAVE; SIDE-ACTION DIES

BUMPER-ACTUATED NOTCHING DIE

The piece part in Fig. 9·1 is a cylindrical tube with one end notched, as shown. These tubes were cut to their required length, after which they were notched in the illustrated die.

Figure **9·1** In this notching die, the length of the punch stroke S is not related to the length of the punch-press stroke. This enables the punch insert (10) to cycle inside the tubular piece part. The major components of this die and the number of each required are: (1) Center-post die set (one). (2) Spring (two). (3) Socket-head cap screw (two). (4) Hex nut (two). (5) Die block (one). (6) Flat key (one). (7) Socket-head cap screw (two). (8) Thrust block (one). (9) Punch yoke block (one). (10) Punch insert (one). (11) Stock rest (one).

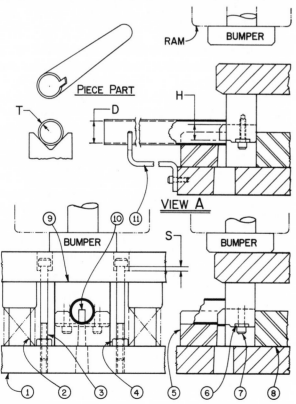

Construction and operation. In this die construction, the punch holder is linked to the die shoe by means of two long screws (3) which are secured at their required setting by locknuts (4). Compression springs are installed around the guideposts of the die set (1). These springs force the punch holder upward through distance S until it is restrained by the linking screws. The punch holder is not secured in any way to the punch-press ram. Instead, a bumper block is clamped in the press ram.

In view A the bumper is shown as it appears at the top of the press stroke. The punch assembly has risen through distance S, permitting the workpiece to be loaded in the die. One end of the tube (workpiece) is gaged against the front face of the punch yoke block (9). The workpiece rests in the mating concave surface in the die block (5) and is further supported by the V in the stock rest (11). Height H of the punch insert (10) is made smaller than the inner diameter of the tube (D) by an amount which will permit the tube to be properly loaded in the die. The punch insert is keyed within the yoke block. The key (6) is held by two screws (7) and serves also as a clamp to hold the insert in assembly.

When the press is tripped, the ram descends, causing the bumper to contact the punch holder and drive the punch assembly through distance S to its closed position shown in the lower sectional view. As the ram reverses its direction and ascends, the punch assembly is forced upward by the springs through distance S. The notched piece part is then unloaded from the die.

AN INVERTED-TYPE TRIM DIE

The piece part pictured in Fig. 9·2 was produced from square unit stock as indicated by the dotted outline. The illustrated die was required to trim the four corners of the piece part to arcs of radius R.

114

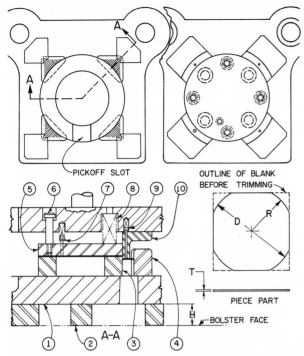

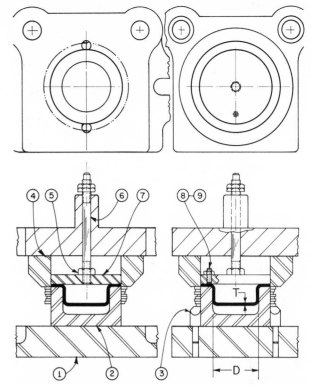

Figure **9·2** Inverted die to trim four corners. The major components of this die and the number required are: (1) Back-post die set (one). (2) Riser bars (three). (3) Punch (one). (4) Nest gage block (four). (5) Shedder (one). (6) Stripper bolt (four). (7) Shedding pin (one). (8) Stripper spring (four). (9) Shedding pin (four). (10) Die segment (four).

Figure **9·3** Inverted trim die with positive shedder and scrap chisels. The major components of this die and the number of each required are: (1) Back-post die set (one). (2) Punch (one). (3) Chisel (two). (4) Die ring (one). (5) Locknut (three). (6) Knockout shaft (one). (7) Shedder (one). (8) Shedding-pin unit (one). (9) Locknut (one).

Construction and operation. The scrap stock material which is trimmed from the piece part is indicated by the shaded areas in the plan view of the lower assembly. These pieces of scrap drop through the openings provided in the die shoe and accumulate on the face of the bolster plate. Riser bars (2) are screwed to the bottom of the die shoe. The risers elevate the die shoe above the bolster plate (H) providing space in which the pieces of scrap can accumulate. The operator removes the scrap from these spaces periodically—before the accumulation becomes excessive. Risers are employed for situations where it is not practical to attempt to pass the scrap through the press bed. Because of this, they are often associated with larger dies where the opening in the press bed is not large enough to encompass the area required for disposal through the bed. Obviously, the foregoing discussion is not restricted solely to the disposal of scrap. It can apply to the disposal of piece parts as well—if and when required.

At first glance, the die segments (10) appear to be punches, and the punch (3) appears to be a die block. However, it is evident by examination

that the four segments (10) create, in effect, a die opening. Radius R and diameter D on the piece part are sized by these segments. The cutting clearance is applied to the punch (3). Note the presence of the shedding pins (9). These are necessary because these scrap slugs will be quite apt to lift upward if shedding pins are not present.

A FLANGE-TRIMMING DIE

Trim dies are often required to correct contour irregularities which occur as the result of drawing operations. The die in Fig. 9 · 3 is one version of a trim die for trimming a flanged shell which was previously drawn to the profile which appears in the illustration.

Nesting. A cavity of diameter D is provided in the punch (2). Diameter D is made a gage fit for the cupped portion of the piece part, thereby positioning the piece part for concentric trimming.

Scrap disposal. To provide for scrap disposal, scrap chisels (3) are installed where and as shown.

These are hardened chisel-pointed members contoured to mount flush against the sidewalls of the lower punch (2). The cutting edge of the chisels must be a safe distance below the face of the punch in order to preclude the possibility of accidental contact between the chisel edge and the face of the die block. A layer (one stock thickness, T) of scrap remains around the punch after each trimming. Each added layer forces the preceding one down the punch walls a distance of T. This process continues until the lowest layer contacts the chisels and is severed by them. The pieces of scrap are then free of the punch and may be cleared away from time to time, when necessitated by the accumulation. The side of the chisel must be in contact with the punch sidewall in order to prevent the scrap from wedging between the chisel and the punch. The number of chisels required depends upon the cutting contour of the die. The chisels must be strategically located in positions that will free the scrap from the punch in order to facilitate the unloading of the scrap.

SHAVING

Shaving is a secondary cutting operation. The purpose of shaving is to improve the surface of a previously cut edge. This purpose is accomplished by removing (shaving) a very small amount of stock material from the previously cut edge. For unusually thick stock material and/or extreme accuracy requirements, more than one shaving operation may be employed.

Figure **9·4** Silhouette showing typical cut-edge condition of a piece part before and after shaving.

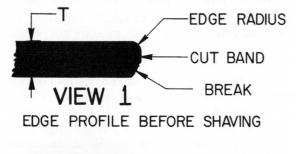

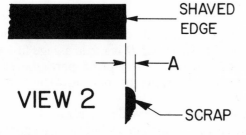

116

Figure 9·4 is a "before-and-after" illustration which depicts the manner in which shaving improves the surface profile of a previously cut edge. In view 1, the edge of a piece part is pictured as it normally appears when produced by a primary operation. This is the typical edge condition which is the result of normal cutting action. (Refer to the principles of cutting action as described and explained in "Basic Diemaking.") The edge condition resulting from the operation prior to shaving can definitely influence the quality of finish attainable by the shave operation. The better the edge condition before shaving, the better will be the edge condition after shaving. Before shaving, these edges should be cleanly cut, with a full break showing evenly throughout; double breaks and/or double cuts should not be present.

Cutting clearances. Cutting clearance for the prior cutting operation should be made at least normal or even larger than normal if necessary. This is emphasized here because it seems that the most common error is to use too little cutting clearance for those cutting operations which precede shaving operations. Cutting clearance for shave dies may be practically nonexistent. It is common practice to use fits between punch and die opening which are as close as possible without incurring interference. However, in cases where the shave allowance is quite large, a cutting clearance equal to 5 percent of the shave allowance will be generally acceptable.

View 2 depicts the edge condition after a narrow piece of material (A) has been cut off by a shaving operation. Note that the edge radius is smaller and that the break has been eliminated. The cut band now spans the entire cut edge from top to bottom. The scrap is pictured in an idealized manner for purposes of illustration. Actually, it will be distorted, for it tends to twist and curl. The distortion is due to the weakness of the scrap and the fact that it is not constrained laterally while the cutting action is taking place. It is an inherent principle of shaving that the scrap must yield in order to produce a clean shave. The scrap must yield enough to prevent the cutting pressure from instigating the fracture phase which is typical for other types of cutting such as piercing, blanking, chopoff, etc.

Allowances for shaving. The width of the scrap web removed by the shaving operation is the shave allowance (refer to A in Fig. 9·4). The following procedure will be generally satisfactory for determining shave allowances: Let

T = stock-material thickness
C = cutting clearance used for previous cutting operation (prior to shaving)
A = shave allowance for single shaving operation or for first shave when more than one shaving operation is employed
A_1 = shave allowance for second shave operation where two shaves are employed

Then, where the stock material is steel,

$$A = C + 0.04T$$

Minimum $A = 0.003$ in.

$$A_1 = \frac{C}{2}$$

Minimum $A_1 = 0.0015$ in.

For shaving brass, copper, and german silver

$$A = 2C$$

Minimum $A = 0.003$ in.

$$A_1 = C$$

Minimum $A_1 = 0.0015$ in.

The above is a generalized procedure, suitable for most shaving applications. Specialized applications may be encountered which will use either smaller or larger allowances than those indicated above. For such applications, the shave allowances are usually determined empirically: by association with similar applications.

Shaving direction. The cutting direction for a shaving operation should be the same as the cutting direction of the previous cutting operation. This directional relationship is illustrated in Fig. 9·5. Views A and B depict the ideal directional relationship of an external shave operation to the blanking operation which precedes it. At A the piece part is shown as it will be produced by a blanking operation: the burr side of its outer periphery is toward the punch. At B the piece part is shown as it should appear when about to be shaved by the shave die: the burr side of its external periphery is toward the punch, just as it was in the previous operation. It is apparent by examination that the cutting direction relative to the piece part is the same for both operations.

Views C and D depict the ideal directional relationship of an internal shave operation to the piercing operation which precedes it. View C is typical for piercing operations: the burr side of the pierced hole is toward the pierce-die opening. View D pictures the manner in which the work should be positioned for shaving: the burr side of

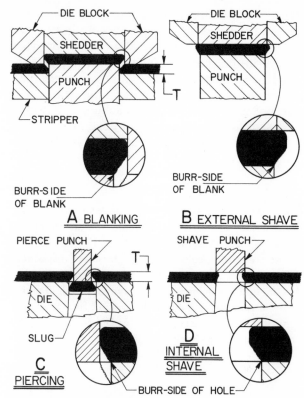

Figure **9·5** Cutting-direction relationship of shaving operations to prior cutting operations.

the previously pierced hole is toward the die opening in the shave die. Here, too, it is apparent by examination that the relative cutting direction is the same for both operations.

The principle of unidirectional cutting action applies, of course, to applications which require more than one shaving operation. The cutting direction for additional shave operations should agree with the cutting direction of the preceding operations.

Exceptions. Departures are sometimes made from the above-described practice of employing unidirectional cutting action for shave operations. One such departure is shown in the exaggerated drawing of Fig. 9·6. Here, the blank was pro-

Figure **9·6** A blank-through operation and a through-type shave operation in which the respective cutting directions are opposed.

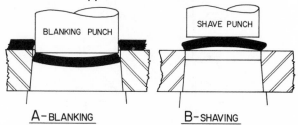

117

duced by a blank-through die (view *A*), which dished the blank as shown exaggeratedly in the illustration. The blank was turned over when loaded in the shave die (view *B*). In this case the underlying purpose was to improve the flatness of the piece part. To a considerable degree, this purpose was achieved. It was achieved, however, by a sacrifice in the quality of edge finish, which was the penalty of reversing the cutting direction for the shave operation. Actually, these two dies

represent a compromise situation. Both the flatness and the edge condition were improved in comparison with the "as blanked" condition, but neither flatness nor edge condition was as good as it could have been if more conventional procedures had been followed.

The poorer edge condition which results from reversing the shaving direction is related to the stock-material thickness: ranging from only slightly poorer for thinner stock to much poorer for thicker stock material. Stock-material hardness is also a factor. Softer materials generally tend to tolerate a reversed shave better than harder materials.

In brief, shaved edges produced by means of unidirectional cutting procedures will be superior to shaved edges produced by means of procedures where the cutting actions are reversed. This applies, of course, to all shave applications, including those where more than one shaving operation is employed.

Stripping. Be certain that stripping provisions are adequate. The amount of stripping force required for shaving operations may be double or even triple the force required for an equivalent blanking or piercing type of cutting operation.

A SHAVE DIE WITH SCRAP CHISELS

A very conventional shave die appears in Fig. 9·7.

Construction and operation. Upon examining the illustration, it is readily discernible that the configuration of shave dies has much in common with that of trim dies. In fact, shaving is a very special type of trimming operation, one in which a minimal scrap web is shaved (trimmed) from the edges of the piece part. However, shave dies are relatively more exacting to make because of the very close fits necessitated between punch and die and because piece parts which require shaving are quite apt to have comparatively stringent dimensional specifications.

On suitable occasions, shave dies may be mounted on back-post die sets. However, to provide more equalized guidance, shave dies will more often employ one of the following die-set types: center-post, diagonal-post, three-post, four-post, and floating-adapter die sets.

The die in Fig. 9·7 is mounted on a four-post die set (1). Always be certain that the die set provides adequate clear space for loading and unloading. Inadequate working space is more likely to occur in using other than back-post die sets. Gaging is accomplished by loading the previously

Figure **9·7** This shaving die is an inverted-type die. The shedder (7) is spring-actuated. Scrap chisels (5) sever the scrap ring at three places. These severance points are strategically located to facilitate disposal of the resulting scrap segments. The major components of this die and the number of each required are: (1) Four-post die set (one). (2) Punch (one). (3) Lifter (three). (4) Pilot (three). (5) Chisel (three). (6) Die block (one). (7) Shedder (one). (8) Shedding pin (one).

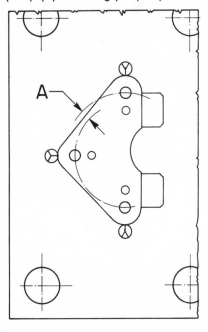

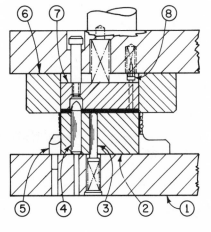

pierced workpiece over the three pilots (4) which are mounted in the punch (2). The centers of these holes in the piece part are asymmetrically located (refer to *A*).

For all practical purposes, then, the loading can be considered to be foolproofed. Either the workpiece will be correctly loaded, or else it will be visibly obvious that it is not correctly loaded. Before proceeding with construction, the diemaker should check and verify the orientation of the workpiece relative to the desired cutting direction.

Three spring-actuated lifters (3) are also installed in the punch. These serve to lift the piece part above the punch face far enough to facilitate unloading (but not so far as to interfere with loading the workpiece on the pilots). The scrap chisels (5) are conventional, made and installed in the manner described earlier for the flange-trimming die(refer to Fig. 9·3). The die opening in the die block (6) sizes the piece part and is made accordingly. The shedder (7) is actuated by springs and suspended by stripper bolts. A shedding pin (8) is mounted in the shedder as a necessary adjunct to the shedding function.

A COMPOUND SHAVE DIE

A compound shave die is shown in Fig. 9·8.

The construction. This die is mounted on a floating-adapter die set (1). The adapter assembly (1*A*) permits the shank to swivel, and the entire assembly floats in relation to the punch holder. This combination is intended to compensate for slight inaccuracies pertaining to the punch press. As furnished, these die sets are intended to operate with the guideposts engaged in the guidepost bushings throughout the entire punch-press cycle. To accomplish this, it is necessary for dimension *A* to be longer than the press stroke. It may sometimes be necessary for the top end of the guideposts to protrude above the punch holder when the die is closed. In this event, it is imperative to be absolutely certain that the guideposts will clear the press ram.

The stripper (2) is hardened. It must be very closely fitted around the entire contour of the external shave punch (3). These conditions are necessary to prevent the relatively wispy scrap from becoming wedged between the stripper and the punch.

The die block (5), punch plate (6), and internal shave punches (7) are assembled in a manner which is typical for conventional compound dies. Conventional perforators serve as internal shave punches (7).

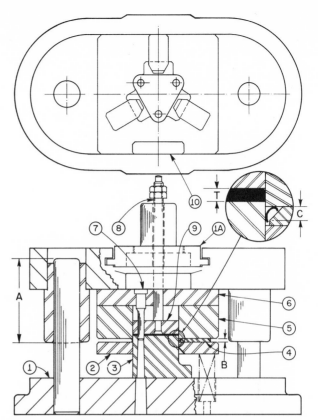

Figure **9·8**   A compound shaving die equipped with a spring stripper. This die is shown mounted in a floating-adapter type of die set. The major components of this die and the number of each required are: (1) Floating-adapter die set (one). (1A) Swivel-adapter assembly (one). (2) Stripper (one). (3) Punch (one). (4) Nest segment (three). (5) Die block (one). (6) Punch plate (one). (7) Internal-shave punch (three). (8) Knockout shaft (one). (9) Shedder (one). (10) Instruction plate (one).

The shedder (9) is peened to the knockout shaft (8). This assembly is retained by locknuts, as shown. The shedding pin does not appear in the illustration but is necessary, nevertheless.

The configuration of this piece part is symmetrical. Thus, it is possible to load this piece with its burr side up or with its burr side down. To aid in proper loading, an instruction plate (10) is installed at the front of the stripper, which states the manner in which the piece is to be loaded.

Nesting is provided by the segments (4). The resulting nest supplies maximum access for removal of the scrap after each shaving operation. The beveled nose on these segments facilitates loading and provides space for the shave scrap to curl away from the punch. One method, when practical, is to make the height *B* of the nest equal to the stock-material thickness *T*. Another

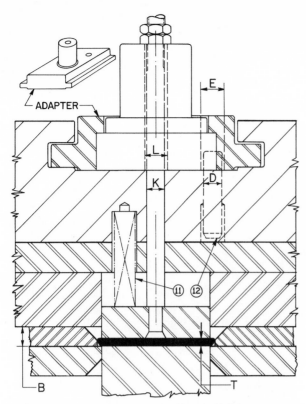

Figure **9·9** An alternative nest and shedder construction. This drawing also pictures the floating-adapter detail.

method is sometimes employed in order to provide a deeper nest. This method is to make

$$B = 1\tfrac{1}{2}T$$

and

$$C = T$$

If this second method proves to be unsatisfactory, the nest height can be reduced or, as an alternative, weak springs can be installed, as shown in Fig. 9·9.

A deeper nest construction. The construction shown in Fig. 9·9 is intended to permit the use of nests where $B > 1\tfrac{1}{2}T$. Light springs (11) are installed to ensure that the shedder will hold the workpiece in gaged position during the interval in which the workpiece is not confined between the nest gages. The illustration depicts the die as it appears during the downstroke. It is readily apparent that, as the die continues to descend, the nest gage will lose contact with the workpiece. It is also apparent that the shedder will hold the workpiece in place until the cutting action begins. Remember that strong spring pressure can be very objectionable when used in conjunction with

a positive knockout. The springs are not intended to assist in shedding. Their sole function is to ensure immobilization of the workpiece during the brief interval in which it would be otherwise unconfined.

As a general rule, the use of springs in conjunction with positive knockouts should be avoided. However, there can be exceptions to the rule, such as this one. These exceptional cases will have one feature in common: the spring pressure should be restricted to the minimum amount necessary for the purpose.

Restricting the adapter. Possible endwise movement of the adapter is restricted by installing a dowel pin (12) as shown. A light drive fit is provided in the punch holder at D. A clearance hole E is provided in the adapter. The clearance hole should be

$$E = D + \tfrac{1}{32} \text{ in. min.}$$

For dies which have knockout rods (or other components) extending into the adapter the clearance should be limited to

$$E = D + \tfrac{3}{64} \text{ in. max.}$$

A slip fit is provided in the punch holder and the punch plate for the knockout rod K. The clearance hole L through the shank is made

$$L = K + \tfrac{1}{16} \text{ in. min.}$$

The purpose of the above clearance relationships is to prevent the knockout shaft from binding. Large dies may need somewhat more clearance at L.

Restricting the adapter in a manner similar to the above can be a distinct asset in setting up the die in the punch press.

A PUSH-OUT DIE FOR SHAVING

The die in Fig. 9·10 is an internal-external shave die. Strictly speaking, this is a type of compound die. However, compound dies of this general kind are commonly referred to as "push-out" dies.

Die action. At view A the die is shown as it appears when in its closed position at the bottom of the press stroke. At view B the die is opening as the ram moves upward during the upstroke. The piece part has been stripped by action of the pressure pad (2). The lifters (7) elevate the piece part as shown in order to facilitate unloading. The two scrap bands are rising with the upper punch (9) to be ejected when the knockout/knockoff assembly is actuated at the top of the press stroke.

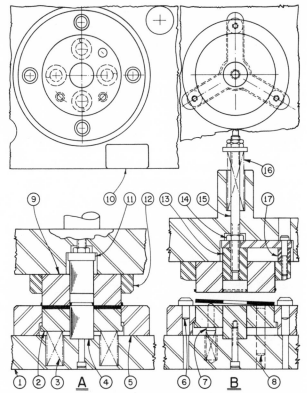

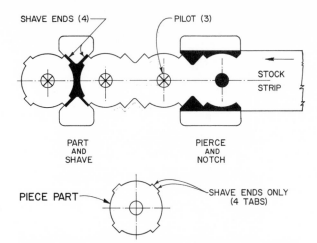

Figure **9·11** Strip layout for a progressive pierce, notch, part, and shave die.

Figure **9·10** This shave die employs a positive knock-out arrangement to remove the two rings of scrap from the compound punch (9). The major components of this die and the number of each required are:

1. Diagonal-post die set (one)
2. Pressure pad (one)
3. Spring (four)
4. Internal-shave punch (one)
5. Die block (one)
6. Nest pin (four)
7. Lifter (two)
8. Guide pin (one)
9. External-shave punch (one)
10. Instruction plate (one)
11. Spider (one)
12. Stripping ring (one)
13. Shedding plunger (one)
14. Locknut (three)
15. Knockout shaft (one)
16. Spring (one)
17. Spacer bushing (three)

SHAVING IN A PROGRESSIVE DIE

Figure 9·11 is a strip layout showing the operation sequence for a progressive die which includes a shaving operation. Note that the shave scrap is a part of the larger piece of scrap which is produced by the parting operation; that is, the shave scrap and the parting scrap are produced as one piece. This is an important principle which should be adhered to when shaving operations are incorporated into progressive dies. Satisfactory dies of this sort are made regularly.

Progressive dies which violate the above principle are notoriously troublesome. Unattached pieces of wispy shave scrap can be a nuisance and a hazard in progressive dies. Shave operations should not be included in progressive dies unless a practical means of scrap disposal can be ensured.

SIDE-ACTION DIES

Side-action dies perform work at an angle to the stroke of the press ram, commonly at any practical required angle. However, the most common direction is 90° to the direction of the press stroke.

The required angular motions may be achieved by the use of cams, toggles, bellcranks, pivots, etc., which are built as part of the die and which derive their motivation from the press stroke. Or the angular motions may be accomplished by means of hydraulic and/or air cylinders, where and when applicable.

Side-action dies are appropriate for many secondary operations. These include cutting operations such as piercing, notching, trimming, etc. Also included are bending, curling, and other forming operations. Side actions can also be incorporated in progressive dies.

A TYPICAL SIDE-CAM PIERCE DIE

The predominant features of a typical cam-actuated side-piercing die appear in Fig. 9·12.

The die-post assembly. In this die, the die post is an assembled unit. The pierce-die openings are

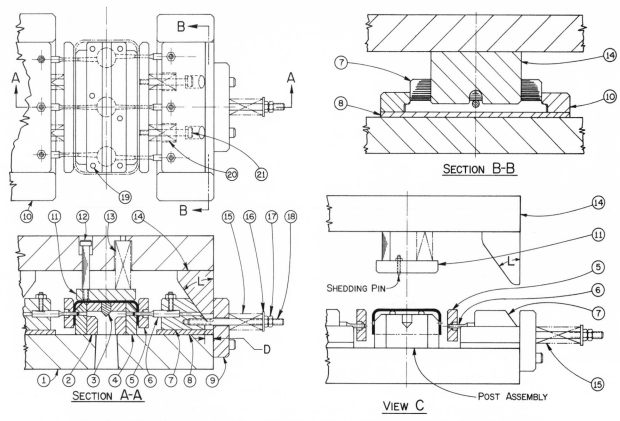

Figure **9·12**   A side-action pierce die. The major components of this die and the number of each required are:

1. Die set (one)	8. Bearing plate (two)	15. Spring (two)
2. Mounting block (one)	9. Thrust block (two)	16. Washer (two)
3. Slug deflector (one)	10. Gib (four)	17. Locknut (four)
4. Die block (two)	11. Pressure pad (one)	18. Stud (two)
5. Stripper (two)	12. Stripper bolt (four)	19. Lifter (six)
6. Perforator (six)	13. Spring (six)	20. Spring (four)
7. Cam slide (two)	14. Cam (two)	21. Stripper bolt (four)

contained in two die blocks (4), which are fastened to the mounting block (2). This construction provides die life by permitting the die blocks to be shimmed outward in order to compensate for sharpening attrition. The slug deflector (3) is a hardened insert which is contoured to deflect the slugs downward for disposal through the die shoe.

The slug deflector is a vital component of this die. The slugs could jam together and wreck the die if the slug deflector were not present. Slug deflectors or their equivalent are required on most side-action cutting dies. In those instances where they are not necessary, the fact will be obvious. Remember that inadequate provision for slug disposal is probably the most common error committed in the construction of side-action cutting dies.

The slide assemblies. The perforators (6) are mounted in the slides (7) as shown. The perforators are headless. They are retained by the setscrews, which act against a whistle notch provided in each shank. Note that a knockout hole is provided behind each perforator to facilitate removal when necessary. The strippers (5) are spring-actuated and are attached to the slides by stripper bolts (21). The stripper springs (20) should be strong enough to perform the stripping act without assistance from the slide-return springs (15). Hardened bearing plates (8) permit each slide to travel back and forth with a minimum of friction and wear. The bearing plates should contain oil grooves in their upper surfaces to facilitate lubrication. The slides are, of course, hardened. They are provided with shoulders (refer to section *B-B*) and are retained by the gibs. The gibs must be very nicely fitted, permitting the slides to move in the required direction only and preventing them from shifting in any other direction. The studs (18) function as drawbars. Each stud, actuated by its spring (15), returns its slide to starting position against its thrust block (9). Thus, each thrust block serves as a stop and retainer for its slide, in addition to its function of providing lateral support for its cam (14). The thrust blocks are, of course, hardened.

The cams. The cams must be hardened (this need should be obvious). Each cam requires a clearance notch to prevent contact with the stud. The notch should be made deep enough to provide for the anticipated die life. Cam angles L are most generally made in the range 30 through 45°. The optimum cam angle for a given application will depend upon circumstances pertinent to that application. A smaller angle yields a greater force advantage, and a larger angle provides a faster action. The distance the slide travels (D) is related to the cam angle L. The working portion of the vertical cam stroke S required to produce a slide travel of D is

$$S = D \cot L$$

The range of cam angles suggested above (30 through 45°) will be satisfactory for most applications.

Operation. At view C the die is shown open, as it appears at the top of the press stroke. The workpiece, a rectangular drawn shell, has been loaded in position on the post assembly and is ready for the press cycle to begin. The post assembly serves as an internal gage (pilot) to position the workpiece properly.

When the press ram descends, the pressure pad (11) contacts the workpiece, ensuring that it is seated on the post. This action ensures the accuracy of the vertical dimensions of the piece part. As the downstroke continues, the cams (14) drive the slides (7) in the desired direction. The matching cam and slide angles L convert the vertical cam motion to the horizontal motion required for the slide assembly. The stripper (5) is part of the slide assembly and moves with it. The strippers must not contact the workpiece before it has been properly seated by the action of the pressure pad (11).

After piercing, when the press ram is returning upward, the strippers (5) act to strip the perforators (6) from the piece parts. The return springs (15) act simultaneously to return the slide assem-

bly to starting (open) position. The lifters (19) elevate the piece part to facilitate unloading (see view C). In this die the piece part is unloaded by hand after the press ram stops at the top of its stroke. Another workpiece is then loaded onto the post, and the cycle is repeated for the duration of the production run.

This cam-and-slide arrangement is probably the general type most frequently encountered. It is a noncaptive arrangement; that is, the cam can be (and usually is) entirely withdrawn from the slide assembly during the normal working cycle. Spring actuation for the return stroke of the slide is typical of this kind of arrangement.

POSITIVE RECIPROCATION

The term "positive cam action" is used in reference to cam-and-slide arrangements where the slide is cam-driven in both directions. Positive cam actions are employed where space limitations prohibit the installation of adequate return springs. They are also recommended where there is any reason to believe that a spring return may not be adequately positive. This last reason applies especially to side-acting stations in progressive dies.

Some typical positive cam actions are illustrated in Figs. 9·13 to 9·15.

To resist reciprocating lateral forces, the cam (4) (Fig. 9·13) is slip-fitted against the end of a slot (at C) provided in the base plate (2).

Figure **9·13** Cam-and-slide construction and relationships for positive reciprocation. The major components are: (1) Die set. (2) Base plate. (3) Thrust cap. (4) Cam. (5) Slide return cap. (6) Slide. (7) Yoke block. (8) Clamp.

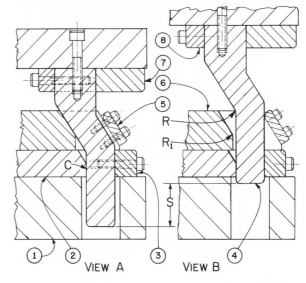

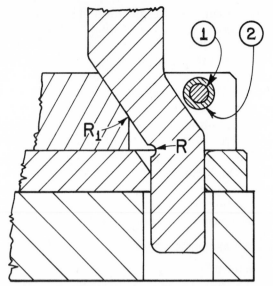

Figure **9·14** This cam acts against a roller during the return stroke.

Thrust in the opposite direction is absorbed through the cap (3) which covers the open end of the slot in the base plate. The slide (6) is returned by the cam action against the slide-return cap (5). The upper end of the cam is confined in the yoke (7) by the clamp (8). The cam is retained against the punch shoe by the socket-head cap screw as shown.

This is a "captive" cam arrangement. At view B, the relationships are shown as they appear at the top of the press stroke S. The cam is entered through the slide and is still confined in the base plate.

For applications where the force requirement is minimal, a clearance is sometimes provided at C instead of a slide fit. If this is done, however, be certain that the cam and its upper mounting are substantial enough to endure and perform adequately.

When making the arrangement, be sure to pro-

vide a slightly larger radius at R_1 on the slide than at R on the cam. To secure a smooth action, R_1 must be equal to or greater than R. Or, instead of a radius at R_1, a bevel can be applied to provide a clearance for R. This last method may be simpler in many cases.

The arrangement of Fig. 9·14 is similar to that of Fig. 9·13 except that the cam acts against a bearing roller (2) for the return stroke. The bearing roller is secured by a shaft pin (1) installed in the slide. The shaft pin should be of adequate diameter and should be made of tool steel, tempered to a hardness within the Rockwell range of C47-54 for toughness. Do not attempt to use standard dowel pins for this purpose. This cam shows a slight radial undercut at R to provide clearance for the slide corner R_1. This will permit R_1 to be almost a sharp corner. However, undercut R must be kept as shallow as possible in order not to weaken the cam.

In Fig. 9·15 the cam is made with an internal track which acts against a shaft pin to drive the slide in both directions. This pin must be free to rotate. As indicated in view B-B, the shaft pin is slip-fitted in the slide, which permits it to ro-

Figure **9·16** Side-pierce die with positive top delivery. The major components are:

1. Die set	9. Bearing plate
2. Die post	10. Pivot pin
3. Slug deflector	11. Pickup latch
4. Pierce-die bushing	12. Latch spring
5. Stripper	13. Pressure pad
6. Punch plate	14. Knockout rod
7. Perforator	15. Knockout spring
8. Slide	16. Cam

Figure **9·15** Cam with internal track.

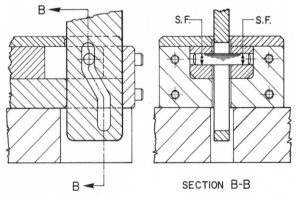

SECTION B-B

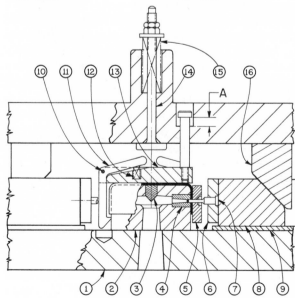

Figure **9·17** A side-action forming and sizing die.

Figure **9·18** A compound shave and repierce die.

tate. As with the pin described earlier, it should be of tough steel, heat-treated to a temper which is within the Rockwell hardness range of C47-54.

SIDE-PIERCE DIE WITH PICKUP LATCHES

Figure 9·16 is a partial section drawing which depicts the die in concept.

Construction and operation. This die pierces a number of holes in two sides of a rectangular drawn shell. The die is shown as it appears when in closed position, at the bottom of the press stroke. The pressure pad (11) is typical: actuated by springs (not shown) and retained by stripper bolts. Action of the pressure pad is the same as that described for the previous side-cam pierce die (refer to Fig. 9·12).

The latches (11) are assembled to the pressure pad (13) by the pins (10), which permit the latches to pivot. The latches are maintained in

stripping position (as shown) by springs (12). The stripper-bolt travel distance A causes the pressure pad to dwell, holding the piece part in position on the die post (2) until the horizontal stripping is completed. Then the pressure pad is carried upward, causing the latches to lift the piece part from the die post. As the press ram approaches its TDC position, the knockout (14) is actuated in the normal manner. The knockout causes the latches to swing open, permitting the piece part to fall free.

The die in Fig. 9·17 is an example of conventional side-action design as applied to a forming type of operation.

Figure 9·18 shows a compound shave and repierce die. The repiercing is a trimming operation which enlarges the required opening in the piece part while the outer contour of the piece part is being shaved. This compound action ensures a very precise relationship of the repierced hole to the shaved outer periphery of the piece part. The workpiece for this die was produced by the die of Fig. 4·21.

CHAPTER 10

DRAWING OPERATIONS: DRAW DIES

DRAWING IS A SPECIFIC KIND OF FORMING

When used in the fundamental sense, the term "forming" is generally descriptive of all noncutting stamping operations. Associated with this fundamental classification are drawing operations, which compose a large and important group of specific forming operations.

Features which distinguish some different kinds of forming operations are readily apparent in Fig. 10·1. Drawing operations are generally distinguished from other forming operations in that the sidewalls of a drawpiece are continuous: in drawing operations, the metal (stock material) undergoes plastic flow throughout a continuous contour.

Practically speaking, applications requiring

Figure **10·1**   Some different kinds of forming operations.

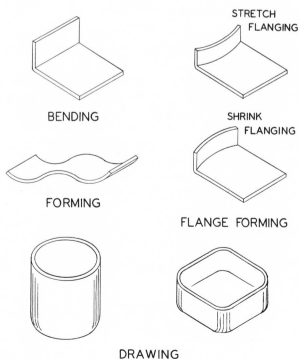

BENDING

STRETCH FLANGING

FORMING

SHRINK FLANGING

FLANGE FORMING

DRAWING

drawn piece parts are virtually unlimited. Their widespread use ranges through most fields of production—from household appliances to outer space vehicles. The size range of drawn piece parts extends from tiny eyelets to bathtubs and larger. It is necessary to produce drawn piece parts in a variety of shapes and contours. Some rather typical drawn shapes are depicted in Fig. 10·2, views *A* to *I*.

BASIC DRAW TERMINOLOGY

Certain basic terms are particularly related to draw operations and draw dies. A common understanding of certain of these terms is necessary. They are defined as follows:

Drawing. A process by which seamless vessels are formed from flat stock material (usually metal).

Redrawing. A drawing operation in which previously drawn vessels are drawn deeper and reduced in their crosswise dimensions.

Vessels produced by the above processes are commonly called "cups" and/or "shells."

Drawpiece. Any drawn piece part or workpiece.

Shallow draw. A drawn piece part which requires only one drawing operation (no redraws).

Deep draw. A piece part which requires one or more redrawing operations.

It should be mentioned that some diemakers define a deep draw as one in which the depth of the draw is equal to or greater than the narrowest crosswise dimension of the piece part. However, this definition is not generally as satisfactory as the definition listed above.

Draw radius. The radius tangent to the die face and the sidewalls of the die opening. This is the radius around which the stock material is drawn.

Draw bevel. A beveled contour sometimes used instead of a draw radius.

Drawn off. If the outer edges of the blank are drawn entirely past the arc surface of the draw radius and into the die opening, the drawpiece is said to be "drawn off" (see Fig. 10·2).

DESIGN AND CONSTRUCTION VARIATIONS

It is generally true of all types of dies that many different constructions and designs are not only possible, but necessary. Draw dies are especially subject to variations in design and construction. Some of the factors which will influence the design and the construction of draw (and redraw) dies are:

1. Size of drawpiece
2. Type and thickness of the stock material
3. Amount of reduction from workpiece diameter to drawpiece diameter
4. Production requirements
5. Type of press equipment
6. Types of materials from which the various die components may be made (such as tool steels, carbides, die bronzes, etc.)

It is not practical to attempt to describe and discuss these possibilities individually. Instead, it is best to study the representative dies, drawing actions, and reactions of the metal (stock material) as they are presented here. If an adequate understanding of these is achieved, the resulting knowledge can be successfully applied, by association, to other situations.

Figure **10·2**   Some representative drawpieces.

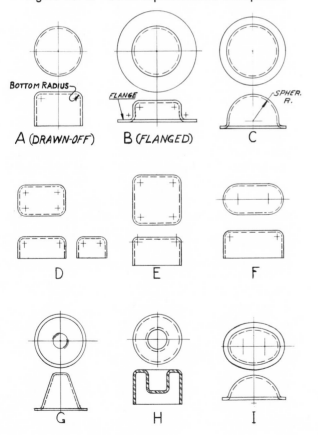

PLAIN PUSH-THROUGH DRAW DIE

In concept, the die in Fig. 10·3 is the simplest kind of draw die. It is a minimal die in construction as well as in concept.

Construction. The die set is not equipped with guideposts. A plain die shoe (1) and a plain punch shoe (5) serve as the die set. If a guidepost-equipped die set is employed instead of the no-guidepost set shown, the die will be somewhat easier to set up for production. However, a die of this type is very easy to set up, even when mounted on a no-guidepost die set. Therefore, the choice of die set is not critical and may be influenced by factors peculiar to individual applications.

The die block (2) contains the die opening through which the stock material is drawn. The draw radius R is fashioned in the die block as shown, tangent to the die face and the sidewalls of the die opening. The arc surface created by the

Figure **10·3**   A simple push-through type of draw die for drawing cylindrical cups. Dies of this general type, which are not equipped with draw pads (blank holders), are called "plain" push-through draw dies. The major components of this die are: (1) Die shoe. (2) Die block. (3) Nest. (4) Punch. (5) Punch shoe.

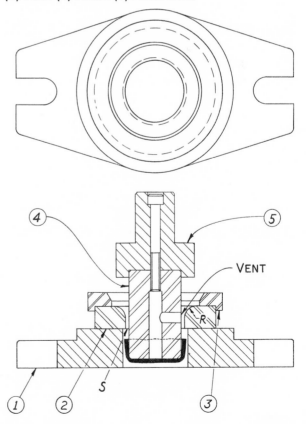

draw radius is continuous, extending around the entire periphery of the die opening. In order to induce an even drawing action, the draw radius must be precisely the same size around the entire periphery of the die opening.

The nest ring (3) is mounted to the die block. The flat blank is positioned by the nest opening. The diameter of the nest opening must be such that it provides the necessary gaging fit for the blank (refer to Chap. 12, *Nest Gages,* in "Basic Diemaking"). The nest opening must be accurately concentric with the die opening. Any eccentricity in the gaging of the blank will tend to be exaggerated by the drawing action. This can be a source of trouble, ranging from lopsided to ruptured drawpieces.

An important feature of the draw punch (4) is the air vent, which, in fact, is vital to successful die function. The die is shown as it appears at the bottom of the press stroke. When the punch ascends, the rim of the drawpiece contacts the base surface of the die block contiguous to the die opening (at S), causing the punch to withdraw

from the drawpiece. This stripping act depends upon the presence of the air vent for successful performance. The diemaker must recognize the importance of air vents in draw dies. Air vents must be adequate in size and strategically located with respect to the specific application. Check especially for interference—be certain that mounting screws, etc., will not interfere with adequate air flow.

Action of the die. For dies of this type the drawing action takes place in the manner shown in Fig. 10·4, views *A, B,* and *C.*

In view *A* the blank has been previously loaded into the nest. The punch is descending, about to contact the blank.

In view *B* the punch is descending into the die opening, drawing the blank around the draw radius *R*. The blank tends to react as shown. The material which has passed over the draw radius is in tension, drawing the outer periphery of the blank toward the center. The circumference of the blank is undergoing a reduction in size. This in-

Figure **10·4** Action of a plain draw die. The flat blank reacts in the manner shown. This reaction is referred to specifically as the "drawing" action.

Figure **10·5** Possible results when relative draw depth is excessive.

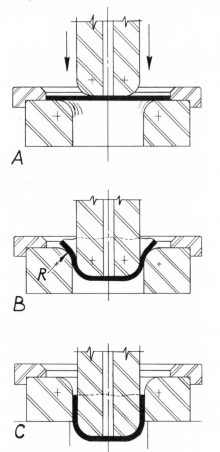

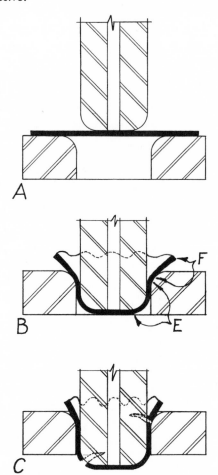

troduces compressive stresses in the material which is outside the draw radius. The combination of opposed forces tends to result in the flared condition shown.

In view C, as the punch continues to descend, the blank is drawn completely into the die. The drawpiece is completely drawn at this stage. Further descent of the punch produces either a wiping effect or an ironing action on the walls of the drawpiece.

After stage C has been attained, the punch descends through the die to its bottom position, as pictured in Fig. 10·3. The drawpiece can then be stripped from the punch in the manner described earlier.

Limitations of plain push-through die. Dies of this type are called "plain" push-through dies because they are not equipped with pressure pads which confine and control the flow of the stock material. Because they lack pressure pads, these dies are limited to drawing either heavy-walled (thick-stock-material) cups or, in thinner stock material, very shallow cups.

For cups which have the same diameter and the same size bottom radius, the blank size required to produce a shallow cup will, of course, be smaller than the blank size required to produce a deeper cup.

Attempting to draw too deeply in a single operation will require a blank diameter which is disproportionately large in relation to the diameter of the drawpiece. If the stock material is relatively thin and the diametral reduction is too great, the drawing action will result in conditions similar to those illustrated in Fig. 10·5.

In view A, the draw punch is descending and is about to initiate the drawing action. As the punch continues its descent, the drawing action develops in the manner shown in view B. As with any normal draw action, the stock material in area E is subjected to tensile forces, and the forces engendered in area F are compressive. However, if the blank is too large (in relation to the amount of reduction and the stock-material thickness) the area in compression (F) will also be too large. As a result, the material tends to wrinkle in this flared flange area. Wrinkling will, of course, cause additional resistance to the flow of the material. Then, as the punch continues to descend, the forces imposed upon the stock material in area E exceed the tensile strength of the material. Exceeding the ultimate strength of the material causes the drawpiece to rupture in a manner similar to that shown in view C. Such fractures may occur anywhere within the tension area but

are most likely to occur near the bottom of the drawpiece. It is evident by examination (refer to the illustration) that the maximum tensile stresses normally develop at the junction of the sidewalls and the bottom of the drawpiece.

Rupturing is often associated with wrinkling. However, wrinkling is not a necessary prelude to rupture. If the difference between the blank diameter and the drawpiece diameter is too large, the work will rupture even though it may not develop wrinkles.

Stock material thickness and stiffness. Stiffness is that property of the stock material which is evidenced by its degree of resistance to bending forces. It follows, then, that resistance to wrinkling is associated with the stiffness of the stock material. For sheet metals, the stiffness is considered to increase approximately as the square of the thickness. Therefore, if the stock material is relatively thick, it will resist wrinkling to a much greater degree than if it is relatively thin. Consequently, plain push-through dies are quite often used for drawing applications where the stock material thickness is $\frac{3}{32}$ in. or more. Plain push-through draw dies are seldom employed for stock material which is less than $\frac{1}{16}$ in. thick unless the depth of the draw is proportionately shallow.

PLAIN PUSH-THROUGH DIE: BEVELED

It has been found to be good practice to use draw bevels on plain push-through dies when the stock material is thicker than $\frac{1}{16}$ in. A very typical push-through die which has a beveled draw edge is pictured in Fig. 10·6. This design has

Figure **10·6** Plain push-through die with draw bevel.

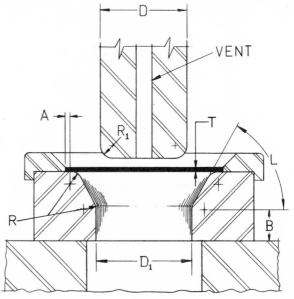

been found to yield satisfactory results where the following proportions prevail:

$T = \frac{1}{16}$ in. min.
$D = 3\frac{1}{4}$ in. max.
$D_1 = D + 2.2T$ to $2.4T$
$R = \frac{1}{8}$ in. approx.
$A = \frac{1}{8}$ in. approx.
$L = 60°$
$B = \frac{3}{8}$ to $\frac{1}{2}$ in.
$R_1 = 4T$ min., recommended for average applications

R_1 may be made $\frac{1}{64}$ in. or less, but the height of the drawpiece must be correspondingly lower.

Draw-edge proportions: push-through dies. Figure 10·7 pictures three typical draw edges in profile. These are a draw radius (view A), a draw bevel (view B), and an elliptical draw edge (view C). The views are partial cross sections, showing one-half the blank diameter ($D/2$) and one edge of the die opening. For plain push-through dies, the following proportions apply

Figure **10·7** Draw-edge profiles and proportions for plain draw dies.

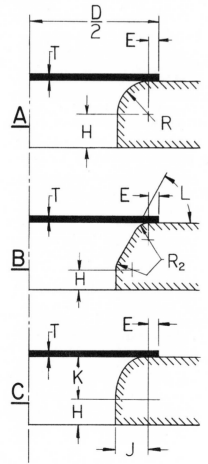

generally to all three of these draw-edge profiles:

$E = 3T$ max.

(Some diemakers simply assign an arbitrary minimum and maximum of $\frac{1}{16}$ in., respectively, for E, with generally satisfactory results.)

$H = \frac{3}{8}$ to $\frac{1}{2}$ in.

However, for smaller diameters and thinner stock material, a shorter H dimension may be desirable. Conversely, for larger diameters and heavier stock material, it may be desirable to use a somewhat longer H dimension.

The following proportions apply in a specific manner to each draw edge:

In view A, $R = 4T$, generally. However, for heavy-gage stock material, it may be necessary to make $R = 6T$ to $10T$. Conversely, for extremely shallow drawpieces, it may be necessary to make $R = T/2$, and possibly smaller.

In drawing heavier stock material, the required draw radius R may be so large as entirely to eliminate the flat bearing surface E. In this event, the draw edge should be profiled as shown in either view B or view C.

In view B, $L = 45$ to $65°$, depending upon thickness T and blank diameter. The degree of angle (L) decreases as the blank diameter and thickness T increase. For the tangent radii R_2 experience has shown them to be somewhat inversely related to the stock thickness T as follows:

$R_2 = 2T$ where $T = \frac{1}{16}$ in.
$R_2 = T$ where $T = \frac{1}{4}$ in.

Others are proportionate.

In view C proportions for the elliptical curve will generally range as follows:

$J = 2T$ to $4T$
$K = 1.5J$ to $2J$

Elliptical draw edge. On occasion, it can be desirable to make the draw-edge profile in the form of an elliptical curve, as shown in view C. This edge profile is employed in situations where it is desirable to give the effect of a smaller draw radius during the initial phase of the drawing action. Then, as the drawing action continues, the effective radius becomes larger, tending to ease the tensile straining which builds up during the act of drawing. The elliptical draw edge is a compromise profile. In effect, it is intended to provide a drawing profile which is directly related to the manner in which strains accumulate in the drawpiece during the drawing act. As a consequence, elliptical draw edges should be considered when difficulties are encountered in the development stage of draw-die construction.

SOME VARIABLE FACTORS WHICH AFFECT DRAW DIES

A great number of variable factors enter into the design and construction of draw dies. As a consequence, these dies are not made by adhering to rigidly established rules. It is impractical to attempt to define precisely the proportions and limitations pertaining to draw operations in a manner which will satisfy all situations. However, the following conditions are generally applicable for plain (no pressure pad) draw dies.

Stock-material thickness. Except for very shallow drawpieces, plain dies are not generally employed for stock material less than 1/16 in. (approx.).

Height of drawpiece. Where the metal thickness is 1/16 in., round shells can be drawn to a depth equal to one-third their mean diameter. In favorable circumstances, shells of these proportions can be drawn from metals which are 3/64 in. thick, although some wrinkling effects may appear at the open end of the shell.

Increasing the metal thickness will permit deeper draws. As the stock-material thickness increases, the possible shell height increases. With heavier stock, heights of three-fourths the shell diameter and higher can be practical.

The above proportions are based on the use of drawing quality steel, brass, aluminum, and copper and are conservatively estimated. If the combined circumstances for a given application are favorable, deeper draws than the above are possible. However, if the combination of factors is less favorable, the above height-to-diameter ratios may be difficult to achieve.

Rim condition. The rim of a cup which is drawn in a plain push-through die will be considerably more uneven than will the rim of an equivalent cup produced by a die which is equipped with a pressure pad (blank holder). And the deeper the draw, the more uneven the rim of the drawpiece.

Drawing speed. Plain push-through draw dies can normally be operated at higher linear velocities (faster drawing speeds) than draw dies equipped with pressure pads. Keep in mind, however, that the metal must have sufficient time to flow. Excessive linear velocities can cause the stock material to fracture. Different materials will have different flow rates. For plain push-through dies, some recommended maximum linear velocities are as follows (the materials are assumed to be drawing grades, drawn with proper lubricants):

Aluminum	150 fpm
Brass	200 fpm
Copper	150 fpm
Steel	55 fpm
Steel, stainless	40 fpm

Carbide dies will normally permit faster linear velocities.

Shallower draws may be made at higher speeds than deeper draws. As with all draw dies, the quality of finish on the die surfaces is vitally important. Better finishes permit faster drawing speeds. Heavier stock material requires slower drawing speeds.

PUSH-THROUGH DIE: FIXED BLANK HOLDER

A push-through die with fixed blank holder is shown in Fig. 10·8.

Construction and action. This die cannot be called a plain push-through die because it is

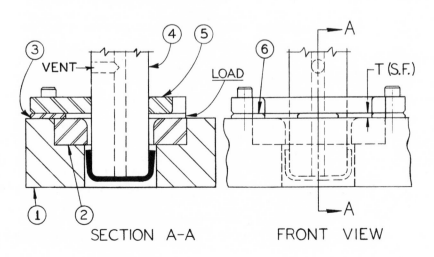

SECTION A-A   FRONT VIEW

Figure **10·8** Push-through draw die with fixed blank holder. The major components are: (1) Die shoe. (2) Die block. (3) Spacer and back gage. (4) Punch. (5) Blank holder. (6) Spacer and side gage (two).

equipped with a blank holder (4). The primary function of the blank holder is to confine the stock material during the act of drawing. The purpose of such confinement is to prevent flange wrinkles from developing during the drawing act.

The blank is loaded into the die from the front, as indicated in the illustration. Height of the cavity in the blank holder provides a slip fit for the blank thickness T as indicated. This height should be held to the practical minimum which will permit satisfactory loading while providing as much confinement as possible for the stock material during the act of drawing. The blank holder should be hardened (Rockwell C60 or harder), and its lower surface should be smooth and highly polished. Hardness and a high quality of finish on the undersurface are essential to the successful function of the blank holder.

Figure **10·9** Push-through draw die with blank holder (double-action press). The major components of this die are: (1) Die shoe. (2) Die ring. (3) Draw punch. (4) Blank-holder pad. (5) Nest. (6) Blank holder.

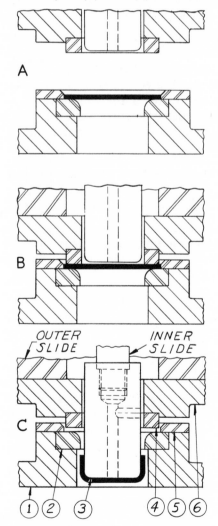

The die from which this illustration was taken was mounted on a no-guidepost die set. The opening through the blank holder was made a slip fit for the punch (4) in order to facilitate setting up the die in the press. The blank holder, in conjunction with the back gage and side gages (3) and (6), serves as a hold-down, securing the die block (2) in the die shoe (1).

In function, this die is similar to the preceding plain push-through dies except for the presence of the blank holder. The blank holder confines and directs the flow of the material during the act of drawing.

The fixed blank holder is not as efficient as an adequate pressure-pad type of blank holder. The presence of the fixed blank holder also makes loading more difficult. However, it is relatively inexpensive to make, and applications to which it is suited may be encountered from time to time.

Fixed blank holders can be applied to temporary dies which are made for development purposes. In such cases, the blank holder may be left soft. When applied to temporary dies the blank holder may be screwed tightly against the blank for each drawing operation. Doing this can simulate the effect of a pressure pad for limited development purposes.

PUSH-THROUGH DIE: DOUBLE-ACTION PRESS

A double-action press has two slides, one within the other. This type of press is ordinarily used for drawing operations during which the inner slide drives the punch while the outer slide actuates the blank holder. The blank holder slide (outer slide) dwells to hold the blank while the punch slide (inner slide) continues to drive the punch downward in order to perform the drawing operation. The holding pressure exerted by the outer slide can be regulated to suit the special requirements of individual drawing operations. In principle, the relationships of a push-through draw die to a double-action press are schematically pictured in Fig. 10·9. This is a common type of draw die.

Action of the die. At view A, the die is shown as it appears in its open position. At view B, the press is closing. The blank holder has descended against the blank, and the punch is about to contact the blank. The blank holder now dwells in this position, holding the blank against the face of the die ring. The inner slide continues its downstroke, causing the punch to draw the blank into the die opening. At view C, the die-and-press relationships are shown as they exist when the die is fully closed. Next, the slides move upward to their open position. Stripping is accomplished during the upstroke of the punch in the same manner as that described for the previous push-through dies.

STRIPPING PUSH-THROUGH OPERATIONS

Push-through dies often require additional provision for stripping; especially for thinner stock materials, or for softer stock material. This also applies especially to operations in which the sidewalls of the drawpiece are subjected to ironing effects.

Air-assisted stripping. As an aid to stripping, pressurized air can be blown through the vent hole in the punch. The air blast should be sequenced to begin at the bottom of the press stroke. If the use of air pressure is anticipated, provisions should be made for air-fitting connections. Consideration should also be given to installing a number of vents in the punch face and to their location. They should be strategically located to provide maximum efficiency for the specific stripping situation.

Latch-type strippers. One of the most commonly used stripping provisions employs side-acting latches to strip the drawpiece from the

punch. This method is generally very practical and satisfactory.

Stripping latches can be made and actuated in various ways. A very typical stripping latch assembly appears in Fig. 10·10. An angular surface or a conical surface (whichever is appropriate) is provided as shown on the nose end of the latches L (1). During the downstroke, the outer surface of the drawpiece contacts the nose angle L. This forces the latches to move outward, permitting the drawpiece to descend through the die opening. When the rim of the drawpiece descends below the latches, the compression springs (2) return the latches to their original position as shown in the drawing. Then, on the upstroke of the punch, the latches strip the drawpiece from the punch.

Two or more latches will be required, depending upon the individual application. Larger work will require more latches. The latches should be wide enough (W) to preclude any likelihood of tearing into the rim of the drawpiece. Radius N on the nose end of the latch should be

$$N = \frac{D}{2}$$

The horizontal upper surface of the latch should not extend into the die opening. Angle L should

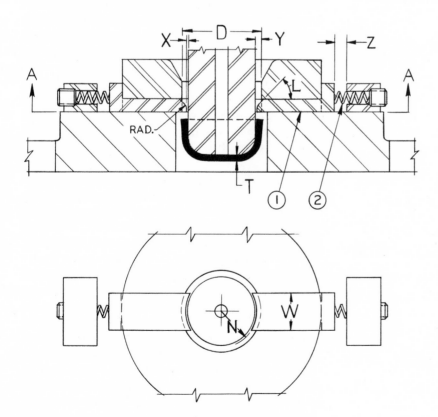

Figure **10·10** Push-through die with sliding latches for stripping.

VIEW A—A

be
$$L \geqq 45°$$

A small clearance X should exist between the latch nose and the punch. If the stripping area provided by the latches is relatively large, then clearance X may be made larger than otherwise. For soft materials such as aluminum, copper, etc., clearance X should be minimal. Depending upon the individual application, clearance X should be

$$X = 5 \text{ to } 20\% \ T$$

Be certain that space Z will amply provide for the necessary latch motion. It is generally practical to consider space Z as

$$Z \geqq 3Y$$

Latches should be made of tool steel, heat-treated to a range of Rockwell C58-64 and appropriate to the particular type of tool steel. The nose end of the latch should be highly polished. In some cases it may be desirable to chromium-plate the latches.

Stripping-latch constructions differing from this one are, of course, possible and desirable. The constructions will, however, be similar in principle. They will involve the same relationships that we have considered here and may be treated accordingly.

Figure **10·11**   Push-through draw die with snap-ring stripper.

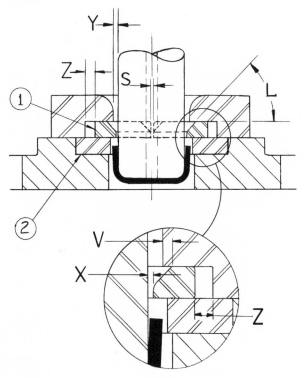

A Snap-ring Stripper. These are sometimes desirable for stripping thin-walled shells. They are not suited to use with heavy-gage stock material. A snap ring for stripping is pictured (1) (Fig. 10·11). The ring is made of tool steel, heat-treated to Rockwell C45-48. It is separated at one point on its circumference as shown (S). The separation allows the ring to expand, permitting the drawpiece to pass through it during the downstroke. After passage of the drawpiece, the ring snaps closed above the rim of the drawpiece. Stripping then occurs in the normal manner during the upstroke of the punch. A hardened bearing ring (2) is generally necessary to carry the snap ring. Angle L should be a minimum of 45°. Angles of 60° and higher are used more often than lesser angles. Space Z must be larger than space Y to permit the necessary expansion. However, space Z must not be too large. The following will be generally suitable:

$$Z = Y + 0.005 \text{ to } 0.010 \text{ in.}$$

Distance V must be large enough to ensure centering the ring. V is related to Z as

$$V > Z$$

The snap ring should not hug the punch. Ideally, a very small clearance should exist at X. However, for thin stock material these rings have proved to be satisfactory when their inner diameter is made a slip fit to the punch.

AN INVERTED DRAW DIE

Dies of this general type are very popular. One reason for their popularity is the fact that they perform double-action drawing operations in single-action presses. Figure 10·12 illustrates a typical inverted draw die.

Construction and operation. Press setup procedures for these dies will often be considerably simplified if the die is mounted on a guidepost-equipped die set. The die in the illustration employs a standard back-post die set (1). With the back-post configuration, the location of the guideposts permits maximum loading access, which facilitates the production operation. The punch (9) is fitted to a recess which is bored in the die shoe. The die block (7) is similarly fitted into the punch holder. This "set-in" construction ensures maximum rigidity and concentricity.

The sidewalls of the punch must be smoothly finished to eliminate the very undesirable effects of excessive friction during the act of stripping the drawpiece from the punch. The lay of the finish should be made parallel to the vertical axis of the punch (in order to agree with the stripping direction). Keep in mind that adequate air vents in the punch are absolutely essential to successful stripping function.

The inner diameter of the draw pad (3) is made a close slip fit to the punch. This fit should be nicely made. If the fit is too loose, the pad may float laterally, causing an eccentric relationship of the pad to the punch. The nest-gage pins (8) are installed in the draw pad. Consequently, any eccentricity of the pad will destroy the concentricity of the nest-gage relationship. The inner diameter of the draw pad should also be smoothly finished in order to minimize friction between the pad and the punch. The draw pad serves as a blank holder to control the flow of the stock material during the act of drawing. The pad is therefore subject to severe wear tendencies which act against its upper face. Therefore, it is necessary for this face to have a very smooth surface finish. It follows, then, that the draw pad should be heat-treated to the maximum degree of hardness practical for the type of material from which it is made. It is often profitable to apply a hard-chrome flash to the upper surface of these pads.

The die block (7) is subject to more total wearing effects than any other component of the die. The die block should be heat-treated to the maximum degree of hardness practical for the material from which it is made. The working face, the draw radius, and the sidewalls of the die opening work in forced sliding contact with the stock material. As a consequence, these surfaces must be finished to the finest practical degree. The die block must be provided with an air vent. The vent is necessary to relieve compression during the drawing operation and to admit air for the shedding action. Adequate die-cavity venting is vital to the overall function of the die.

Shedding action and construction are conventional and in accordance with the principles described in "Basic Diemaking." The shedding pin (4) is a standard, commercially available spring-pin unit. It is installed in a tapped hole provided in the shedder plate (6) and secured with a locknut. The spring-pin unit protrudes behind the shedding plate, requiring clearance in the punch holder. An annular slot is provided in the punch holder to clear the spring-pin unit. The annular slot ensures clearance even though the spring-pin location is not radially fixed. And the annular slot permits a better bearing condition for the knockout shaft (5).

The transfer pins (2) transmit the pad travel to the pressure source. The pressure source may

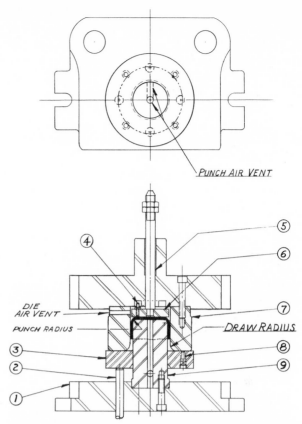

Figure **10·12** Inverted draw die. The major components of this die and the number of each required are: (1) Back-post die set (one). (2) Transfer pin (four). (3) Draw pad (one). (4) Commercial spring pin (one). (5) Knockout shaft (one). (6) Shedder plate (one). (7) Die block (one). (8) Disappearing pin (four). (9) Punch (one).

be a coil spring (or springs), a rubber pad, an air cushion, or a hydraulic cushion. Choice of pressure media depends upon the requirements of the specific application and is influenced to some degree by the type of press equipment which is available for the operation. Length of the transfer pins must be accurately equal in order to provide an equalized drawing action and to preclude the possibility of tilting the pad. A tilted pad can produce a severe binding action against the draw punch.

Action of inverted draw die. Figure 10·13 depicts the die as it appears during various stages of its cycle.

In view *A* the die is shown with the blank nested in position on the draw pad. The press ram is descending. The die block has just contacted the blank. The nest pins are depressed flush with the blank.

In view *B* as the press ram continues to descend,

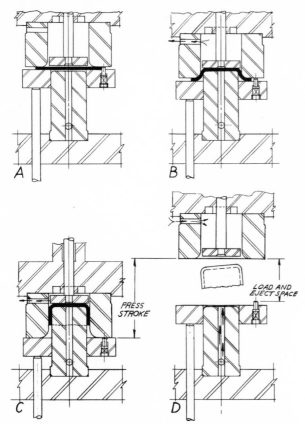

A

B

PRESS
STROKE

LOAD AND
EJECT SPACE

C

D

Figure 10·13   Sequence showing action of inverted draw die.

drawing action is initiated and proceeds as shown. The air within the die cavity is being compressed and forced out through the vent hole, as indicated by the arrows. Further descent will cause the outer edge of the drawpiece to draw around the draw-die radius. The die block will then further depress the nest pins and contact the draw pad.

In view C the drawing operation is complete. The die is shown as it appears when closed at the bottom of the press stroke. Note that the die face is in contact with the face of the draw pad. Also note the volumetric difference within the die cavity (view A and view C). In comparing these views, the need for die-cavity vents is readily apparent by examination. It is equally obvious that die-cavity vents must be large enough to preclude the possibility of any objectional amount of impedance to the air flow.

During the upstroke, the pad will act as a stripper, to strip the drawpiece from the punch. The drawpiece will then remain in the die opening and will be carried upward, to be ejected at the top of the press stroke.

In view D the die is in its open position at the top of the press stroke. The drawpiece has been ejected from the die opening and is about to be

disposed of by a timed air blast, which will blow it clear of the die (usually into a tote pan or other container placed behind the press). Or if the die is run in an inclined open-back press, the drawpiece may fall clear without requiring an air blast. Keep in mind, however, that many piece parts may require an air blast even when run in an inclined press.

The directional arrows at the die air vent indicate the return air flow into the die cavity which occurred during the shedding act. This return flow through the vent is essential to the act of shedding and must be considered to be indispensable to satisfactory die function.

The directional arrows at the punch air vent indicate the flow of air as it occurred during the stripping act.

Minimum vent-hole diameters for both punch and die opening should be:

¼ in. for drawpieces, 1 to 2 in. diameter
5/16 in. for drawpieces, 2 to 4 in. diameter
3/8 in. for drawpieces, 4 to 8 in. diameter

For larger drawpieces, the vents should be correspondingly larger—or install more than one vent, whichever is most appropriate. For smaller drawpieces, make the air vents as large as practical in proportion to the size and strength of the specific component.

DRAW-PAD FUNCTION

Paradoxically, draw-pad function is best illustrated by visualizing the possible results of attempting to operate the die without its draw pad. Figure 10·14 depicts some of the possible results associated with various stages of the die cycle.

In view A the blank is shown balanced on the nose of the punch. Removing the draw pad also removed the nest gage. It is, of course, true that some other means for nest gaging the blank could be devised. However, as this view serves to illustrate, the presence of a draw pad would have provided a most desirable site for the nest-gage installation.

In view B the blank is in the process of being drawn into its ultimate cuplike shape. Wrinkles are developing in the outer area of the blank. The wrinkling is due to the proportional relationship of the stock-material thickness to the draw depth, plus the fact that there is no draw pad to confine and control the flow of the stock material. The presence of the wrinkles causes extra resistance to the flow of the material into the die opening, which induces extra tensile straining of the material at the bottom radius of the drawpiece (N).

In view C the die is closed (at the bottom of

the press stroke). The drawpiece shows a fracture in the area of the bottom radius. The fracture is the result of excessive stretching and attendant work hardening, which was caused, in this case, by permitting the blank to develop wrinkles while it was being drawn.

In view *D* the die is open (top of press stroke). This view serves to emphasize another (and very important) function of the draw pad, that of stripping the drawpiece from the punch. In some cases, the drawpiece may strip easily and be carried upward in the die opening without benefit of a stripping action from below. In many cases, however, the drawpiece may cling very tightly to the punch, necessitating proper application of strong stripping force to remove it.

Primary function of draw pads. A draw pad is a specific kind of pressure pad. Its primary function is to control the flow of the stock material during the process of drawing. The primary function of a draw pad is the same as that of a blank holder. Draw pads and blank holders differ as follows:

Blank holder. Attached to a press slide; dwells to control the flow of stock material

Draw pad. Not attached to a press slide; must travel in order to control flow of stock material

The primary function of draw pads (and blank holders) can be correlated with the prevention of wrinkle formation in the stock material. By preventing the occurrence of extra flow resistance due to wrinkling, deeper draws are feasible in relatively lighter-gage materials. A draw pad can prevent the occcurrence of fractured drawpieces only to the extent that the fracture is induced by wrinkling. It cannot prevent fractures if the attempted diametral reduction (from blank diameter to drawpiece diameter) is too large.

Secondary function of draw pads. Draw pads are multifunctional die components, as described in "Basic Diemaking." Stripping is a secondary function of draw pads: a secondary function which is just as important as the primary function when considered in the light of overall die operation. Remember that successful stripping also depends upon other factors. The punch must be adequately vented. The punch must be smoothly finished. The lay of the finish should be parallel to the stripping direction. It is generally practical to taper the punch, making it slightly smaller at the nose end. Such tapers may be (and generally should be) very slight. Tapers of only 0.0005 to 0.001 in. per in. per side have proved to be effective as an aid to stripping.

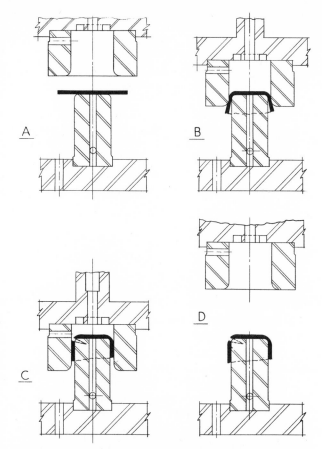

Figure **10·14** Inverted draw die with draw pad removed demonstrates necessity for draw pad.

NEST PLATES ON DRAW PADS

The dies pictured in Fig. 10·15 are equipped with nest plates. Height *H* of the nest rings and associated die configurations are related to the stock-material thickness *T*.

In view *A*, space *S* between the die face and the pad face is equal to the height of the nest plate (*H*). This is of course the simplest construction and should therefore be employed whenever practical. However, this construction is feasible only when *T* is heavy enough to allow heights at *H* which are adequate for loading purposes.

In view *B, T* is thinner than in the previous view. It is therefore necessary to make $H > S$ in order to facilitate loading the blank into the nest.

Nest plates and pad pressures. Remember that the act of drawing tends to produce an increase in the stock-material thickness toward the outer areas of the blank. As a consequence, if the blank is gripped between the die face and the pad at the beginning of the operation, the gripping effect will tend to increase progressively during the process of drawing. This effect is the result of the

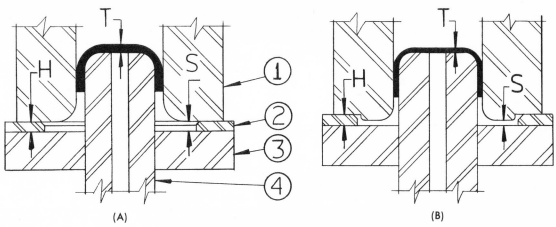

Figure **10·15** Nest gages for draw dies.

normal physical reaction of the stock material to the drawing process. It is not normally practical to attempt to eliminate the thickening tendency by means of pressure pads. Rather, pressure pads are intended to prevent the wrinkles which may develop as a result of this thickening tendency.

Another factor which influences the gripping action of draw pads is the source from which the pad pressure is derived. If the pressure source is a pneumatic cushion (or equivalent), the resulting draw-pad pressure can be regulated and controlled throughout the drawing cycle. If, however, the pressure source is a conventionally installed coil spring (or equivalent), the vertical pad travel compresses the spring, causing the spring pressure to accumulate. As a consequence, the resulting draw-pad pressure will increase progressively throughout the drawing act.

In Fig. 10·15, nest plates are related to draw pad pressures as follows:

Maximum Applied Pressure. For operations where maximum gripping effect is desired, space S is made equal to or slightly smaller than T.

EXAMPLE

$$T = 0.078 \pm 0.002 \text{ in.}$$

Make

$$S \leqq 0.076 \text{ in.}$$

Limited Applied Pressure. For many applications it can be desirable or necessary to make S slightly larger than T. For these applications, make $S = 1.1T$.

EXAMPLE

$$T = 0.078 \pm 0.002 \text{ in.}$$

Make

$$S = 0.088 \text{ in.}$$

If, in tryout, wrinkling tendencies are apparent, reduce S accordingly. The reduction should be made decrementally—by grinding small amounts from height H until the desired pressure balance is achieved.

Note that with the second method (where $S > T$) it is a simple matter to convert to the first method (where $S \leqq T$) if this should prove to be necessary. Also note that the second method can prevent the adverse effects of pressure build-up for draw pads which are actuated by springs (or the equivalent).

INFLUENCE OF BOTTOM RADIUS

The bottom radius of a drawpiece is the radius which is tangent to the inner surfaces of the sidewalls and bottom of the drawpiece (see Fig. 10·2). The bottom radius is formed by, and derives its size from, the radius on the nose of the draw punch. The size of the punch-nose radius strongly influences the depth to which a drawpiece may be drawn in a single operation. Practical draw depths are severely limited when draws are made over minimal punch-nose radii. This condition is visually apparent in Fig. 10·16. The illustration depicts two draw operations which are identical except for draw depth. Equivalent operation stages are shown side by side for purposes of comparison.

The operation shown on the left (views A to D) is a very shallow draw operation. It is successful in spite of the virtually nonexistent nose radius (N). It is successful because it is shallow. The fact that it is shallow eliminates the development of excessive tensile straining around N. The amount of stretch, and resultant thinning (view D), has not exceeded the tensile strength of the stock material.

This operation (views A to D) also depicts

138

some construction features which can often be advantageous for very shallow draw operations where the stock material (T) is relatively thick. These are:

1. Height H of the nest plate (2) is higher than normal. This prevents the outer edge of the blank from dragging across the pad (3) during the drawing act (views B and C). Of course, this also prevents the pad from acting as a draw pad. Therefore, this feature is suitable only for applications where the stock material is heavy enough to draw without benefit of pressure pad action.

2. The draw radius R is smaller than normal. A smaller draw radius is more compatible with the small volume of material which undergoes plastic flow in a very shallow draw operation. If, during tryout, the radius is found to be too small, it is a simple matter to increase its size. Keep in mind that it usually requires more time and effort to rework the die block (1) in order to make a smaller radius than it does simply to enlarge the draw radius. Therefore, if there is any doubt as to the optimum draw-radius size, it is most practical to start with a smaller radius and enlarge it, if required.

The draw operation shown on the right (views A' to D') is too deep in proportion to the size of the punch-nose radius (N). Therefore, the operation is not successful. The failure is directly attributable to the small radius at N, which causes the required contour change to be too abrupt in relation to the volume of material which must be drawn. The abrupt change at N causes the normal stretch condition to become severely localized. This, in turn, causes the tensile straining rapidly to exceed the ultimate strength of the stock material, resulting in failure, as shown in view C'.

Of course, there are other factors which can contribute to failure. If we assume that radius N is adequately large, then:

Draw radius R_1 may be too small, causing too much flow resistance.

Draw radius R_1 may be too large, permitting wrinkles to develop.

Pad pressure may be too great, causing too much flow resistance.

Pad pressure may be insufficient, permitting wrinkles to develop.

Nest height H_1 may be too low, permitting application of excessive pad pressure to blank.

Nest height H_1 may be too high, permitting wrinkles to develop.

Surface finish of component areas in contact with the stock material may not be smooth enough.

Any of the above factors can be a source of draw failure for any application. However, in the

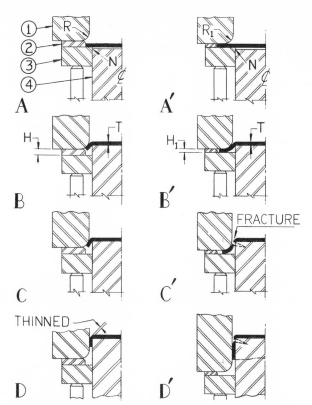

Figure **10·16** Comparative action sequences illustrating relationship of bottom radius to draw depth.

instance illustrated, the failure is due to the fact that the punch-nose radius is disproportionately small.

It is interesting to note that the depth of this attempted draw operation is less than one-half the diameter of the drawpiece. However, it must be classed with deep-draw operations in the sense that it could not be produced in a single draw operation. If overlooked, situations of this kind can be very undesirable, since they may lead to unanticipated tooling and production costs.

SOME SINGLE-OPERATION DRAWPIECES

Figure 10·17 depicts a range of drawpiece proportions which can normally be produced successfully from a flat blank in one drawing operation. These drawpieces represent an average. If all associated conditions are ideal, the proportions shown here may be somewhat conservative. If any of the associated conditions are dubious, these proportions could then be extreme. The associated conditions mentioned above include type and quality of stock material, quality and condition of the die, drawing lubricants, condition of the punch press, drawing speed (linear velocity of the press), etc.

This illustration can be a convenient comparison reference. It can be used in an associative

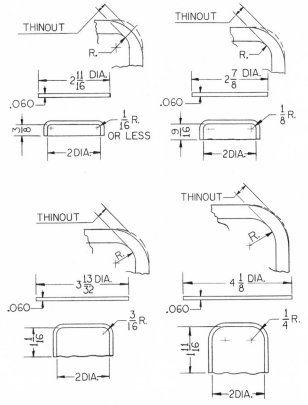

Figure **10·17** Comparison sketch showing relative proportions of a range of typical single-operation draws.

Figure **10·18** Schematic of inverted draw die, showing proportional relationships.

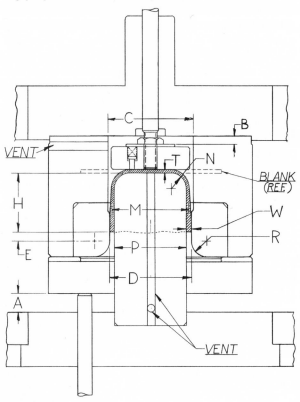

manner as a guide for a great many applications (on the assumption, of course, that an adequate understanding of the preceding text material has been achieved).

When referring to this illustration, especially note the relationship of the bottom radii R to the draw depths. Note also that the thin-out becomes more extreme as the size of the bottom radius R decreases.

OPTIMAL DIE AND DRAWPIECE PROPORTIONS

Figure 10·18 pictures a typical inverted draw die in which a flat blank has been drawn off. Important proportions and relationships are indicated by the various designations in the illustration. These are:

T = stock-material thickness
P = draw-punch diameter
P = inner diameter of drawpiece
D = diameter of die opening
D = outer diameter of drawpiece
$M = P + T$ = mean diameter of drawpiece
C = die opening relief
H = height (or depth) of drawpiece measured from inside drawpiece
R = draw radius
N = nose radius on draw punch
N = bottom radius of drawpiece
$W = \dfrac{D - P}{2}$ = space between punch and die sidewalls
E = distance from rim of drawpiece to center of draw radius
A = space under draw pad
B = space behind shedder

On the assumption that a maximum practical depth of draw is intended, then

$$H = 0.75M$$

This is an average practical maximum.

$$N \text{ min.} = 4T \text{ or } \tfrac{1}{16} \text{ in.}$$

whichever is larger.

$$R = 4T \text{ to } 8T$$

or occasionally larger; when in doubt as to optimum draw-radius size, start with $4T$ and enlarge, if and as proved necessary.

$$E = \tfrac{1}{8} \text{ in. min.}$$

Allow extra to permit enlarging R, if required.

$$W = 1.08T \text{ to } 1.15T$$

This dimension varies according to the stock-material thickness and type as well as according to the relative depth of draw.

$D = P + 2W$
$C = D + 0.005$ in. and up (in proportion to T)
A min. $= \frac{1}{8}$ in. or T, whichever is larger
B min. $= \frac{1}{8}$ in. or T, whichever is larger

The spaces at A and B provide safety and convenience for die setup and operation. For normal draw operations (similar to the illustration), the desirability of these spaces should not be disregarded. It is a misconception to assume that space B should be eliminated in order to spank the drawpiece in this type of operation.

DRAW CLEARANCE

Draw clearance is the space between the sidewalls of the die opening and the sidewalls of the punch. This space is indicated as W in Fig. $10 \cdot 18$. For normal draw operations, this space should be made equal to the stock-material thickness, plus an allowance. The purpose of the allowance is to prevent excessive wall friction and minimize the stretching forces which, if excessive, can rupture the drawpiece. Allowances will generally range from 8 to 20 percent of the thickness of the metal which is to be drawn. The specific allowance for any given operation depends upon:

1. Thickness T of the metal to be drawn. The allowance percentage of T increases as T increases. That is, thicker stock material requires larger percentages than does thinner stock material.
2. Type of metal (stock material). Generally, weaker metals require larger allowances than do stronger metals. This can be equated with the shearing strength of the stock material (metal) and stated as follows: The allowance percentage should increase as the shear strength of the stock material decreases. However, there are exceptions to this rule. For example, stainless steels normally require comparatively large allowances in spite of their relatively high shear strength.
3. Type of operation. It has been found that the draw-clearance allowance for redraw dies should be slightly larger than for first-draw dies. For sizing draws, the clearance allowance will be somewhat less than for first draws. Sizing draws are secondary press operations whose purpose is to improve dimensional accuracy of the drawpiece and/or secure smaller bottom radii and/or smaller flange junction radii, etc.
4. Depth of draw. For shallow draws, the allowance percentage may be made smaller than those required for deeper draws.
5. Diameter of draw. For a given draw depth, the allowance percentage required for a large diameter is smaller than that required for a smaller diameter.

NOTE

When the ratio of the draw depth to the diameter is such that the draw is considered quite shallow, the allowance may be eliminated, making the draw clearance equal to the original blank thickness. In Fig. $10 \cdot 18$ this would be $W = T$.

For most applications, the draw clearances suggested in Fig. $10 \cdot 19$ will yield satisfactory results.

In many applications the size of the draw clear-

Figure **10·19** Suggested draw clearances.

T	FIRST DRAW	REDRAW	SIZING DRAW
< 0.016	$1.08\,T$	$1.09\,T - 1.10\,T$	$1.04\,T - 1.05\,T$
$0.016 - 0.050$	$1.08\,T - 1.10\,T$	$1.10\,T - 1.13\,T$	$1.05\,T - 1.06\,T$
$0.050 - 0.125$	$1.10\,T - 1.13\,T$	$1.13\,T - 1.15\,T$	$1.06\,T - 1.08\,T$
> 0.125	$1.13\,T - 1.15\,T$	$1.15\,T - 1.20\,T$	$1.08\,T - 1.10\,T$

T = THICKNESS OF ORIGINAL BLANK, INCHES.

Figure 10·20 Draw dies of various types were involved in the production of these drawpieces.

ance can be critical, and, naturally enough, the more severe the application, the more critical the draw clearance. As mentioned earlier, if the draw clearance is too tight, excessive friction and attendant problems will appear. If the draw clearance is too large, puckering and other associated difficulties may arise. (Puckers are broad wrinkle-like waves which develop in the sidewalls of the drawpiece.)

The draw clearances suggested in Fig. 10·19 have proved to be generally satisfactory. If the draw clearance is in accordance with these recommendations and trouble is encountered in try-out, the trouble is more apt to be due to the following:

1. Pad pressure, too light or too heavy
2. The draw lubricant not suitable for the application
3. Poor surface finish on die components
4. Draw radius—too large or too small
5. Punch-nose radius—usually too small
6. Attempted reduction too great
7. Type and/or condition of stock material

DRAWING OPERATIONS: REDRAW DIES COMBINATION DIES

REDRAW DIES

As defined earlier, redrawing is a drawing operation in which previously drawn vessels are drawn deeper and reduced in their crosswise dimensions. Basic types of redraw operations are shown in comparison in Fig. 11·1. In each upper view, the workpiece (which is a previously drawn cup, as stated above) is shown as loaded in the die. The respective press rams are descending, and the work (drawing act) is about to begin. In each lower view, the dies are closed (bottom of press stroke). The respective drawpieces have been redrawn in the manner indicated in each view.

The simplest type of redraw die, the plain push-through die, is shown in view A. Its basic components are the die block (1), nest gage (2), and punch (3). This type is desirable from the die-cost standpoint but is limited to relatively heavy stock material and/or comparatively small reductions.

The double-action push-through die shown in view B is operated in a double-action press. It employs redraw sleeves (4) which are actuated by the blank-holder slide of the double-action press. This type of die can very successfully redraw light-gage stock material and is capable of producing maximum practical reductions.

The inverted redraw die shown in view C per-

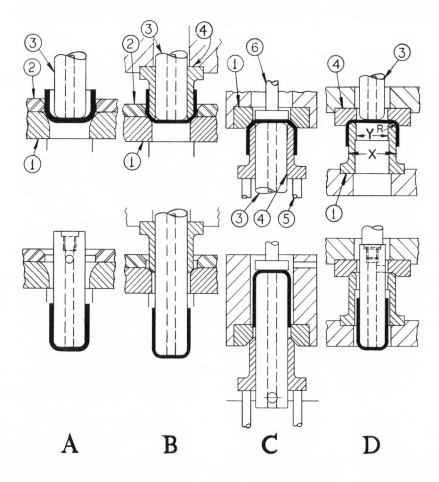

Figure 11·1 Comparison sketch typifying various basic redraw dies. View A: Plain push-through die. View B: Double-action push-through die. View C: Inverted redraw die. View D: Die to perform reverse drawing. The main components are: (1) Die block. (2) Nest gage. (3) Punch. (4) Redraw sleeves.

A   B   C   D

forms the double-action type of redraws in a single-action press. The redraw sleeve (4) may be actuated via the transfer pins (5) by an air cushion, hydraulic cushion, spring, etc. Such dies are quite versatile. They can be employed for light-gage stock material and are capable of performing maximum practical reductions.

"Reverse" redrawing is defined as a redraw operation performed in the direction opposite to the draw direction of the preceding operation. The workpiece, a previously drawn cup, is loaded on the die block (1) (view D). The blank holder (4) descends as shown to confine the flow of the stock material around the draw radius R. Then, as the punch (3) continues to descend, the workpiece is turned inside out, producing the draw-piece as shown in the lower view. Because of this action, these dies are often referred to as "inside-out dies."

Aluminum, brass, copper, and steel of the types most commonly in use have similar reactions to being drawn. They require decreasing amounts of deformation for successive draws. However, some other materials (for example, austenitic steels of the 17 to 25 percent chromium nickel-free variety) may require a very moderate first draw, followed by redraws of increased severity. Reverse redrawing is well suited to materials of the latter sort where severe redraws are necessary. This is true because very high reductions are possible with reversed redraws. In fact, the reductions must be large in order to afford adequate die wall thickness. When referring to the die block (1), it is readily apparent that, if the difference between diameters X and Y is slight, the resulting die wall will be too thin and weak to successfully contain the forces exerted against the wall during the act of drawing.

A TYPICAL PUSH-THROUGH REDRAW DIE

A die construction which is quite typical for push-through redraw dies appears in Fig. 11·2. Details of its construction are as follows.

The die set (1) may be equipped with guideposts, or it may be a no-guidepost die set. The choice will depend upon specific circumstances pertaining to the particular situation. The press stroke must be quite long to accomplish the operation. This fact must be considered in relation to the die set. If guideposts are used which are long enough to be engaged in the guidepost bushings before the work begins, they will extend above the top of the punch holder when the die is in the closed position. This can be done only if the guideposts are located outside the area of the press ram. Always check and be certain that there will be no interference of any sort between the guideposts and the punch press.

Another approach is to make the guideposts a safe amount shorter than the shut height of the die. Then there is no danger of interference, and the guideposts will still serve to facilitate die set-up in the press. They will also serve to unitize and protect the die for storage, etc. (Refer to Chap. 16, *Die Sets,* in "Basic Diemaking.")

It is not practical to attempt to designate one die-set type as generally superior for redraw applications. Different applications will require different die sets, and it will often be desirable and/or necessary to use special die sets for redraw dies.

The socket-head cap screw (2) retains the punch. Of the next two punch constructions (3), the first calls for a plain punch which is set into a fitted counterbore provided in the punch holder and retained by a single screw (2). In the alternative construction, which is indicated by the dotted lines, the punch is made with an integral flanged

Figure 11·2 Plain push-through type redraw die (single-action). The major components are: (1) Die set. (2) Socket-head cap screw. (3) Draw punch. (4) Nest gage. (5) Draw-die ring. (6) Yoke. (7) Spring-retainer block. (8) Spring. (9) Stripping latch. (10) Dowel. (11) Screws.

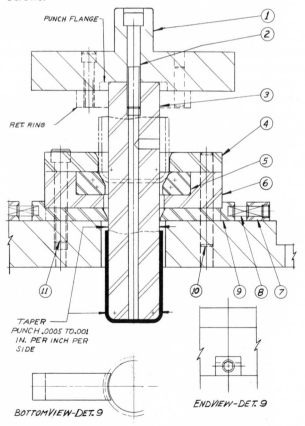

PUNCH FLANGE

RET. RING

TAPER PUNCH .0005 TO .001 IN. PER INCH PER SIDE

BOTTOM VIEW-DET. 9

END VIEW-DET. 9

144

head and secured by a retainer ring, as shown. The material from which the punch is made should be selected to be suitable for the type of stock material being redrawn. This is also influenced by the production requirements (high production, low production, etc.). The punch must be adequately vented and very smoothly finished in the manner described for various draw dies earlier in this text. Note the slight taper provided on the punch in order to facilitate the stripping action.

The nest gage (4) positions the workpiece in its required concentric relationship to the die. The nest plate must be deep enough to ensure that the workpiece will not be loaded in a tilted attitude. The nest plate also serves as a retainer, securing the draw-die ring (5) into its yoke (6).

Material for the die ring (5) must be compatible with the specific application. Range of materials for draw-die rings can include special cast irons, die bronzes, tool steels (including graphitic types), and sintered carbides. Choice of material for the die ring will depend upon the type of stock material being drawn, severity of the operation, size of the drawpiece, quantity of production, etc.

The manner in which the die ring is fitted into the yoke depends upon the individual application. Fits can range from a wring fit through shrink fits. Choice of fit will be influenced by the physical proportions of the die ring and the material from which it is made. The severity of the draw operation can also influence the type of fit— heavier work generally requires more massive die proportions and may require heavier fits.

The draw-edge profile may be any of those described earlier, draw radius, draw bevel, ellipse, depending upon which is deemed most appropriate for the specific application. The illustration shows a beveled draw edge. This type of edge was employed here because it minimized the severity of the plastic flow required for the reduction in this specific application. This is often the case with redraw operations. Keep in mind, however, that wrinkling is more likely to occur in conjunction with a draw bevel than with a draw radius.

The yoke (6) contains the die ring. It also provides a mounting for the nest and acts as a housing for the stripping latches. Yokes may be made of a variety of steels, depending upon their desirability for the specific set of circumstances. A good general choice is an alloy steel, heat-treated to provide toughness.

The spring-retainer block (7) for the spring (8) is usually made of cold-drawn steel, as a matter of convenience. The stripping latches (9) should be made in accordance with the earlier discussion

under the heading "Latch-type Strippers." Two dowels (10) are required. The screws (11) and dowels (10) should be installed in accordance with practices described in "Basic Diemaking."

DOUBLE-ACTION REDRAW DIES

The push-through type of redraw dies for double-action redrawing are very similar to single-action push-through dies such as the die we have just considered. The basic difference exists in the fact that double-action dies require redraw sleeves (see view B, Fig. 11·1).

The redraw sleeve in a double-action push-through die derives its actuation from the outer (blank-holder) slide of the double-action punch press and must be adapted to this slide. The punch is actuated by the inner (punch) slide of the press and must be adapted to this slide. As a consequence, both the punch and the redraw sleeve must be made to suit the requirements dictated by the specific press equipment associated with the operation.

INVERTED REDRAW DIES

Some representative inverted redraw-die assemblies appear in Figs. 11·3 to 11·6.

In Fig. 11·3, typically speaking, the construction is most appropriate for smaller dies. The draw punch (4) is a pedestal-type punch, which is inherently stable. Its integral base flange provides

Figure **11·3** A very typical inverted redraw die. The pressure pad (5) acts internally with respect to the workpiece, which is a previously drawn cup. These pressure pads are called "redraw sleeves." The main components are: (1) Die set. (2) Pressure-transfer pins. (3) Mounting screws. (4) Draw punch. (5) Redraw sleeve. (6) Die block. (7) Dowel. (8) Shedder-knockout. (9) Locknuts. (10) Socket-head cap screw. (11) Shedding pin.

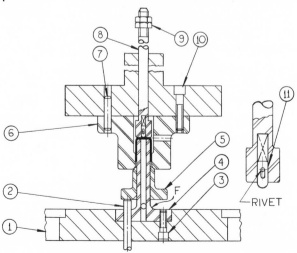

an area of surface in which the mounting screws (3) are conveniently and effectively installed.

The die block, too (6), has a pedestal-type configuration. The die-block flange extends well outside the area covered by the shank of the punch shoe. This facilitates die construction by eliminating possible interference between the shank and the mounting screws and dowels (7) and (10). The relatively large base area contributes significantly to the stability of the die block in assembly.

The integral flange on the redraw sleeve (5) strengthens the sleeve and increases its base area. This base area permits a most practical installation of the pressure-transfer pins (2). The sleeve should be countersunk as shown (from its bottom surface) to clear the punch fillet F.

The shedder-knockout (8) is a one-piece unit. The locknuts (9) stop the downward motion of the shedder after ejection, keeping the shedder within the die opening. The one-piece shedder-knockout construction is very often the most practical one for smaller dies. The shedding pin (11) is made and installed as shown in the enlarged partial view. It is retained by a soft rivet, installed crosswise.

Redraw dies often require special die sets, special adapters, etc. (This, of course, is true for all kinds of draw dies.) The die in Fig. 11·4 is a redraw die which employs a special adapter instead of a more standard punch shoe. This adapter (1) is, in effect, a special punch shoe. It is made of cast iron. The shank is cast as an integral part of the adapter. The insert-type die ring (4) is fitted into the counterbore provided in the adapter. The die ring is retained by a clamp ring (2), which is

assembled to the adapter by the socket-head cap screws (3). The knockout shaft (8) is threadedly engaged in the shedder (7) and secured by a locknut. Although the shedding pin does not appear in the illustration, it should be incorporated in the shedder in the course of making the die. The shedder face is made concave, with a radius at N_1. This practice is associated with draw dies for light-gage stock material, especially where the radius N on the punch nose is relatively large. The shedder radius N_1 supports the stock material to prevent a possible collapse of the drawpiece in this area during the shedding stroke. Size of radius N_1 should be

$$N_1 = N + T$$

It is not normally necessary to allow for thinning of the stock material in determining the size of radius N_1.

Adapters similar to this one are often made of machine steel. These, in turn, are very often made as weldments assembled from two or more pieces welded together. Adapters of this general type are often very appropriate for large dies. Whether the adapter should be a weldment or a casting will depend upon the specific set of circumstances which pertain to the individual application.

The construction pictured in Fig. 11·5 is appropriate for a large die.

The construction. The draw-die ring (12) is conventionally fitted to a counterbored pocket in the adapter unit and is retained in assembly by a clamp ring (11). The adapter unit is a weldment, composed of a cylinder (10B), two end rings (10A) and (10D), and four supporting ribs (10C). The cylinder (10B) can often be made from a section of seamless mechanical tubing. The end rings (10A) and (10D) can be made from hollow cylindrical stock, or they can be of torch-cut plate, whichever is most appropriate. The support ribs (10C) will usually be made from cold-drawn steel. The number of ribs required for a given die will vary with the size of the die: the larger the dies, the greater the number of ribs. These separate items are assembled together, as shown, and welded. The weldment is screwed and doweled to the punch shoe, as shown. Do not forget the air vent!

The transfer pins (2) are generally made from cold-drawn steel, ground shafting (alloy steel), or drill rod, whichever is most appropriate for the particular application. The number of pins required will vary according to the size of the die: the larger the dies, the greater the number of pins. Transfer pins may be left soft for low-production

Figure **11·4** Construction of this inverted-type redraw die incorporates a die ring (4) inserted in a housing (1), which is adapted to fit the shank opening in the ram of the punch press. The main components are: (1) Adapter. (2) Clamp ring. (3) Socket-head cap screws. (4) Die ring. (5) Draw punch. (6) Redraw sleeve. (7) Shedder. (8) Knockout shaft.

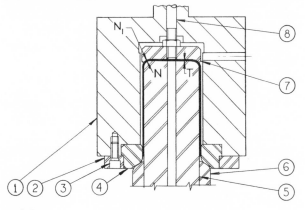

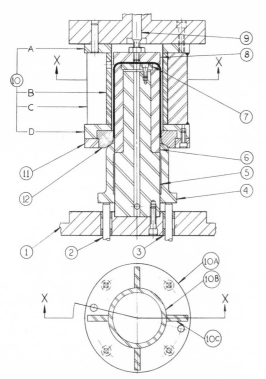

Figure **11·5** Inverted redraw die, composite construction. The major components are:

1. Die set
2. Transfer pins
3. Bushings
4. Redraw sleeve
5. Punch post
6. Punch collar insert
7. Retaining cap
8. Shedder
9. Knockout shaft
10. Adapter unit (weldment)
11. Clamp ring
12. Draw-die ring

light-duty dies. High-production severe-service dies will require heat-treated transfer pins. Guide bushings (3) are an asset for dies with thick die shoes and/or for high-production severe-service applications. Standard drill-jig bushings or liners are often appropriate. These bushings can also be made of graphitic steels or lubricant-impregnated bronze, if deemed necessary.

This die employs a composite punch construction. The hardened, vertically polished collar (6) is assembled on the post (5) and retained by a cap disk (7), as shown. The collar is generally made of a suitable tool steel, heat-treated to maximum practical hardness. The post should be made of a tough steel (and, preferably, a cheaper steel), heat-treated accordingly. Remember that the air vent opening must be adequate in size and that it must extend through both the cap and the post.

Another typical redraw-die construction is depicted in Fig. 11·6.

The construction. This die is very similar to the preceding one except that it has a one-piece punch (7), and the adapter (6) is simply a section

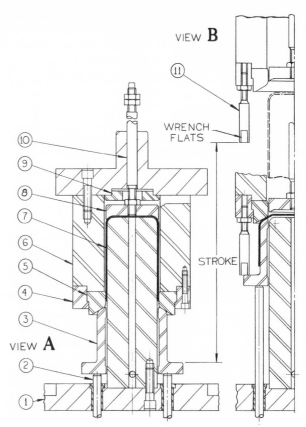

Figure **11·6** Another typical inverted redraw die. This die employs spacers (11), which control the relationship between the redraw sleeve (3) and the draw-die insert (5). The major components are:

1. Die set
2. Transfer pins
3. Redraw sleeve
4. Clamp ring
5. Draw-die ring
6. Adapter
7. Draw punch
8. Shedder
9. Locator plug
10. Knockout shaft
11. Spacer
12. Bushing

of seamless mechanical tubing, machined as required. The adapter is positioned on the punch shoe by means of a locator plug (9). In using this type of construction, be certain that the locator does not interfere with the air vents. Spacers (11) are often employed on redraw dies. The spacers control the transmission of pressure to the draw-piece. They also act to level the redraw sleeve, eliminating any tendency for the sleeve to bind against the punch.

FUNCTION OF REDRAW SLEEVES

The manner in which redraw sleeves act to control the flow of the stock material is pictured progressively in Fig. 11·7, views *A*, *B*, *C*, and *D*.

The redraw sleeve of view *A* is a multifunctional component. Its prime function is to control the flow of the stock material during the act of redrawing. One of its secondary functions is to strip

147

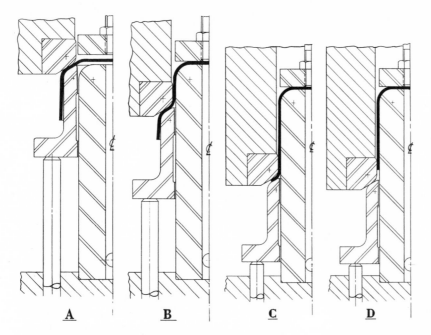

Figure 11 · 7 Views *A* and *B*: Initial stages in the redrawing process, showing action of the redraw sleeve. Views *C* and *D*: Final stages in the redrawing process, showing action of the redraw sleeve.

<u>A</u>   <u>B</u>   <u>C</u>   <u>D</u>

the drawpiece from the punch after redrawing. Another secondary function is piloting. The sleeve serves as a locator on which the workpiece is loaded, as shown in the illustration. Here, the previously drawn workpiece has been loaded in position. The die is descending and has just contacted the workpiece. The act of redrawing is about to begin.

In view *B* conditions are shown as they exist during most of the redrawing process. Note how the die ring and the redraw sleeve confine the stock material, directing its flow. For successful redrawing, the stock material must flow as freely as is possible without developing wrinkles. Too much confinement will impede the metal flow. Too little confinement will permit wrinkling. Therefore, it is necessary to achieve a balanced condition of optimum conditions. This is done by employing suitable draw-edge profiles and pressures. Remember that it is not generally practical to attempt drawing operations which require that the stock material be strained to an extent that approaches its maximum physical capacity.

In view *C* the draw action is nearing completion. Note that the stock-material flow is still controlled by confinement between the die draw edge and the redraw sleeve. This confinement will be maintained until the rim of the drawpiece passes the top of the redraw sleeve. By then, if the die is properly proportioned, the remaining draw-action requirement should be almost nil, permitting the drawpiece to be drawn off without developing wrinkles.

In view *D* the drawpiece has been drawn off and the relationships are shown as they appear

when the die is closed, at the bottom of the press stroke. In the next phase, as the die ascends to its maximum open position, it permits the redraw sleeve to return to its starting position. In the course of returning, the redraw sleeve ensures that the drawpiece will be stripped from the punch.

It might be well to note the following:

Flared cup. This die could be used to produce flared cups by setting its closed position, as shown in view *C*.

Stepped cup. This die could also be used to produce stepped cups by setting its closed position, as shown in view *B*.

Thus, it follows that dies which are intended solely to produce such drawpieces will be very similar to dies in which the work is drawn off.

MATERIALS FOR DIE COMPONENTS

There was a time when it was a simple matter to select the most suitable material for any given die component. This was true for the simple reason that only a very few materials were available. However, this situation no longer exists. Today, there are many different materials which are readily available. Many of these materials are especially appropriate for different specific applications. To acquire information in regard to various materials for die components, a manual of tool steels and associated materials should be consulted. Information of this kind is also available in handbooks such as the "Tool Engineer's Handbook." [1] Keep in mind that this applies to all dies—not solely to draw dies.

[1] "Tool Engineer's Handbook", 2d ed., McGraw-Hill Book Company, New York, 1959.

In order to select the most appropriate materials, it is, of course, necessary to understand the functions of the various die components in relation to wear effects, etc. For example, by referring to the redraw die in Figs. 11·6 and 11·7, it is possible, by examination, to determine some factors which will influence the choice of materials for the various die components. Analysis of the die action reveals that the redraw sleeve (3) and the draw-die ring (5) (Fig. 11·6) are in strong pressure contact with the stock material which slides over their working surfaces. Consequently, these components are subjected to maximum friction and wear. The materials from which these components are made should be selected accordingly. Friction and wear induced by normal drawing action are much less severe in relation to the punch (7). Thus, it is often desirable to select a different material for the punch.

Structural considerations, such as size, shape, and massiveness of each component, will also influence the type of material from which it should be made.

Production requirements can have a decided effect upon the choice of materials. Tooling costs can ordinarily be equated with production requirements. It is generally undesirable to make a die which is capable of producing 1 million or more piece parts when only 100,000 parts are required. It is also generally undesirable to make a die which is capable of producing only 100,000 parts when millions are required. Admittedly, it is not always possible to tailor the die precisely to the production requirements. However, the best possible compromise should always be effected.

Compatibility is another factor which influences the selection of tool steels and/or other die materials. For example, a die which is intended to draw a stainless-steel drawpiece will normally be made of different materials from a die which is intended to draw a brass drawpiece, etc.

Keep in mind, also, that it is often desirable to apply chromium plating to die components, or to carbide-spray them, etc.

TYPICAL CONSTRUCTION RELATIONSHIPS

Typical dimensional relationships for the construction of sleeve-type redraw dies are shown in Fig. 11·8. The illustration depicts an inverted redraw die. Keep in mind that the following discussion also applies to sleeve-type redraw dies which are not inverted (used in double-action presses).

T = stock-material thickness—same as thickness of original blank

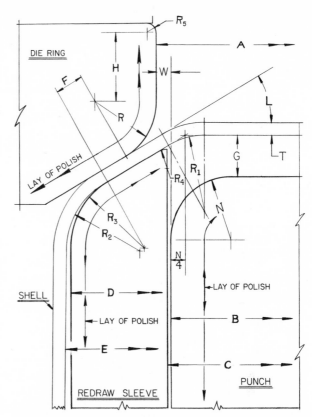

Figure 11·8   Relationships for sleeve-type redraw dies.

W = draw clearance per earlier discussion and table (Fig. 10·19)
A = inner diameter of die ring
B = diameter of draw punch

Assuming this die is the final operation, then

If the piece-part print specifies the outer diameter of the drawpiece, make dimension A in accordance with the piece-part dimension, and make $B = A - 2W$

If the piece-part print specifies the inner diameter of the drawpiece, make B in accordance with the piece-part dimension, and make $A = B + 2W$

If this die is followed by another redraw operation, or a sizing operation, etc., make dimensions A and/or B to suit the specific situation, with the difference between A and B equal to $2W$. $C =$ inner diameter of redraw sleeve. It should not fit too snugly and should permit a slight equalizing float. One procedure is to relate the clearance between C and B to the punch diameter B within the following limits:

$C = B + 0.001$ in. per in. of punch diameter

with a minimum of $C = B + 0.0004$ in. for small

dies and a maximum of $C = B + 0.010$ in. for larger dies

D = outer diameter of redraw sleeve body

It should be a free slip fit for the inner diameter of the previously drawn shell (workpiece). It should not be a push fit or a binding fit. Make

$D = E - 0.001$ to 0.002
E = inner diameter of previously drawn workpiece, measured at sidewalls near center line of bottom radius R_2
F = width of annular pressure surface
G = clearance space between inside bottom surface of workpiece and top of punch when redraw sleeve is in up position

This space may vary from $\frac{1}{64}$ to $\frac{1}{8}$ in. or more depending upon the application but generally $G = \frac{1}{32}$ in. approx.

H = straight land on die wall

This dimension will be shorter for small dies and longer for large dies. In a general way, H can be considered

Minimum $H = \frac{1}{8}$ in.
Average $H = \frac{3}{8}$ in.
Maximum $H = \frac{3}{4}$ in.

If H is made too long, excessive friction will be induced, which will rub out the lubricant and tend to gall the drawpiece.

N = radius on nose end of punch

$$N \leqq R_1$$

$\frac{N}{4}$ = theoretical intersection of inner surfaces at bottom of workpiece shell
R = draw radius

The size of draw radius should be appropriate for the stock-material thickness and the amount of reduction performed by the die. For average circumstances

$$R = 4T \text{ to } 6T \text{ approx.}$$

R_1, R_2 = inside tangent radii of workpiece shell, from previous draw operation
R_3 = draw-sleeve radius

$$R_3 = R_2$$

R_4 = radius on sleeve to clear R_1
R_5 = lead radius on back of die ring to facilitate ejection of drawpiece from die

This radius, too, should be highly polished to prevent scoring the drawpiece.

L = angle of bottom bevel on workpiece, as previously drawn

Angle L will normally be

$L = 30°$ where $T \leqq 0.031$ in.
$L = 40°$ where $T = 0.031$ to 0.062 in.
$L = 45°$ where $T > 0.062$ in.

Angle L of the annular pressure surfaces on the die ring and the redraw sleeve should agree precisely with the angle of the workpiece. One method of checking fits in this area is to carefully cut a workpiece in two (vertically). Then use one of the halves as a gage to check visually the fit of the die ring and the redraw sleeve in relation to the workpiece.

The working surfaces of these components should be highly polished. The lay of the finish should be like that indicated in Fig. 11·8. Generally speaking, draw surfaces cannot be too well finished. Surface finishes for all draw dies should generally be within the range of 2 to 8 μin. average surface roughness and should be appropriate for the specific application.

For the die ring, the highly finished area should include R_5, die-opening sidewalls, draw radius R, and the angular face.

For the punch, the highly finished area should include all of radius N and should extend down the sidewalls to a distance beyond the rim of the drawpiece.

For the redraw sleeve, the highly finished area should include all the upper surfaces and should extend around radius R_2 and down the outer sidewalls to a depth slightly greater than the depth of the workpiece.

A COMPARISON OF REDRAW-EDGE PROFILES

Figure 11·9 is a comparison drawing which depicts two different sleeve-type redraw dies. Each draw-edge profile creates a different path of transition for the metal (stock material). The difference is apparent by examination of the illustration.

In view A, the transition is relatively abrupt, tending to induce greater tensile stress within the stock material.

In view B, the transition is more gradual, tending to induce lesser tensile stress within the stock material.

Method A would be used for applications which prove to require a maximum of flow restraint. Method B would be used for applications where freer flow is desirable. For average draw work, under average conditions, method B would be most generally desirable for sleeve-type redraw operations, whether they are performed in inverted dies or in dies which are not inverted.

Remember, of course, that both these profiles can be modified to provide either freer flow or greater restraint.

COMBINATION BLANK AND DRAW DIES

A combination die is one in which cutting and noncutting operations are performed in a single station. A combination blank and draw die combines blanking and drawing operations to produce the drawpiece from strip stock in one operation. A basic blank and draw-die combination is pictured in Fig. 11·10.

The construction. This die assembly is mounted on a back-post die set (1). Guidepost die sets are a real asset for dies of this type, greatly facilitating diemaking and die setup, maintenance, and storage as well. The blanking die block (2) is chamfered (L), leaving a sharpening land contiguous to the cutting edge. This is done to facilitate die sharpening in the course of die maintenance. The die block is secured by screws and positioned by dowels. Die-block mounting is foolproofed by differential doweling as shown (X and Y). The die block is counterbored to accommodate the shoulders of the pressure pad (3), which is actuated by the pressure-transfer pins (5). The stop (6) and the stripping arrangement (10) are a conventional hook-pin construction. The shedder plate (7) and the knockout shaft (8) are combined as shown, creating a typical flangeless positive shedder.

The sharpening land, the pressure-pad proportions, the hook-pin construction, and the positive shedder should all be made and assembled in accordance with the detailed descriptions given in "Basic Diemaking."

The draw-die opening is contained within the combination punch (9), which is also the blanking punch. Cutting clearance is provided in the orthodox manner between the die cut edge and the punch cut edge. Draw clearance is provided in the usual way between the sidewalls of the draw-die opening (9) and the sidewalls of the draw punch (4). Both components (4) and (9) must be vented in the manner described earlier for inverted draw dies.

Construction relationships. Figure 11·11 depicts the die as it appears when in open position. When the die is in this position, the top surface of the draw pressure pad (3) should be flush with, or slightly lower than, the cutting face of the die block (2), as shown (B).

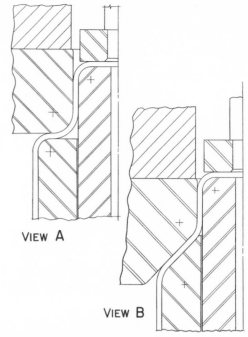

VIEW A

VIEW B

Figure **11·9** Plastic flow of the metal (stock material) related to different draw-edge profiles. The profile on the redraw sleeve acts in conjunction with the die draw-edge profile to create the desired flow configuration.

Figure **11·10** A combination blank and draw die. The major components are: (1) Die set. (2) Blanking-die ring. (3) Draw pad. (4) Draw punch. (5) Transfer pins. (6) Stop. (7) Shedder. (8) Knockout shaft. (9) Combination punch. (10) Stripper and guide.

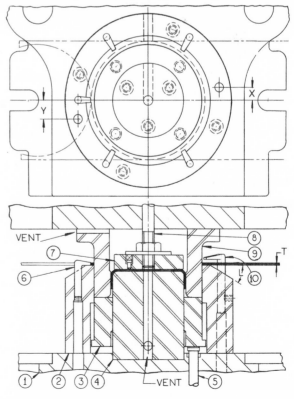

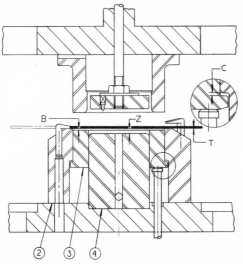

Figure **11·11** Relationships when die is in open position.

$$B = 0 \text{ to } 0.010 \text{ in. approx.}$$

Dimension Z indicates that the top surface of the draw punch (4) is below the cutting face of the die block. Z must be at least equal to T in order to ensure severance of the stock material before the drawing action begins. However, Z is generally made greater than T. This is a die maintenance provision which is typical for combination blank and draw dies. The difference in levels (Z) permits the die block to be sharpened down a distance equal to $Z - T$ before it becomes necessary to perform any maintenance grinding on the punch. Generally

$$Z = T + \frac{1}{8} \text{ in. approx.}$$

Figure **11·12** A procedure to facilitate the making of a combination blank and draw die.

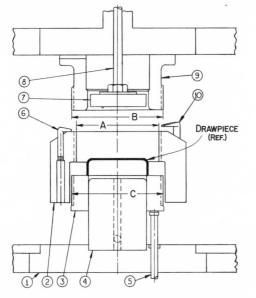

As an exception, for heavy stock material (T), it will usually be desirable to make $Z > T + \frac{1}{8}$ in.

The recess in the die block provides a keeper ledge for the shoulder of the draw pad. Remember that the lower pressure unit should not drive the pad shoulder against the keeper ledge. The length of the transfer pins should be such that when the die is open, as shown, a clearance C exists as indicated in the inset view. This clearance should ordinarily be

$$C = \frac{1}{32} \text{ in. approx.}$$

A diemaking procedure. The die we have been discussing is shown again in Fig. 11·12. This illustration is an associative illustration, arranged to depict the relationship existing among dimensions A, B, and C during the blank-development stage of making the die. Before a combination die can be entirely completed, it is necessary to determine the actual blank size in order to finish dimensions A, B, and C.

PROCEDURE

Make all components hardened and completely finished except for dimensions A, B, and C. These dimensions should be made to the theoretical blank size plus or minus (as pictured in the illustration) an extra amount of grinding stock to be removed after the actual blank diameter has been determined. Extra grinding stock should also be provided on the nose of the stripper hook pins (10). (See Fig. 11·10.)

The draw punch (4) and the transfer pins (5) are completely finished and mounted to the die shoe (1). The draw pad (3) is left oversize on diameter C and assembled as shown. The combination punch (9) is left oversize on diameter B and mounted to the punch shoe. The shedder assembly (7) and (8) is completed and installed in the normal manner. The die block can be completely finished except for diameter A, which is left undersize. Mounting the die block is, however, held in abeyance. The die block is set aside and not mounted until after the required actual blank diameter is determined.

The assembled die (except for the die block, which has been put aside) is then set up in the press. A trial blank is lathe-turned from a piece of the actual stock material which is intended to be run. This first trial blank is turned to the calculated theoretical blank diameter. It is then loaded centrally on the draw pad (remember, the die block is not present) and drawn. This procedure is continued until the required blank diameter is accurately determined.

After the developed blank diameter has been

accurately ascertained, the blanking-die opening diameter A is finish-ground to the same diameter as the developed blank. Diameter B on the combination punch is then finished equal to the final die diameter A minus the necessary cutting clearance. The draw pad is then finished on diameter C to provide a slip fit in the blanking die opening. The nose end of the hook pins (10) is then finished, and the die block is mounted to the die shoe. After checking to verify the general mounting and alignment, the die should be ready to run.

COMBINATION DIE: COMPOSITE CONSTRUCTION

Combination dies, like any other general class of dies, are necessarily designed and constructed in many different ways. This is because each die is an individual tool specifically designed and constructed to satisfy best a set of unique circumstances. Design of the die in Fig. 11·13 differs from the preceding one. Essentially, the difference is due to the fact that this die is intended for a larger drawpiece.

The construction. The number of mounting screws (4), (10), (18), (20), and (21) will depend upon the individual application. Larger dies will require more mounting screws than will smaller dies.

The screws and dowels for the stripper (12) are not shown in the illustration. The stripper is conventionally doweled to the blanking-die block (22) with two dowels. The stripper screws are installed from the top, extending through the stripper and the blanking-die block into tapped holes provided in the filler block (15).

The shedder plate (5) is contoured to support the drawpiece during ejection. The shedding pin is a standard, commercially available spring pin. A vent hole is also provided in the shedding plate as an aid to the shedding action. The knockout shaft (6) is peen-assembled to the shedding plate and is fitted with a cap (7) at its top end. The cap is cross-pinned to the shaft. The pin (8) is made from cold-drawn steel or from drill rod and left soft. Do not use a standard dowel pin for this purpose. The draw-die insert ring (3) is fitted into the blanking punch (2) and retained by the socket-head cap screws (4). The purpose of the insert-ring construction is to permit the blanking punch to be sharpened without reworking the draw-radius profile. To sharpen the blanking punch, remove the insert ring. Drift holes should be provided in the blanking punch, as shown, to facilitate removing the draw-die insert ring. After sharpening the blanking punch, grind precisely the same amount from the back of the insert ring

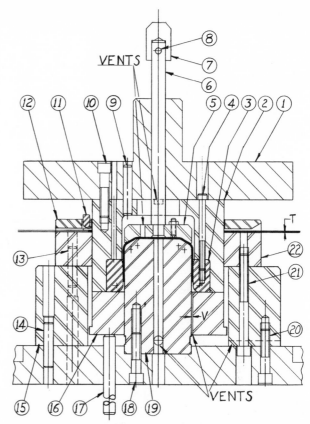

Figure **11·13** Composite construction is a feature of this combination blank and draw die. The major components are:

1. Die set
2. Blanking punch
3. Draw-die insert
4. Socket-head cap screws
5. Shedder plate
6. Knockout shaft
7. Knockout cap
8. Cross pin
9. Dowels
10. Socket-head cap screws
11. Sidewinder stop
12. Stripper
13. Dowels
14. Dowels
15. Filler block
16. Draw pad
17. Transfer pins
18. Socket-head cap screws
19. Draw punch
20. Socket-head cap screws
21. Socket-head cap screws
22. Blanking-die block

in order to maintain the smoothly flush face surface which is essential for the act of drawing. Tapped depth of the screw holes in the insert ring must be deep enough to permit grinding the back of the insert for maintenance. Remember, however, that the holes must be blind holes in order to ensure an uninterrupted plane surface on the drawing face. This applies generally to all draw dies. Screw holes, dowel holes, etc., should not be drilled through the die face or the pad face in the areas over which the metal (stock material) moves during the drawing act.

Figure 11·14   A combination blank and draw die. Note air-vent hole in draw punch.

The stop (11) is a sidewinder stop. Action of these stops, their installation proportions, etc., are thoroughly described under the heading "Pivoted Auto Stops" in "Basic Diemaking."

The blanking-die block (22) is assembled to the filler block (15) by means of two dowels (13) and an appropriate number of socket-head cap screws (21). The filler block can be made of cast iron or machine steel, whichever is most convenient. This composite construction effects a saving in the cost of material for the die and in the heat-treating costs. In addition to these advantages, it can facilitate the actual making of the die. The filler block is mounted on the die shoe of the die set (1), positioned by two dowels (14), and retained by an appropriate number of socket-head cap screws (20).

A pocket, bored in the die shoe, positions the punch (19). The base end of the punch is fitted to the pocket, and the punch is secured in the pocket by its mounting screws (18).

The draw pressure pad (16) is provided with one vent slot (or more, if needed). These slots are made in the inner sidewall of the pad as shown (V). Depth of such slots should be

$$V \leqq \tfrac{1}{2}T$$

Large dies and/or thinner stock material will tend to require more vent slots of this kind than will smaller dies and/or heavier stock material. The purpose of these vents is to expedite the escape of air, which, at the beginning of the drawing act, might be entrapped in the area of the bevel (or radius) at the nose end of the draw punch. This air normally escapes between the walls of the punch and the pad. However, since the pad is generally rather closely fitted to the punch, it is often necessary to provide extra venting by means of slots made as shown in Fig. 11·13.

CHAPTER 12 DRAWING OPERATIONS: COMPUTATION PROCEDURES

DETERMINING BLANK DIAMETERS

To be truly accurate, the blank diameter must be finally verified by actually producing drawpieces from the proper stock material by means of the actual draw die (or dies) concerned. However, it is not practical to use random cut-and-try procedures for the determination of blank diameters. Instead, it is necessary to be able to calculate (in advance) the theoretical diameter of the blank. Among the reasons for calculating the theoretical blank diameter in advance of die design and construction are the following:

1. To calculate the stock-material requirement for production-cost estimates.
2. To determine the ratio of the blank diameter to the drawpiece diameter in order to calculate the number of draw operations required, and whether or not annealing will be needed, etc.
3. To know the approximate blank diameter for designing the blanking die or the blanking portion of a combination die, etc.
4. To know the approximate diameter of the punch and die cutting edges in order to facilitate diemaking procedures (see Fig. 11·12).

Equivalent areas. A drawpiece and the blank required to produce it are depicted in Fig. 12·1. If the drawpiece were placed on one side of a balance scale and the blank were placed on the other side, it would be evident that the weight of the blank is exactly the same as the weight of the drawpiece. It follows, then, that the volume of the stock material in the blank is precisely the same as the volume of the stock material in the drawpiece. It is therefore possible to determine the blank diameter D by calculating the volume of stock material in the drawpiece and converting to find the diameter D of the flat blank which has the same volume and thickness T. For normal draw operations, however, this procedure would be too cumbersome, entailing much calculation that is unnecessary for the purpose. Instead, for normal draw operations it is most practical to compute the mean surface area of the drawpiece and convert this area to find the diameter D of the required flat blank.

In Fig. 12·1, thickness T of the stock material is, of course, the same for both the drawpiece and the blank. Also, in computing blank sizes for normal draw operations, any thinning or thickening effects due to normal draw action are ignored. Thickness T is considered to be constant throughout the entire cross-sectional contour of the drawpiece. Consequently, for computation purposes the mean surface of the drawpiece is considered to exist at the center of the stock material T as indicated by the dotted outline in the illustration.

As mentioned earlier, the volume of the stock material in the blank is equal to the volume of the stock material in the drawpiece. Therefore, if

Figure **12·1** A drawpiece and the blank from which it is produced.

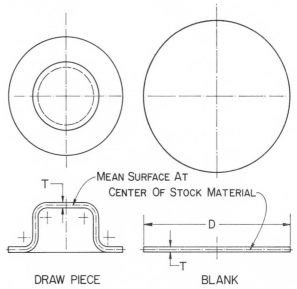

MEAN SURFACE AT CENTER OF STOCK MATERIAL

T

D

T

DRAW PIECE   BLANK

thickness T is considered to be constant, the area of the mean surface of the drawpiece is equal to the area of its required blank. In practice, slight discrepancies will be encountered. These, however, will usually be so slight that they may generally be disregarded for the practical purposes of computing trial-blank sizes.

The above-described condition of equivalent areas provides a means for computing the theoretical required blank diameter. Since the area of the blank is the same as the mean surface area of the drawpiece, the procedure for finding the theoretical blank diameter is:

1. Calculate the mean surface area of the draw piece. Call this the area of the required blank.

Figure **12·2** A circular drawpiece divided into elements for area computations.

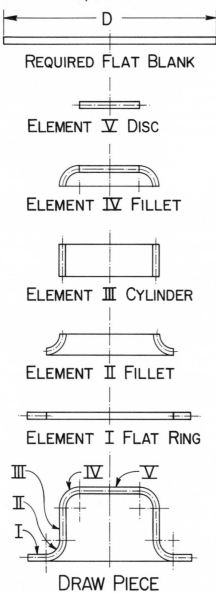

2. Convert this area to its diameter. This will be the diameter of the required flat blank.

Element-area method. A very practical and satisfactory method for computing the mean surface area of a drawpiece is the element-area method, which is illustrated in Fig. 12·2. Procedure for the element-area method is:

1. As shown in the illustration, divide the cross-sectional contour of the drawpiece into its simple geometric elements. For this particular drawpiece, these are the elements indicated I, II, III, IV, and V.
2. Calculate the mean surface area of each element, as a separate unit. Since the elements are simple, the calculations are simple. They are very easily performed by applying the appropriate formulas from Fig. 12·3.
3. It is axiomatic that the whole is equal to the sum of its parts. Therefore, the mean surface area of the drawpiece is equal to the sum of the mean surface areas of its elements. Then, in the illustrated case, if A = mean surface area of the drawpiece, then areas I + II + III + IV + V = A. Also,

$$A = \text{area of required flat blank}$$

Figure **12·3** Equations for areas of circular-drawpiece elements (A = area).

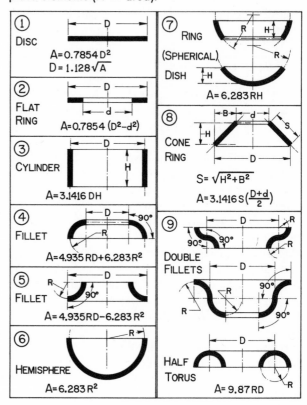

4. Convert area A to its diameter. To convert, call the blank diameter D. Then D will be equal to the $\sqrt{A}$ multiplied by the reciprocal of $\sqrt{\pi/2}$, or

$$D = 1.128 \sqrt{A}$$

EXAMPLE: ELEMENT-AREA METHOD

A piece part is shown at view A, in Fig. 12·4. This piece part is a drawn cup which is dimensioned

    3.000 in. diameter (inside)
    ¼ in. bottom radius (inside)
    $1.875 \begin{smallmatrix}+0.005\\-0.000\end{smallmatrix}$ in. height (inside)

The height dimension is too stringent to be produced without trimming. Therefore, it is necessary to add the amount of stock material desired for trimming. The trim allowance must be added to the height of the cup before the blank diameter is calculated. Do not use the net cup height to calculate the blank diameter and then attempt to add the trim allowance to the blank diameter. This applies to all draw operations in which trimming is a factor. The trim allowance should be properly sequenced in the calculations—it should *not* be added to the net blank diameter.

CALCULATION PROCEDURE

1. Convert the piece-part sizes to their equivalent mean dimensions, and add in the trim allowance as shown in view B.
2. Divide the resulting drawpiece into its simple geometric elements, as shown, (I), (II), and (III).
3. Using the formulas in the preceding illustration, calculate the individual element areas.

Area I:

$$A\mathrm{I} = (3.1416)(3.06)(1.75)$$
$$= 16.823 \text{ sq in.}$$

Area II:

$$A\mathrm{II} = [(4.94)(0.28)(2.5)] + [6.28(0.28)^2]$$
$$= 3.458 + 0.492$$
$$= 3.950 \text{ sq in.}$$

Area III:

$$A\mathrm{III} = 0.7854(2.5)^2$$
$$= 0.7854(6.25)$$
$$= 4.909 \text{ sq in.}$$

Total area A:

$$A = A\mathrm{I} + A\mathrm{II} + A\mathrm{III}$$
$$= 25.682 \text{ sq in.}$$

Blank diameter D:

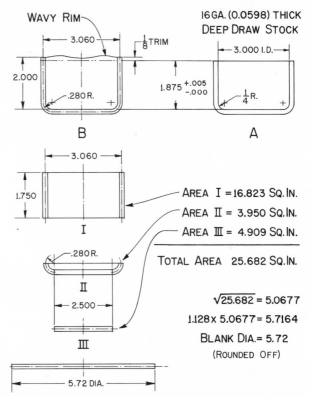

Figure **12·4** Procedure for determining a blank diameter, using the element-area method.

$$D = 1.128 \sqrt{25.682}$$
$$= 1.128(5.0677)$$
$$= 5.7164$$

After determining the blank diameter D as in the above, D is generally rounded off to the nearest two-place decimal figure as shown in the illustration,

$$D = 5.72 \text{ in.}$$

DEEP-DRAW COMPUTATIONS

By definition, a drawn piece part which requires only one drawing operation is considered to be a shallow draw, and a drawn piece part which requires more than one drawing operation is considered to be a deep draw.

Number of draw operations required. The *probable* number of draws required for a piece part may be reckoned by using the relationships shown in Fig. 12·5.

Shallow draws:

$$\frac{H}{D} = \text{⅝ to ¾}$$

Deep draws:

When the H/D ratio exceeds the above, then more than one reduction is required.

157

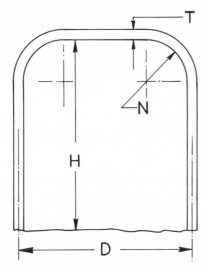

D = MEAN DIAMETER
H = INSIDE HEIGHT
N ≅ 4 T

H ÷ D	P
< .75	1
0.7 – 1.5	2
1.5 – 3.0	3
3.0 – 4.7	4

P = PROBABLE NUMBER
OF REDUCTIONS

Figure **12·5** Relationships for estimating probable number of reductions.

The table in the illustration enumerates the probable number of reductions (P) for a series of H/D ratios.

Bottom radii related to redraws. As described earlier in this chapter, the bottom radius of the drawpiece is formed by the radius on the nose of the draw punch. Consequently for drawpieces which are in the deep-draw category, a new bottom radius is formed by the punch-nose radius in each redraw operation. The optimum condition of radius-to-radius relationships for a series of successive redraw operations is pictured in Fig. 12·6. The illustration depicts a typical deep-draw sequence, which, in this particular instance, requires five draw operations—a first-draw followed by four redraws. The punch-nose radii (N_1 to N_5) should be related as follows:

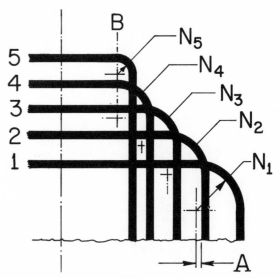

Figure **12·6** Relationships of bottom radii for successive redraw operations.

N_4 and N_5 should originate from approximately the same center line B. The remaining radii should generally be centered a slight distance to the inside of the redraw operation which is subsequent, as indicated at A. Dimension A can be subject to considerable variation. However, for many applications A may generally be made one-fourth of the nose radius of the subsequent redraw operation. That is,

$$A = \frac{N_2}{4} \qquad A_1 = \frac{N_3}{4} \qquad \cdots$$

Bottom-slant proportions. Instead of bottom radii, redraw operations may employ a bevel at the sidewall-and-bottom junction of the drawpiece. Such bevels, incorporated for redraw purposes, are called "bottom slants." Optimum proportions for relating bottom slants to redraw operations are indicated in Fig. 12·7.

These proportions originate with the final drawpiece (No. 3) and are then related successively to each preceding drawpiece. In the illustration, T is the stock-material thickness, R is the bottom radius of the final drawpiece, and L is the angle of the bottom slants.

Angle L of the bottom slant for the last preliminary drawpiece (No. 2) should intersect its drawpiece bottom at a distance of approximately one-fourth R, measured inward from the inner sidewall of the final drawpiece (No. 3). The slant-angle intersection for the next preceding drawpiece (No. 1) is at a distance of one-half A from the inner sidewall of drawpiece 2. If there were another drawpiece in this sequence, its slant angle would begin at a distance of one-half B from the

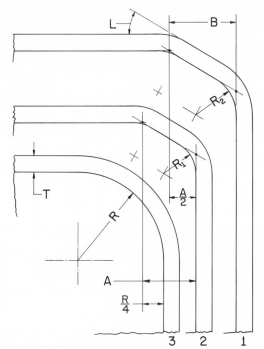

Figure **12·7** Proportional relationships for redraws using bottom slants *L*.

inner wall of No. 1, and so on for others, if required.

Other proportions are

$R_1 = 0.6A$
$R_2 = 0.6B$
$L = 30°$ where $T < 0.31$ in.
$L = 40°$ where $T = 0.031$ to 0.062 in.
$L = 45°$ where $T > 0.062$ in.

Draw reduction percentages. When a drawpiece is drawn from a flat blank, the diameter of the drawpiece is, of course, smaller than the diameter of the flat blank. This difference in diameters can be expressed as a percentage of the original flat-blank diameter. To determine this percentage, let

Z = flat-blank diameter
Y = mean diameter of drawpiece
X = reduction as a percentage of Z

Then

$$X = 1 - \frac{Y}{Z}$$

Each time a drawpiece is redrawn, its diameter is reduced. This reduction in diameter can be expressed as a percentage of the diameter from which the reduction is made. To determine this percentage, let

Z' = drawpiece diameter before reducing
Y' = drawpiece diameter after reducing

X' = the reduction as a percentage of Z'

Then

$$X' = 1 - \frac{Y'}{Z'}$$

A range of reduction percentages for various materials and stock thicknesses is given in Figs. 12·8 and 12·9. Experience has shown that these percentages are practical for average conditions.

STEEL —DRAW QUALITY, OR BETTER				
STOCK MAT'L. THICKNESS	% 1ST. DRAW	% 2ND. DRAW	% 3RD. DRAW	% 4TH. DRAW
< 0.063	40–48	20–25	18–20	16–18
0.063—0.125	40–48	15–18	14–15	13–14
0.125—0.187	40–48	12–15	11–12	10–11
0.187—0.250	40–48	10–13	9–10	8–9
> 0.250	40–48	8–10	7–8	6–7

BRASS— DRAWING QUALITY				
< 0.063	44–50	20–29	18–23	18–20
0.063—0.125	44–50	16–23	15–17	12–15
0.125—0.187	44–50	14–17	12–14	11–13
0.187—0.250	44–50	10–14	9–11	8–10
> 0.250	44–50	9–11	8–9	7–8

Figure **12·8** Practical reduction percentages for drawing and redrawing brass and steel.

Figure **12·9** Practical reduction percentages for drawing and redrawing various types of aluminum.

ALUMINUM				
STOCK MAT'L. THICKNESS	% 1ST. DRAW	% 2ND. DRAW	% 3RD. DRAW	% 4TH. DRAW
O (ANNEALED) 0.020 — 0.125	40–42	14–22	14–22	14–22
> 0.125	42–45	20–28	14–22	14–22
H12 AND H32 0.020 — 0.125	32–34	15	15	15
> 0.125	34–36	15	15	15
H14 AND H34 0.020 — 0.125	25–28	15	15	15
> 0.125	22–28	15	15	15
H16, H36, H18, H38 0.020 — 0.125	20–22	NOT RECOMMENDED		
> 0.125	22–24	NOT RECOMMENDED		
61S-T4 AND R301-T3 0.020 — 0.125	24–28	NOT RECOMMENDED		
> 0.125	28–32	NOT RECOMMENDED		
6061-T6, 2024-T3 2014-T6, 7075-T6 0.020 — 0.125	20–22	NOT RECOMMENDED		
> 0.125	22–25	NOT RECOMMENDED		

If conditions are unfavorable, the percentages may be too large. On the other hand, it can be practical to exceed the percentages if conditions are favorable. Keep in mind, however, that, if the reduction is too great, the resulting drawpiece will be overstressed.

It is only natural to attempt to minimize the number of operations required to produce the piece part. But remember that, in relation to draw work, the most common error is to attempt reductions which are too large. It is very often better to use relatively conservative reductions than to run the risk of production troubles and poor work quality, which are all too commonly associated with attempting to eliminate a redraw operation.

A TYPICAL DEEP-DRAW CALCULATION

EXAMPLE

It is desired to produce a piece part which is a cylindrical cup. It is to be drawn from cold-rolled steel (commercial draw quality). Required piece-part dimensions are:

$$\text{Diameter, inside} = 4.00 \text{ in.}$$
$$\text{Height, inside} = 6.000 \text{ in.}$$
$$\text{Bottom radius} = \tfrac{1}{2} \text{ in.}$$

The piece-part dimensions are shown in view Z (Fig. 12·10). The stock-material thickness is specified as 0.0299 in. This thickness dimension is considered to be 0.030 in. for calculation purposes (and for diemaking purposes, too).

For drawpieces which require trimming, the trim allowance must be included in the calculations. The trim allowance should be incorporated in the calculations at the draw operation which immediately precedes the trimming operation. In this example, the trim allowance is therefore added to the required final piece-part height, as shown in view Z. As a consequence, it is necessary to compute (and make dies for) a cup which has a height of $6\tfrac{5}{16}$ in.

PROCEDURE FOR COMPUTING

1. Add in the trim allowance as explained above.
2. Determine the probable number of draws.
3. Calculate the flat-blank diameter.
4. Determine the optimum number of draws.
5. Calculate the bottom slants (if used).
6. Calculate the height of each draw.

These heights are required in order to determine the necessary die proportions such as die-cavity depth, punch length, redraw sleeve length, etc. These heights are also needed in order to relate the operations to the press equipment for factors such as die space, press stroke, loading and ejection conditions, etc.

CALCULATIONS

1. Piece-part height plus trim allowance = final drawpiece height

$$6.000 + \tfrac{5}{16} = 6\tfrac{5}{16} \text{ in. final drawpiece height}$$

2. Probable number of draws required (see Fig. 12·5)

$$6\tfrac{5}{16} \div 4.03 = 1.57$$

(using dimensions in Fig. 12·10)

This H/D ratio is within the range which indicates that three draws will probably be required. Actually, since the bottom radius is relatively large, this might be considered to be a borderline case, one which may be possible in two draws. However, in view of the fact that the stock material is of less than deep-draw quality, it is best to assume the probability of the three draws.

3. Flat-blank diameter. Use mean dimensions as shown in illustration.

Area I:

$$3.1416 \times 4.03 \times 5.812 = 73.583 \text{ sq in.}$$

Area II:

$$4.935 \times 0.515 \times 3.0 = 7.625$$
$$\text{plus } 6.283 \times 0.515^2 = \underline{1.666}$$
$$9.291 \qquad 9.291 \text{ sq in.}$$

Area III:

$$0.7854 \times 9 = \underline{7.069 \text{ sq in.}}$$
$$\text{Total area} = 89.943 \text{ sq in.}$$

$$\text{Flat-blank diameter} = 1.1287\sqrt{89.943}$$
$$= 1.128 \times 9.484$$
$$= 10.698$$
$$\therefore \text{Flat-blank diameter} = 10.7 \text{ rounded off}$$

4. Refer to table (Fig. 12·8). The practical reduction-percentage ranges applicable to this piece part are

$$\text{1st draw} = 40\text{–}48\%$$
$$\text{2nd draw} = 20\text{–}25\%$$
$$\text{3rd draw} = 18\text{–}20\%$$

It was determined earlier (refer to number 2 above) that a conservative approach will be desirable for this application. As a consequence, the reduction percentages will tend to approach the low end of the recommended ranges given in the table. With this in mind, the optimum reduction-percentage range for this application is narrowed to

$$\text{1st draw} = 40\text{–}42\% \text{ of blank diameter}$$
$$\text{2nd draw} = 20\text{–}22\% \text{ of 1st draw diameter}$$
$$\text{3rd draw} = 18\text{–}19\% \text{ of 2nd draw diameter}$$

Then 1st draw diameter will be between

40% reduction = 10.7(100 − 40) = 6.42 diameter
42% reduction = 10.7(100 − 42) = 6.206 diameter

From this range of diameters (6.206 to 6.42) select a tentative diameter for the first draw. (This diameter will be considered tentative until all the reduction percentages and diameters are calculated.)

Tentative 1st draw diameter = 6.28 in.

Then 2nd draw diameter will be between

20% reduction = 6.28(100 − 20) = 5.024 diameter
22% reduction = 6.28(100 − 22) = 4.898 diameter
Tentative 2nd draw diameter = 4.93 in.

Then 3rd draw reduction percentage based on the above tentative diameters will be

$$4.03 \div 4.93 = 0.817 \qquad 1.000 - 0.817 = 0.183$$
$$\therefore 3\text{rd draw} = 18.3\% \text{ reduction}$$

It is now evident that the above tentative diameters will be satisfactory. Therefore, they are no longer considered tentative and are used as actual dimensions for this application. Consequently, the actual mean drawpiece diameters and reduction percentages are

1st draw = 6.28 in. diameter, 41.3% reduction
2nd draw = 4.93 in. diameter, 21.5% reduction
3rd draw = 4.03 in. diameter, 18.3% reduction

5. Bottom slants (see Fig. 12·7)

$$L = 30°$$
$$A = \frac{4.900 - 4.000}{2} + \frac{R}{4}$$
$$= \frac{0.900}{2} + \frac{0.500}{4}$$
$$= \frac{2.300}{4}$$
$$= 0.575$$
$$B = \frac{6.250 - 4.900}{2} + \frac{A}{2}$$
$$= \frac{1.350 + 0.575}{2}$$
$$= 0.962 \text{ rounded off}$$

To determine the mean dimensions of the bottom slants use the following equations:

$$\text{Mean } A = A + \frac{T}{2} - \left(\sin \frac{L}{2}\right)\frac{T}{2}$$
$$= (0.575 + 0.015) - (0.25882)0.015$$
$$= 0.590 - 0.004$$
$$= 0.586$$
$$\text{Mean } B = B + \frac{T}{2} - \left(\sin \frac{L}{2}\right)\frac{T}{2}$$
$$= (0.962 + 0.015) - (0.25882)0.015$$
$$= 0.977 - 0.004$$
$$= 0.973$$

Figure **12·10** Procedure for deep-draw calculations.

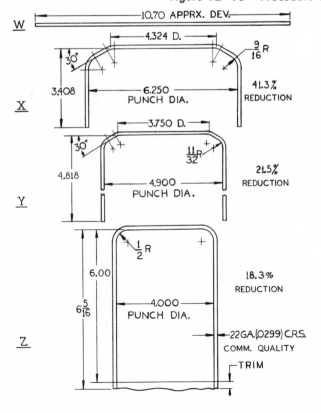

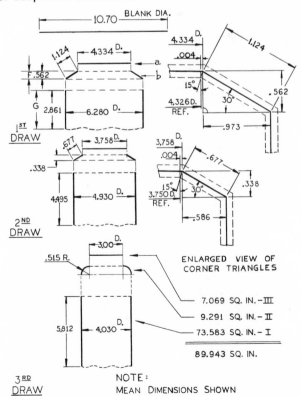

These mean dimensions are used to determine the height and length of the bevels as shown in the enlarged views (Fig. 12·10).

6. Height of 1st draw. Referring to the illustration, F = mean height of bevel, G = height of cylinder, and H = inside height of drawpiece. Then

$$H = G + F - \frac{T}{2}$$

To find H, it is necessary to calculate for G.

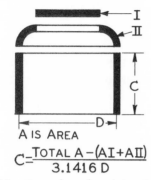

$$C = \frac{\text{TOTAL } A - (A\,\mathrm{I} + A\,\mathrm{II})}{3.1416\ D}$$

A IS AREA

Figure **12·11** Procedure for determining height of sidewall for drawpieces which have a bottom radius.

$$G = \frac{\text{blank area} - (\text{area } a + \text{area } b)}{\pi \times \text{mean dia.}}$$

$$= \frac{89.943 - (14.753 + 18.740)}{\pi \times 6.280}$$

$$= \frac{56.450}{19.729}$$

$$= 2.861$$

$$G + F - \frac{T}{2} = 3.408$$

$$H = 3.408, \text{ for 1st draw}$$

Height of 2nd draw:

$$G = \frac{89.943 - 20.331}{3.1416 \times 4.930}$$

$$= \frac{69.612}{15.488}$$

$$= 4.495$$

$$H = 4.495 + 0.338 - 0.015$$

$$= 4.818$$

You will note that in the above calculations the $1\frac{1}{32}$ and $\frac{9}{16}$ radii were not used. The bottom slants were treated (as shown in the enlarged

Figure **12·12** Production of these piece parts involved draw computations and some experimental work in conjunction with the calculating.

views) as sharp-cornered intersections. This procedure simplifies the calculation. It is a proved procedure—entirely satisfactory for the purpose. However, for shells which have a single fillet-type bottom radius (instead of bevels), the bottom radius must be considered in the shell-height calculation. For these, the procedure is that shown in Fig. 12·11.

This chapter has emphasized the fundamental principles of draw operations and related die constructions. The order of presentation is a logical sequence, beginning with the basic factors and evolving through a naturally ascending order into the necessarily more sophisticated aspects of draw work. This has been done in a manner which is as simple and clear as possible in relation to the requirements of the subject matter. This information, supplemented by judicious use of reference books, can enable the diemaker to deal logically with other phases of draw work, such as rectangular draws, etc. (the basic principles are the same).

A serious study of this chapter can provide the real understanding which is essential to diemaking proficiency in regard to draw operations. It should also be remembered that, although this study was developed for the diemaker, it is at least equally essential for the designer and for the men who process and estimate draw work as well.

INDEX TO DIES

GENERAL INDEX